Meta Incognita: A Discourse of Discovery

Martin Frobisher's Arctic Expeditions, 1576–1578

Edited by
Thomas H.B. Symons, CC, FRSC

with the assistance of
Stephen Alsford and Chris Kitzan

Mercury Series
Directorate
Paper 10

Published by
the Canadian Museum of Civilization
with the authorization of the Meta Incognita
Project Steering Committee

Volume 2

D1280545

© Canadian Museum of Civilization 1999

CANADIAN CATALOGUING IN PUBLICATION DATA

Main entry under title:

Meta Incognita: a discourse of discovery: Martin Frobisher's Arctic expeditions, 1576–1578

(Mercury series)
(Directorate paper/Canadian Museum of Civilization; no. 10). Consists of 2 volumes.
Includes an abstract in French.
"With the authorization of the Meta Incognita Project Steering Committee"
Includes bibliographical references.
ISBN 0-660-17507-X (Vol. 1 and Vol. 2)

1. Frobisher, Martin, Sir, 1535?–1594 — Journeys — Northwest Territories — Baffin Island.
2. Explorers — Arctic Regions.
3. Arctic regions — Discovery and exploration — English.
4. Frobisher Bay (N.W.T.) — Discovery and exploration.
5. Baffin Island (N.W.T.) — Discovery and exploration.
6. Metallurgy — Northwest Territories — Baffin Island — History.
7. Mineralogy — Northwest Territories — Baffin Island — History.
I. Symons, T.H.B. (Thomas Henry Bull), 1929–
II. Alsford, Stephen, 1952–
III. Kitzan, Chris, 1970–
IV. Canadian Museum of Civilization.
V. Meta Incognita Project Steering Committee.
VI. Series.
VII. Series: Directorate paper (Canadian Museum of Civilization); no. 10.

G650.M47 1999   971.9'501   C99-980068-X

PRINTED IN CANADA

Published by
Canadian Museum of Civilization
100 Laurier Street
P.O. Box 3100, Station B
Hull, Quebec
J8X 4H2

Senior production officer: Deborah Brownrigg

Cover design: Roger Langlois Design

Cover illustrations:
© Bodleian Library (Frobisher portrait); Trustees of the British Museum (female Inuk); Canadian Museum of Civilization (ship model).

OBJECT OF THE MERCURY SERIES

The Mercury Series is designed to permit the rapid dissemination of information pertaining to the disciplines in which the Canadian Museum of Civilization is active. Considered an important reference by the scientific community, the Mercury Series comprises over three hundred specialized publications on Canada's history and prehistory.

Because of its specialized audience, the series consists largely of monographs published in the language of the author.

Titles in the Mercury Series can be obtained by calling 1-800-555-5621; by e-mail to <publications@civilization.ca>; by internet to <cyberboutique.civilization.ca>; or by writing to

Mail Order Services
Canadian Museum of Civilization
100 Laurier Street
P.O. Box 3100, Station B
Hull, Quebec
J8X 4H2

BUT DE LA COLLECTION MERCURE

La collection Mercure vise à diffuser rapidement le résultat de travaux dans les disciplines qui relèvent des sphères d'activités du Musée canadien des civilisations. Considérée comme un apport important dans la communauté scientifique, la collection Mercure présente plus de trois cents publications spécialisées portant sur l'héritage canadien préhistorique et historique.

Comme la collection s'adresse à un public spécialisé, celle-ci est constituée essentiellement de monographies publiées dans la langue des auteurs.

Vous pouvez vous procurer les titres parus dans la collection Mercure par téléphone, en appelant au 1 800 555-5621, par courriel, en adressant votre demande à <publications@civilisations.ca> par internet à <cyberboutique.civilisations.ca> ou par la poste, en écrivant au :

Service des commandes postales
Musée canadien des civilisations
100, rue Laurier
C.P. 3100, succursale B
Hull (Québec)
J8X 4H2

Canada

Abstract

The Meta Incognita Project was initiated to cast new light on the Arctic voyages of Martin Frobisher and their significance for the histories of North America and Britain. The papers published here are the result of several years of research in British and European archives, undertaken by an Archival Research Task Force set up in England under the chairmanship of Sir Ian Gourlay and with the guidance of the Meta Incognita Project Steering Committee. Leading scholars have broken new ground in examining the sociopolitical, technological, and historical contexts, the conduct of the expeditions, the roles and complex motivations of some of the key players, the significance of the voyages for the future both of English oceanic exploration and of imperial and entrepreneurial ambitions, and questions about intercultural contact between Inuit and Europeans. Although the Elizabethan venture failed in its goals to discover a northwest passage, to mine precious metals, and to establish a colony in the future Canadian Arctic, it left valuable legacies which have not been fully demonstrated until now. The collection is edited by one of Canada's most renowned scholars, Professor Thomas Symons, chairman of the Steering Committee.

Résumé

Le projet Meta Incognita a été mis sur pied dans le but de jeter un nouvel éclairage sur les voyages de Martin Frobisher dans l'Arctique et sur leur importance dans l'histoire de l'Amérique du Nord et de la Grande-Bretagne. Les articles publiés ici sont le résultat de plusieurs années de recherches dans les archives britanniques et européennes. Ces recherches ont été entreprises par un groupe d'étude en recherche archivistique mis sur pied en Angleterre sous la présidence de M. Ian Gourlay et sous la direction du comité directeur du projet Meta Incognita. Des spécialistes de premier plan ont fait œuvre de pionniers en étudiant les contextes sociopolitique, technique et historique, la conduite des expéditions, les rôles et les motivations profondes de certains des principaux protagonistes, l'importance des voyages relativement à l'avenir de l'exploration des mers par l'Angleterre et de ses visées impériales et commerciales ainsi que les questions relatives au contact interculturel entre les Inuit et les Européens. Bien que l'entreprise élisabéthaine consistant à découvrir un passage vers le nord-ouest, à exploiter des métaux précieux et à établir une colonie dans ce qui deviendrait l'Arctique canadien ait échoué, elle a laissé de précieux héritages dont on n'a pas fourni toutes les explications jusqu'à maintenant. La collection est publiée sous la direction d'un des plus éminents savants du Canada, M. Thomas Symons, président du comité directeur.

Contents

<u>VOLUME 1</u>

Frobisher's Ships: the Ships of the North-Western Atlantic Voyages, 1576-1578

Ian Friel

A total of fifteen sailing ships were used on the English voyages to north-eastern Canada between 1576 and 1578. This paper discusses the technical information available for some of these vessels, and attempts to place them in the context of the maritime world of their time.

There are surviving details of the equipment of four of these ships, the *Aid*, the *Gabriel*, *Michael* and *Judith*, with some supplementary technical and other information relating to three of these vessels.

This study is divided into a number of sections: the first is aimed at providing an overview of the shipping provided for the Frobisher voyages, whilst the second looks in detail at the evidence for the construction, rig and equipment for some of the vessels used.

The Nature of the Evidence

Most of the evidence for Frobisher's ships is contained in documents. There are no known archaeological remains, and only a single surviving picture that purports to be an image of one of the vessels. Michael Lok's financial accounts for the voyages do not contain a great deal of detailed information about the ships used, but what they do tell us is a valuable supplement to the inventories of the *Aid*, *Gabriel*, *Michael* and *Judith* which are to be found in the Calendars of State Papers, Domestic, at the Public Record Office, together with other incidental references to the ships. The inventories are the key technical documents for this study, and are summarised below in tabular form. Some technical information can be gleaned from the accounts of the voyages, and this is also discussed. The material relating directly to Frobisher's ships is viewed in the light of other evidence for sixteenth-century ships, with the aim of putting them in their proper historical context. The author would like to express his gratitude to Jim McDermott for supplying transcripts of those sections of the Lok accounts relating to shipping.

The ships of the 1576 voyage

The only vessels purpose-built for the north-western voyages were the 30-ton bark *Gabriel* and a number of pinnaces. In 1576, as Michael Lok's accounts show, the royal master shipwrights Matthew Baker and John Ady were contracted for building the *Gabriel* and a 7-ton pinnace. Baker had been hired the previous year to build a ship for the venture, but the scheme "tooke none effecte for lake of venturars money," and he was paid £5 for releasing the bargain.[1] The venturers had got so far as to hire a man named John Cocke as the ship's master, and he was likewise paid £5 for closing the contract.

In 1576, Matthew Baker and John Ady were paid £105. 16s. 8d for building the *Gabriel* and the pinnace, the money covering "carpenters worke to furnish the same (ships)," and planks, timber, masts and their "stuff." This works out at approximately £2. 17s. 1½d per ton, although the exact total costs of these vessels are difficult to ascertain, as the expenses of the *Gabriel* and the pinnace may be mixed in with those of work on the *Michael*. A note of costs of the 1576 voyage in the government records gives the cost of the hull of the *Gabriel* as £83, and that of the pinnace as £20. There is a slight discrepancy between this and the Lok data, but it indicates that the cost per ton of the hull of the *Gabriel* was about £2. 15s. 4d, and that of the pinnace was slightly greater, at £2. 17s. 1½d.[2]

That same year, Martin Frobisher spent £6. 16s. 2d employing ten carpenters for more than 60 man/days' work, along with two sawyers for one day, and two caulkers for eight days each. It is not stated whether or not this was work on just the *Gabriel* or the pinnace, or if the *Michael* was included. Certainly another shipwright named Richard Estwood was paid £3. 6s for timber and for work on the *Gabriel* and *Michael*, and three smiths were paid a total of £10. 18s. 6d for bolts, spikes, nails and other ironwork. A joiner was paid £1. 5s. 4d for "selinge" the cabin of the *Gabriel* (i.e. putting ceiling planking on the inside of the cabin walls), for making a "bytakle" (compass binnacle), and a further £10. 2s. 6d was spent on masts and other gear for the *Gabriel*. The *Michael*, a ship of 30 tons burden, was purchased from Christopher Andrewes and Robert Martin "with apparell, takell, and furnyture redy made" for a total of £120, and was thus valued at £4 per ton. It is probable that the second ship was purchased because there was insufficient time to build another new one. The venturers had considered buying another ship, for a man was sent to Aldeburgh in Suffolk to buy a Master Foxe's "shippe flybote," possibly before the purchase of the *Michael* was decided. The work on the ships was evidently undertaken with a sense of urgency, as £2 was spent on bread, drink and "brekfastes to the carpentares to hasten their workes."[3] The launch of the *Gabriel* was accompanied by a small celebration. Frobisher bought beer and bread for it, and also paid for the mariners' dinners, perhaps also supplying some spirits ("aquavite": OED) for the occasion.[4] In total, £458. 2s were spent on the ships for the 1576 voyages, including the £120 purchase-price of the *Michael*.

The ships of the 1577 voyages

The Queen's ship *Aid* was hired for the second voyage of 1577, at a cost of £750. The *Michael* and the *Gabriel*, both described as "barkes" were given new decks, made by the shipwright John Ady. Seventy-two oars were purchased for the barks and the boats, more than would have been required for the pinnace and small boats alone. This may suggest that the *Gabriel* and *Michael* could be worked under oars — an advantage for ships on a reconaissance voyage. The other shipping expenditure of the year was largely in the areas of construction and repair work on the vessels, with the 200-ton *Aid* absorbing a considerable amount of the money. A new mainmast for the *Aid* alone cost £20 (a ship of this size would have required a made mast), with a half-ton anchor for the ship at £9, and two 120-fathom (720 ft or 219.5 m) cables weighing 2½ tons and costing £58. 6s. 8d. The rebuilding and refurbishment expenses were relatively routine, apart from the number of small boats purchased or built. Matthew Baker made two "pynaces botes for shipps service rowinge"; a "bote gondelo" was supplied for the *Aid*, and Frobisher had two skiffs made at Ratcliffe. The supply of five small craft for three ships, two of which were themselves small, underlines the importance accorded on this voyage to the needs of coastal exploration and the transhipment of men and gear.

Another significant feature of the year's expenditure was the payment of £7. 11s. 10d "for reparinge and newe makinge divers Instrumentes of navigatione" for the voyage by the leading instrument maker Humphrey Cole.[5]

The ships of the 1578 voyages

For the 1578 voyage, an additional ship was purchased, the *Judith*, a vessel of 80 tons burden, bought from William Burrow (or Borough) of Limehouse. The *Judith* cost £320, and was therefore valued at £4 per ton. More small craft were also purchased, in the form of four "pynasse botes," three of which were provided by Matthew Baker, at £14 each. The fourth was smaller and came from Steven Burrow, costing £7. Cordage and canvas were also acquired, including seven cables, sailcloth for the *Judith* and *Michael*, and 209.75 ells of canvas to make sails for three of the small pinnaces. Another 72 oars were also bought, presumably for the four new small craft. A carpenter named Thomas Bodnam supplied some small cranes or "Crabes for the Landing of the Shippes that shall remayne in the new Land." A ton (20 cwt) of corned gunpowder was purchased for the *Gabriel*, *Michael* and *Judith*, along with sixty bows, 180 sheaves of arrows (over 4300 arrows if each sheaf contained 24 arrows) and 1440 bowstrings. The ships were also supplied with materials to make incendiary weapons, in the form of six pounds of mastick, 2 pounds of camphor and a quart of linseed oil, bought from an apothecary named John Turpin.[6]

Most of the ships were used on the third voyage of 1578. The *Gabriel*, *Michael* and pinnace of the 1576 voyage were small ships, even by Elizabethan standards, of between 20 and 30 tons, smaller than many of the tiny coasters that served the ports and muddy creeks around the English coast. The reason for using ships of this size is clear: the loss of such small vessels on a risky transoceanic venture would not financially cripple their owners. The addition of the 200-ton warship *Aid* on the second gave the expedition added "muscle," in both the literal sense of greater manpower, and in terms of the firepower of the fleet should it meet with attack by other ships. The dozen extra ships of the third voyage were intended to carry enough men and stores to make the mining operations viable, and to be able to carry back the mined ore. Most of them were in a tonnage range of between 100 and 160 tons. A 1577 government survey of merchant shipping showed that out of 791 vessels listed, only 131 (about 16%) were of 100 tons burden or more, and 121 of these were in the 100-199 ton-range.[7] Although the survey was incomplete, it does indicate that the 1578 voyage used a significant proportion — perhaps ten per cent — of the country's "defensible" merchantmen, a sign of the importance accorded to the venture (the construction of private vessels of 100 tons or more attracted a government bounty, for ships of this size could be pressed into royal service as warships).

Table 1: the ships of the 1578 voyage
(excluding vessels identified as pinnaces)
Arranged in descending order of tonnage
Aid, 200 tons
Thomas Allen, 160 tons
Hopewell, 150 tons
Anne Francis, 130 tons
Francis of Fowey, 130 tons
Thomas of Ipswich, 130 tons (deserted 8/8/1578)
Salomon of Weymouth, 120 tons
Armonell of Exmouth, 100 tons
Beare Leicester, 100 tons
Barke Dennis, 100 tons (sank near Resolution Island, 2/7/1578)
Emanuel of Bridgwater, 100 tons
Mone (probably pronounced Moon) of Fowey, 100 tons
Judith, 80/100 tons (1578)
Michael, 25/30 tons
Gabriel, 20/30 tons
(The author wishes to thank Professor D.B.Quinn for supplying this complete list)

Apart from the *Judith*, it is very difficult to be able to say much about the additional ships of the 1578 expedition. Vessels of similar names and sizes can be found in other documents, but it is impossible to give anything approaching complete histories for any of them.

From the archaeological point of view, it might be worthwhile looking for the wreck site of the *Bark Dennis*, which sank near Resolution Island in July 1578, after being holed by floating ice.[8] The fact that this was the only one of the large sailing vessels in the any of the three voyages to succumb to ice, rocks or storm is surely a testament to the skills of the shipwrights who built them, and of the mariners who sailed in them.

The *Gabriel, Michael, Aid* and *Judith*: a detailed study

This section focuses on the detailed evidence for the construction, rig and equipment of these vessels, the only four of the fifteen used for which any technical data survive, in the form of inventories and some other material. When these inventories are compared with the inventories and appraisals of other contemporary non-royal vessels, one overriding impression emerges: with the possible exception of their level of armament, and bearing in mind that the *Aid* was a royal warship, there was nothing particularly unusual about their equipment. They were ordinary Elizabethan sailing vessels.

The sizes of the ships

With one exception, the dimensions of these ships are unknown, and there is little to tell us about their design or internal structures. The only ship of the 1576-78 voyages for which an original set of dimensions survives is the *Aid*. A list of the measurements of the royal ships was prepared c.1590-1591, and this is extant in two forms, an incomplete contemporary version, and a complete but clearly somewhat garbled eighteenth-century copy.[9] When checked against a further list of 1602, it is possible to produce a "restored" set of dimensions, as accurate as we are likely to get short of the discovery of the full original list. The list concentrated on those measurements basic to Elizabethan ship design, the keel length, breadth, depth in hold, rake forward (i.e. horizontal length of the rake of the stempost) and rake aft (horizontal length of the rake of the sternpost) (Figure 1). The dimensions of the *Aid* were as follows:

Table 2
Dimensions of the Aid, c.1590-91 (metric equivalents in brackets)

Rake forward	Keel	Rake aft	Beam	Depth in hold
25'	73'	4' 5"	22'	14'
(7.62)	(22.26)	(1.35)	(6.71)	(4.27)

Using the Tudor tonnage calculation method known as Baker's Old Rule, attributed to Matthew Baker, the results are as follows:

$$\frac{\text{Keel} \times \text{Beam} \times \text{Depth in hold}}{100} = \text{tons burden}$$

$$\frac{73 \times 22 \times 14}{100} = 224.84 \text{ tons burden}$$

This approximates to the 225 tons burden, or theoretical carrying capacity, that the list gives for the *Aid*. This is a ship 25 tons larger in size than the *Aid* of the 1570s voyages! As far as can be ascertained, the *Aid* was not enlarged or altered in any significant way between the 1570s and the early 1590s, suggesting that the earlier figure was an approximation. Sixteenth-century tonnage measurement can be very problematical, due to miscalculations, or to the deliberate "fudging" of figures, but the dimensional figures are fairly clear. They were prepared for an internal naval document, presumably for

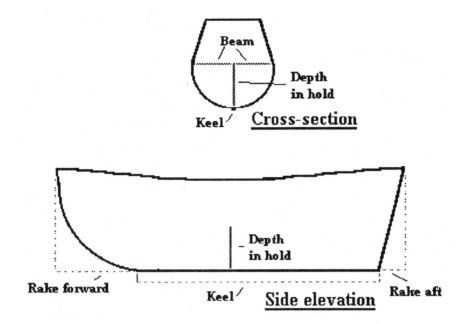

Figure 1: Schematic diagram showing Elizabethan ship measurements

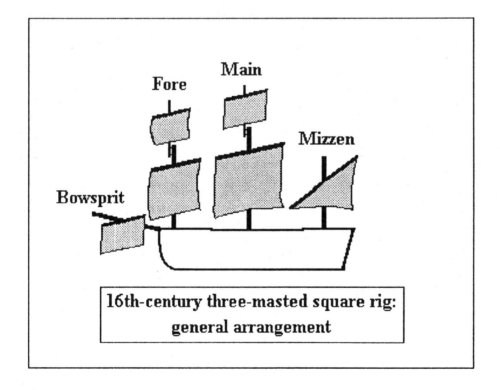

16th-century three-masted square rig:
general arrangement

Figure 2: Sixteenth-century three-masted square rig: general arrangement

technical reasons, and there is no reason to believe that they were deliberately falsified, or that there was any incentive to do so.

We can at least get some impression of the scale of the *Aid*. There are no known surviving dimensions for any of the other ships in the voyages, but the 1590-91 dimensions for another royal ship do give some grounds for working out the approximate size of the *Gabriel*. The Queen's ship Cygnet was a small scouting vessel of 29 tons burden, constructed in 1585. Her measurements were as follows:

Table 3				
Dimensions of the Cygnet, c.1590-91 (metric equivalents in brackets)				
Rake Forward	Keel	Rake aft	Beam	Depth in hold
10' (3.05)	40' (12.20)	2' (0.61)	12' (3.66)	6' (1.83)
(Sources: see previous note)				

The tonnage calculation, by Baker's Old Rule, is 28.8 tons, or 29 tons to the nearest ton. The *Gabriel* is said to have been a vessel of 30 tons, and only a slight change in the dimensions of the Cygnet would "give" us the *Gabriel*. For this purpose, I have assumed that the beam and depth-in-hold figures have remained at 12 and 6 feet respectively. The 1590-91 list invariably gives these as whole feet, whereas keel lengths and rakes are often quoted in terms of feet and inches. By adjusting the keel length to 41 feet, 8 inches, and then using the Baker's Old Rule, we get 29.99 tons burden, close enough to 30 tons to satisfy most Elizabethan shipwrights. As the rake forward and rake aft figures for the Cygnet are, respectively, 25% and 5% of the keel length, those for the *Gabriel* have been adjusted accordingly:

Table 4				
Possible dimensions of the Gabriel, 1576 (metric equivalents in brackets)				
Rake forward	Keel	Rake aft	Beam	Depth in hold
10' 5" (3.18)	41' 8" (12.70)	2' 1" (0.64)	12' (3.66)	6' (1.83)

There does not appear to be any way of knowing if these dimensions are close to those of the real *Gabriel*. A ship with a keel length of 33 feet, a beam of 13 feet, and a depth-in-hold of 7 feet would have had about the same tonnage. The "longer" keel length gives the "*Gabriel*" the proportions of a small warship, like the Cygnet; the "shorter" keel would create a tubby merchantman. The *Gabriel*'s builder, Matthew Baker, was first and foremost a warship designer, but would have been perfectly capable of creating a beamy coasting vessel. However, the longer and narrower "*Gabriel*" would probably have been faster and more manoeuvrable than the shorter version, and better suited for a reconnaissance voyage. The 1576 voyage was such a voyage, and for this reason I believe that the figures in Table 4 may well be close to those of the original ship.

"Reconstructing" any of the ships of the north-western voyages would be a difficult enterprise, not just because of the problems of designing seaworthy vessels, or of reviving 16th-century shipwrightry, but because the original data is very thin indeed. The best that could be hoped for is a generalised interpretation, based on sixteenth- and early seventeenth-century design techniques, similar to those made for the *Mayflower* and the *Susan Constant*.[10]

Hulls, superstructures and cabins

None of the sources tell us much in detail about the construction or shapes of the vessels used by Frobisher, but it is fairly certain that all of the sea-going ships (with the possible exception of the smaller pinnaces and boats) will have been skeleton-built. This was a technique which had been introduced into England in the fifteenth century, and there is little doubt that by the sixteenth century it had become the predominant shipbuilding method in the country, as in much of Northern Europe.[11] Certainly Matthew Baker's design drawings of c.1586, contained in the manuscript known as "Fragments of Ancient English Shipwrightry," all relate to skeleton-built vessels.[12]

Skeleton construction involved fastening a shell of planking to a pre-erected skeleton of frames, with the planking flush-laid, so that the hull exterior had a smooth appearance. Much remains to be learned about the detail of the construction techniques used, evidence that is only likely to come from archaeological remains, but there are indications that large numbers of wooden nails, or trenails were used in English hulls of the period. For example, when a pinnace of about 25 tons was built for the Sussex town of Rye in the years 1587-8, the construction work required the use of at least 2375 trenails and 1000 wooden "needle wedges" (presumably pieces of sharpened timber driven into the outboard ends of some of the trenails to help hold them in position), and the account does not, significantly, mention the purchase of iron nails.[13]

The Lok accounts do throw some light on the construction and equipment of the ships for the 1576 voyage. The *Gabriel* possessed a cabin, as we have seen, presumably for Captain Frobisher, who was also provided with an expensive "Ducke upholster for beddinge" that cost £3. 16s. 5d. The provision of interior ceiling planking for the cabin, installed by a joiner, would have helped to protect the interior against wind and weather, and would have given some protection against rats and other vermin that were commonplace in the ships of the period.[14] The hulls of the *Gabriel* and *Michael* were fastened with iron nails, bolts and spikes, in addition, presumably, to wooden trenails; six tons of Russian ironstone was purchased as ballast for the *Gabriel*. Some £4. 5s. was spent on painting the ships, and a further 10s went on carving a "dragones head" as the *Gabriel*'s figurehead.[15] It is probable that most of the cabins, with the exception of the master's or captain's cabins, were fairly cramped structures, similar to those found in the wreck of the Mary Rose.[16]

The only direct evidence for the deck-levels and superstructures of the ships is to be found in the picture of the *Aid* on the Smerwick Bay map of 1580 (Figure 3).[17] This shows the port aspect of the ship, with a row of some five gunports on its side, above the line of a wale, or horizontal strengthening timber. The wale is at about the right level for the gundeck on which the guns would have stood. In the flat transom stern there are two small ports at about the same level as the wale, perhaps indicating a lower section of deck. Above the gunports is the line of the gunwale, suggesting a weather deck over the guns. The aft superstructure or aftercastle rises significantly: the lowest part of this superstructure would have enclosed part of the weather deck, giving space to build cabins. The superstructure has two stages, with a longer, partially open deck above the weather deck: the second stage consists of a poop deck that carries the mizzenmast. The forecastle structure at the bow is in part obscured by smoke from a cannon, but it clearly has only one deck above the weather deck. The suggested arrangement of decks is demonstrated in Table 5. The gunsmoke also obscures the bow, so that it is not possible to see if the *Aid* has a beakhead, a platform projecting out beyond the bow, but they are a commonplace sight in ship pictures of the period, and can indeed been seen depicted on many of the ships shown on the Smerwick Bay map.

Superstructures on sixteenth-century ships functioned both as fighting platforms and as shelters for cabins, and it is likely that all of Frobishers's ships possessed them to some degree, apart from the pinnaces and small boats. As we have seen, the *Gabriel* had a cabin and one account says that the ship was open in the "waist." As this was a term used to describe the section of the weather deck between the fore and aft superstructures, this clearly implies that the ship did have them.[18] The possession of superstructures may have been one of the things that distinguished a small sailing ship from a large pinnace.

The sources have little to say about how the ships were steered. All possessed stern rudders, but it is unclear if these were worked by simple tillers, or by a vertical pole called a whipstaff, attached to the end of the tiller. Such an arrangement was certainly in use by the late sixteenth century, but it is not known exactly when, or where, it was introduced.[19] The loss of steerage was something to be feared: in July 1576 a storm blew the *Gabriel* over on her beam ends, so that she would not answer to the helm, and a year later bad weather broke the steering-gear of the *Michael*.[20] Although the sails could be used to help steer the ship, the rudder and helm were also of crucial importance, for in bad weather a mis-timed movement of the rudder could sink a ship. On 19 July 1577 a fierce storm put Frobisher's small fleet in danger. Through the efforts of the crew all was saved, but in the account of the incident it was natural for a sixteenth-century writer to link steerage with divine providence, "God being our best steresman."[21]

**Figure 3: The *Aid* in 1580 (from the Smerwick Harbour map);
reproduced by permission of the Public Record Office, MPF 75.**

Table 5: possible arrangement of decks in the Aid		
BOW	WAIST	STERN
		Aftercastle deck 2
Forecastle deck 1		Aftercastle deck 1
Beakhead?	Weather deck	
	Gundeck .	
		Lower deck section?

Little seems to have been done, before the ships left England, to reinforce their hulls against floating ice. Once in the Arctic, oars, pikes and poles were used to help fend off this peril, and sections of cable, masts, bedding, planks and other items were hung overboard to add a protective layer to the hulls. In July 1578 the *Michael* was also equipped with a reinforced stem, when the bow of the bark was "armed" with three-inch thick planks, capstan bars and cut-up sections of cable. Such an encumbrance would probably have adversely affected the ship's performance, and it is not clear if this idea was taken up in other ships. It is apparent that this was intended as a defence for the ship rather than as a means of attacking the ice, so the *Michael* cannot be described as history's first "icebreaker."[22]

Cooking facilities and victuals

All of the sailing ships involved in the voyages, with exception of the pinnaces and small boats, are likely to have had cooking facilities of some kind. This must have been true of even the *Gabriel* and *Michael*, for the purchases for the 1576 voyage included a list of culinary equipment, such as a baking pan, meat pot, trivet, dripping pan and a pair of spits, that were only of use if heat could be applied to them.[23] Exactly where these cooking facilities were is very difficult to say. In a contemporary royal warship, the cook-room seems to have been normally in the hold, with a substantial tiled hearth and sometimes an oven built over the ballast, and the smoke taken up to deck level by a chimney.[24] Given the evidence that the hull of the *Gabriel* was open amidships (see above), it is possible that the bark's cooking facilities were in the superstructure. The *Aid* certainly had a below-decks kitchen with an oven and a chimney: during the 1577 voyage the cook allowed the oven to overheat, and this, coupled with a faulty chimney, almost set fire to the ship. Fortunately, one of the ship's boys saw what was happening and the fire was put out.[25]

The victuals purchased for the voyages were little more than the standard fare provided to English seafarers. The allotment for the 115 men embarked for the 1577 voyage gives a good idea of what was carried.[26] Elizabethan dietary laws decreed that certain days in the week had to be "flesh" or meat days, with no fish served, and others had to be fish days, on which no meat could be consumed. For victualling estimates for a notional 504-day voyage see Table 6.

In addition, there were other items of food and drink that would have probably been for the exclusive use of the officers: 2 barrels of honey, 1 hogshead of "sallet" (salad — OED) oil, 1 ton of vinegar, 2 hogsheads of spirits ("aquaviete") and 4 bushels of mustard seed. The surgeon was also given a supply of prunes, raisins, almonds, liquorice and other things for the treatment of sick men.

The fuel to be supplied consisted of 14 tons of firewood, 30 tons of sea coal and 1 ton of charcoal. In addition, these crew were provided with fishing nets, hooks, lines and harping-irons (large hooks used for spearing whales or large fish, OED), to enable them to catch fresh food.

Table 6: victualling estimates for the 1577 voyage		
Victuals	Tons carried	No. of days covered by supply
Biscuit	16	140
Meal/grain (to make biscuit)	30	364
Beer	80½	168
Wine	5	Probably officers only
Beef	5	48
Pork	15½	420
Stockfish	2½	108
Butter	2	108
Cheese	4	108
Oatmeal	1½	To make up for lack of fish
Rice	1½	To make up for lack of fish

The 1577 estimate was a planning document, but indicates that only the biscuit (or meal), the salt meat and the pease were expected to last for the whole of the notional 504-day voyage. On an average meat day in the early weeks of the voyage, each mariner would have received one pound of beef or pork, one pound of biscuit, just over eleven ounces of pease, four ounces of butter, half a pound of cheese and eight pints of beer. The total burden, or carrying capacity, of the three ships was between 240 and 260 tons. The 205-215 tons of victuals and fuel would therefore have occupied between about 80% and 85% of the available internal space.

Different cooking methods may well have been used to vary the monotony of the diet. The cooking gear supplied for the first voyage would have made it possible to boil or to stew meat and fish, to roast meat on spits or on a gridiron (there was also a dripping pan to collect the fat that ran off), or to fry it in a frying pan. The officers on this voyage (probably Frobisher in particular) had three great painted wooden Muscovy platters (from Russia), a great pewter basin or ewer, three pint butts or mugs for beer and wine, and a pewter salt cellar, items comparable with some of the fine tableware that emerged from the wreck of the *Mary Rose*.[27]

The 1578 inventories show that the *Gabriel*, *Judith* and *Michael* each had a cook room equipped with a great kettle or cauldron, containing an array of spits, gridirons, pots, frying pans ladles, wooden platters and trays. The *Gabriel* had a chain and a hook for its kettle, and the *Judith* had two iron hooks for its kettle, perhaps suggesting that these cauldrons were suspended over a cooking fire, rather than being part of a fixed brick oven. The *Aid* possessed a bar with a chain and three hooks for hanging a kettle, along with a copper kettle, a meat kettle and a "very small" meat kettle, although other details of the cook-room's equipment are unclear.

The importance of cooking facilities on board these ships should not be under-rated. Wet and cold can rapidly reduce the physical capacity of a crew, and just as seriously, can erode their morale. The men involved in the north-western voyages were sailing into regions far colder than those normally visited by English sailors, and it is likely that hot food, when it was available, became even more important than on a more routine voyage. In this way, the cook-rooms of Frobisher's ships may have helped to ensure that the casualty rates in these voyages remained — in sixteenth-century terms — relatively low.

Rig and rigging equipment

The *Aid*, *Judith*, *Gabriel* and *Michael* were all three-masted, square-rigged vessels; that is to say, each had a foremast and mainmast rigged with square sails, and a mizzenmast rigged for one (or probably two, in the case of the *Aid*) triangular lateen sails (Figure 2). In addition, each ship carried a square spritsail, set on a yard slung underneath the bowsprit, and square sails set on fore- and main topmasts. This was probably the commonest type of seagoing rig to be found in northern Europe, and it had been in use since the fifteenth century. The list of vessels appraised by the English High Court of Admiralty between 1579 and 1590 includes 77 ships for which the type of rig can be determined. Forty-one (53.2%) were three-masters, with 25 two-masters (32.5%) and 11 (14.3%) one-masters.[28]

The square sails operated best with the wind from astern, or on the beam, and were the main driving sails of a ship; the lateen sail, a fore-and-aft rigged sail best adapted for sailing to windward, was of particular use in manoeuvring a vessel, and so was set on the mizzenmast, closest to the rudder.

There was nothing particularly unusual about the actual rigging ropes and other equipment used by the four ships: parallels for the items listed could be found in many other sixteenth-century inventories. The operation of the rigging of sailing ships until the nineteenth century depended very largely on the muscle power of the crew, aided by pulleys, and occasionally by mechanical winding gear such as windlasses or capstans. The sometimes confusing (or indeed, confused) array of ropes found in ship pictures of Tudor times, whether precisely accurate or not, did at least accurately reflect the multiplicity of ropes and other gear required to work the yards and sails of even quite small ships.   Table 7 lists the total numbers of running rigging ropes (pairs of ropes counted as two; parrals excluded) listed as being on the four ships in 1578:

Table 7: Numbers of running rigging ropes listed in the inventories

Mast/spar	Gabriel	Judith	Michael	Aid	Aid (pulleys, blocks, etc)
Bowsprit	4	10+	7	6+	9
Fore topmast	8	10+	10	12+	20
Foremast	11	17	8	16+	28+
Main topmast	9	16+	15	8+	24
Mainmast	13	19+	12	24+	48+
Mizzen topmast	-	-	-	*	*
Mizzenmast	5	7	6	5+	8+
Total no. of ropes	--- 50	--- 79+	--- 58	--- 71+	
				Total no. of pulleys	----- 146+

*mast rigged with standing rigging only: no yard, sail or running rigging listed.

Even allowing for the fact that some items that were normally carried had not been listed because they had been lost or stolen, the totals of ropes are large, and give some idea of the skill required to operate one of these sailing ships. The numbers of running rigging ropes on the *Judith* and the *Aid* are undercounted, as in some cases the existence of a piece of gear was registered without a note of how many items there were. The 80-ton *Judith* and the 200-ton *Aid* naturally had heavier yards and larger sails than the *Gabriel* and *Michael*, and therefore needed more ropes to handle them: in addition, there was a certain amount of redundancy built into sailing ship rig in the form of extra ropes, to provide back-ups in the case of storm or battle damage.

The numbers of pulleys, blocks and other fixed, sheaved items (such as knightheads) on the three smaller ships was not counted, but those of the *Aid* were, presumably because some of them contained valuable bronze sheaves. The total of pulleys and blocks, etc., gives a vivid impression of the mechanical complexity of a Tudor sailing ship: in addition to those pulleys listed in the rigging, there were at least ten more stored in the ship.

In 1576 the *Gabriel* was equipped with three masts, and two "smalle mastes", that is the three lower masts and two topmasts. The lower masts cost a mere £2. 5s, suggesting that they were probably pole masts, made from a single tree, rather than the expensive "made" masts that were composed of several different pieces of timber. Made masts were first developed in the Middle Ages as a response to the difficulty of finding trees that were both tall and straight enough to be made into large masts.[29] Larger ships, such as the *Aid*, would have required made masts for the lower masts.

Sails were made of canvas, of which much had to be imported. Despite attempts to encourage the production of canvas in England, a good deal of the sailcloth used in English ships still came from abroad.[30] The sails of all the ships on the 1576 voyages were made new by a man named Adrian Prussom, a Dutchman or Fleming to judge from his name.[31]

General ships' gear

Sailing vessels needed a wide range of ancillary gear of different kinds. The purchases for the 1576 voyage included miscellaneous gear such as a wooden binnacle for the *Gabriel*'s compass, five anchor stocks, two anchor buoys made from spun oakum, nine baskets, barrel-hoops, scupper-leathers and a new small boat or skiff.[32]

Anchors and the ropes and other gear that went with them, known collectively as ground tackle, were of key importance. The three 1576 vessels were supplied with eight anchors, weighing 9 cwt, 1 qtr and 12 lb (1048 lb or 476.4 kg), along with 42 cwt (4704 lb or 2138.2 kg) of cordage, including 6 cables. The inventories may not be the best guide to the numbers of anchors carried by each ship, for it was not unusual for anchors to be lost, but it can be seen that the *Michael* and the *Judith* had at least four each, while the *Gabriel* had three. The *Aid* possessed four great anchors, together with six large cables (of up to 11 inches in circumference) and two 12-inch mooring cables. The ship also had two capstans for raising and lowering the anchors, a fore capstan, and a main capstan, which was presumably further aft in the ship, and was worked with at least removable capstan bars. There are no references to capstans or windlasses in the inventories of the three smaller vessels, although it is difficult to believe that their anchors and cables could have been handled efficiently without some kind of winding gear. It may be that the inventories are deficient here: other clearly identifiable gaps include the absence of pumping gear in the *Aid*'s inventory. This was probably a clerical omission, for a ship the size of the *Aid* would have required one or possibly two pumps for ejecting water from the hold.

The navigational equipment listed in the sources is, with one or two exceptions, fairly basic. The *Gabriel* was supplied with a compass binnacle or mount in 1576, and the 1578 inventory shows that the ship had at least four compasses. The same document lists five compasses in the *Judith* and four in the *Michael*, together with an old "compass of variation." The *Gabriel* and *Michael* had five and three running glasses respectively (hourglasses used for timing runs and manoeuvres) and all of the ships had sounding leads and lines, including some specifically for "deep sea" use. The *Aid*'s listed navigational equipment was similar, although it should be pointed out that the items in the inventories, important as they were, were only part of the range of gear available to sixteenth-century navigators. Individual pilots and master mariners possessed their own sets of implements, charts and tables which did not figure in the ships' inventories.

Also lacking in the inventories are references to shipwrights' tools. Pitch, tar and rosin were carried for caulking and timber preservation, but ships' carpenters seem to have brought their own toolkits aboard. It is very rare to find mention of such tools in sixteenth-century ships' inventories.[33]

Weaponry

Armed ships were very common in European waters at this time, but by no means did every vessel carried guns. Out of 97 English and foreign ships with tolerably complete inventories appraised by the High Court of Admiralty between 1579 and 1590, 60 (61.9%) carried cannon, ranging from small swivel "pot pieces" to large cannon such as sakers.[34] Given that shipboard weaponry was common in the 1570s and 1580s, the twelve additional ships of the 1578 voyage doubtless carried their own cannon, in addition to small arms.

Piracy and privateering were endemic, and it seems likely that the heavy weapons carried by Frobisher's ships were intended to defend the vessels against attack by other Europeans, rather than to ward off assaults by the indigenous Arctic people. Cannon could have been taken ashore to help fortify any English settlements, but hand weapons were of much more use in confrontations with the local inhabitants.

The armament supplied to the ships in 1576 consisted entirely of firearms — 25 calivers or muskets, and one musket with a "fyerlocke" (in the sixteenth century this meant a wheel-lock musket rather than a flintlock — OED), together with powder flasks, other gun furniture and 24 lb (10.9 kg) of lead for making into shot.[35]

The merchant ships involved in the voyages will have carried some guns, but there is little doubt that the most powerful single vessel used by Frobisher was the *Aid*. The total weight of roundshot that could be fired by the *Aid* (both broadsides) was probably between 80 and 90 lb; the combined total carriage-piece shot-weight of the *Gabriel* and the *Michael* was little more than 10 lb; that of the *Judith* was about 30-35 lb.

The 1578 inventories show that the ships were equipped with an array of infantry weapons, including calivers (heavy muskets), bows and arrows and pikes. The *Aid* alone had 32 "stocked" calivers (i.e. with wooden stocks) and a further six unmounted ones, 25 bows and 45 archery sheaves, containing perhaps more than 1000 arrows.[36]

Small craft, boats and oar power

The small boats and pinnaces used by the Frobisher expeditions lacked the glamour of some of the larger ships, and did not even have names, but they proved to be of enormous significance. The Lok accounts show that seven pinnaces and three other small boats were supplied for the voyages, underlining the importance accorded to small craft both in coastal exploration and in the transhipment of men, equipment and goods to and from the ships in an area where there were no quays or other harbourworks.

The exact sizes of the small craft supplied for the expeditions is uncertain: the dimensions of the three "new pynnasse boats" supplied by Baker were meant to be included in the 1578 accounts, but the spaces for the figures were left blank. However, the boats were priced at £14; the 7-ton pinnace built by Baker in 1576 cost £20,[37] suggesting that the 1578 pinnaces were slightly smaller, perhaps of the order of 4-5 tons burden. The *Aid* possessed a one-masted ship's boat that was large enough to have its own windlass, together with a 12-oared skiff.

Data on boats and pinnaces supplied for the navy in 1588 gives some idea of the sizes of vessels that Elizabethans regarded as pinnaces. These vessels ranged between 28 ft and 32 ft (8.54-9.76 m) in length, and 6 ft 6 ins and 7 ft 4 ins (1.98-2.21 m) in breadth, giving a range of length:beam ratios from about 1:4.1 to 1:4.5. These were priced at between £9. 10s. and £11 each, suggesting something slightly larger than the "small pynnasse bote" supplied by Steven Burrow to Lok in 1578. Eight larger boats sold to the navy in 1588 ranged between 33 ft and 43 ft in length and from 8 ft 6 ins to 9 ft 9 ins in breadth. The largest cost £30 each; the closest in price to the 1578 pinnaces supplied by Baker to Lok cost £15, and measured 33 ft by 8 ft 6 ins, a length:beam ratio of 1:3.88.[38] Illustrations of the sixteenth and seventeenth centuries often show ship's boats with rounded stems and sterns. A 17th-century Dutch plan of a ten-oar boat measuring 28 by 9½ (Dutch) feet depicts a clinker-built craft with a rounded stem and stern, a pronounced sheer and a shallow draught.[39] Considerable sheer would have made such a boat stronger, and its shallow draught would have enabled it to operate from beaches and river banks. Bluff-bowed boats can be seen in English paintings and other images of the sixteenth century, sometimes with a seemingly exaggerated hull curvature, suggesting that English ships' boats of this period may not have been very different from the later Dutch example (Figures 4a and 4b).

What may be the earliest record of English boatbuilding in the New World comes from one of the accounts of the Frobisher expeditions. In August 1578, Captain Best of the *Anne Francis*, which with the *Mone* was separated from the rest of the fleet, ordered the construction of a pinnace for use in reconaissance. This was a very difficult job, for suitable nails and timber were lacking. Whilst there happened to be a smith in the company, there were no smithing tools. A miner's pickaxe was used to serve as a sledgehammer, and a gun chamber became an anvil. With two small bellows to heat a furnace, broken-up tongs, a gridiron and a fire-shovel were made into nails. A carpenter put the boat together, but as it "lacked some of principall knees and timbers," he declared

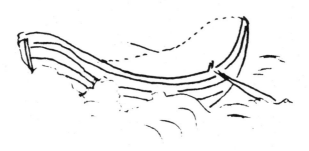

**Figure 4a: Conventional Tudor representations of ships' boats
(figures of crew omitted) — after Rule, 1983, p.21.**

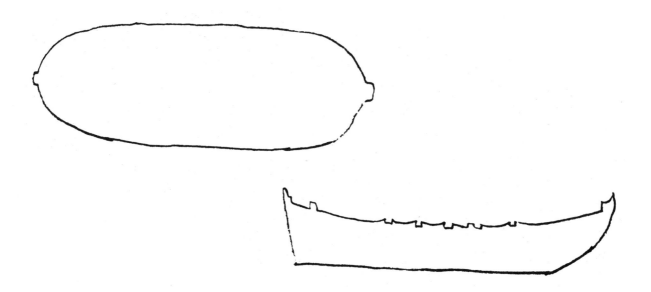

**Figure 4b: Outline plan and elevation of a 10-oar Dutch ship's boat,
seventeenth century — after Howard 1987, p.160**

"that he woulde not adventure himselfe therein for five hundreth poundes, for that the boat hung togither but onelye by the strength of the nayles!" (the boat was probably clinker-built, with a shell of overlapping planks, for there seems to have been insufficient timber to build it in any other way). The "poore pinesse" was equipped with a sail as well as oars, and Best set off on what proved to be a four-day voyage with a crew of nineteen volunteers, eventually locating another English encampment.[40]

In Frobisher's voyages, pinnaces and small boats were used for transporting men and gear between the ships and the shore, and for both long-range and short-range reconaissance. For example, in July 1578, the boats were sent ahead of the ships to sound the depth of shallow waters. When the *Bark Dennis* was fatally holed by floating ice in 1578, they also served to rescue the ship's crew. The small craft later became casualties themselves. Of the three Lok ships inventoried in 1578, only the *Judith* was listed as having a small boat, a skiff with four oars. A contemporary source gives the probable reason for this: "well neere xx (20) boates and pinesses" were lost in a storm during the return journey in 1578, although the ships survived. These humble craft were vital to the success of any transoceanic venture.[41]

The experience of seafaring

The north-western voyages took Frobisher's crews and ships to the limits of their capabilities, but the majority of them survived to come home again. It was considered remarkable that "not above fortie persons" died in the 1578 voyage. In view of the perils of storm, ice and rocks faced by men sailing thousands of miles in wooden sailing vessels, one might be inclined to agree. Only one of the larger sailing vessels, the *Bark Dennis* in 1578, was lost, although several came very close to total disaster. In July 1576 an "extreme storme" knocked the *Gabriel* on to her side: only the timely loosing of the foresail and the jettisoning of the mizzen mast enable to ship to come upright again. The following year the master and boatswain of the same vessel were washed overboard, despite the presence of chest-high safety ropes rigged fore and aft. The boatswain was saved, after vainly trying to keep hold of the master, who drowned. In the same voyage the *Aid*'s rudder was broken in two, and was ready to fall off: during a calm, six men dived underwater to repair the rudder with ropes and planks, returning more than half dead from the task. In 1578, some ships were caught in the ice, and pushed nearly a foot out of the water above their waterlines, whilst their internal timbers bowed or snapped under the strain.[42]

The fact that these ships were able to survive such dangers says much for their construction and for the skills and ingenuity of the men who crewed them. As noted above, there seems to have been little prior provision against ice damage. The makeshift defences of masts, planks, and bedding hung overboard might have prevented sharp ice from piercing the hull, but would have been little help against the crushing forces of ice floes. It seems to have been the basic strength of the ships' hulls that helped to save them when they were caught in the ice.

There is very little evidence of the sailing performances of the ships used, although it is apparent that they were manoeuvrable enough to avoid fatal damage from the floating ice. At one point in the 1577 voyage, with a strong wind and little sea room, the *Aid* was forced to tack fourteen times in four hours, an average of one tack every seventeen minutes. A substantial part of the crew would have been involved in this tiring operation, which required shifting the yards and sails round from one side to the other, and turning the ship to sail on another tack in the process. Later, in the same voyage, the *Gabriel* was unable to keep pace with the *Aid* during a storm. The *Aid*, "being higher in the poope, and a tall ship," had a good deal more windage than the *Gabriel*, which was unable to rig any sails because of the strength of the wind. The wind acting on the *Aid*'s superstructure "wheron the wind had more force to drive" simply blew the larger ship ahead, and out of sight[43]

What became of the ships

The eventual fates of Frobisher's ships are difficult, if not impossible, to determine. The *Aid* remained in royal service for another twenty years, but even the exact circumstances of her disposal are unclear (see Appendix 5). The *Gabriel*, *Michael* and *Judith* seem to disappear from the record. When the *Gabriel* was offered for sale in March 1579, the sale price had to be knocked down from £100 to £80, as "no mane wyll by her at that pryce" perhaps indicating that the *Gabriel* was in a bad way after three transatlantic voyages, or merely that the value of a small ship declined rapidly.[44] It was an ignominious fate for what seems to have been the first ship in English history to be the subject of a ship portrait.[45]

Manuscript Sources (originals and copies)

East Sussex Record Office, Lewes
RYE47.   Rye Borough Records

National Maritime Museum, London
PST20A and B.   Photographic copies of Magdalen College MS.2820

Public Record Office, London
E351.   Exchequer, Pipe Office, Declared Accounts
SP12.   State Papers Domestic, Elizabeth
HCA 24.   High Court of Admiralty, Files of Libels

Bibliography and abbreviations

Anderson 1957.	R.C.Anderson, "A list of the Royal Navy 1590-1591," *Mariner's Mirror*, Vol.48, pp.322-3.
Blackmore 1976	H.L.Blackmore, *The Armouries of the Tower of London.* Vol.I, Ordnance, London.
Collinson 1867.	R.Collinson (ed)., *The Three Voyages of Martin Frobisher...* 1576-8, Hakluyt Society, London.
Dell 1966.	R.F. Dell, *Rye Shipping Records 1566-1590,* Sussex Record Society, Lewes.
Friel 1995.	I. Friel, *The Good Ship. Ships, Shipbuilding and Technology in England 1200-1520*, London
Glasgow 1966.	T.Glasgow, "English ships pictured on the Smerwick Map, 1580. Background, authentication and evaluation," *Mariner's Mirror*, Vol.52, pp.157-62.
Glasgow 1970.	T.Glasgow, "List of ships in the Royal Navy from 1539 to 1588...," *Mariner's Mirror,* Vol.56, p.305.
Howard 1987.	F.Howard, *Sailing Ships of War 1400-1860*, London.
Kemp 1979.	P.Kemp (ed)., *The Oxford Companion to Ships and the Sea*, Oxford.
Lavery 1988.	B.Lavery, *The Colonial Merchantman Susan Constant 1605*, London.
Manwaring and Perrin 1921.	G.E.Manwaring and W.G.Perrin (eds)., *The Life and Works of Sir Henry Mainwaring*, Navy Records Society, Vol.56, London.
NMM 1988.	National Maritime Museum, Armada 1588-1988. The Official Catalogue, London.
OED.	*Oxford English Dictionary.*
Oppenheim 1896.	M.M.Oppenheim, *A History of the Administration of the Royal Navy 1509-1660*, London.
Rule 1983	M.Rule, *The Mary Rose*, 2nd. edn., London.

Notes

[1] 1576 Lok Accounts, p.9.
[2] PRO SP12/119, 32, f.1.
[3] 1576 Lok Accounts, pp.9-12.
[4] Collinson 1867, x-xi.
[5] 1577 Lok Accounts pp.99-102.
[6] 1578 Lok Accounts, pp.6-9.
[7] Oppenheim 1896, pp.173-4.
[8] Collinson 1867, p.236.
[9] PRO SP12/243, 111 and Anderson 1957.
[10] Lavery 1988.
[11] Friel 1995, pp.170-80.
[12] NMM PST20 a and b; original manuscript is in the Pepysian Library, Magdalen College, Cambridge, MS 2820.
[13] East Sussex Record Office RYE 47/37 (2); Dell 1966, pp.1-3.
[14] PRO SP 12/224, 45: a 1589 warship contract specified that the captain's and master's cabins should be "seeled to the Plancke, with Spruce delles or wainscott, for avoydinge of myse & Ratts."
[15] 1576 Lok Accounts, pp.9-12.
[16] Rule 1983, pp.120-2.
[17] Glasgow 1966.
[18] Collinson 1867, p.81.
[19] Lavery 1988, p.20.
[20] Collinson 1867, pp.81 and 127.
[21] Collinson 1867, p.132.
[22] Collinson 1867, p.294.
[23] Collinson 1867, xi.
[24] Oppenheim 1896, pp.127-8; Rule 1983, pp.107-9.
[25] Collinson 1867, p.132.
[26] Collinson 1867, pp.105-7.
[27] Collinson 1867, x-xi.
[28] PRO HCA 24/50-57, passim.
[29] 1576 Lok Accounts, pp.9-12.
[30] Oppenheim 1896, pp.103, 181-2.
[31] 1576 Lok Accounts, p.11.
[32] 1576 Lok Accounts, pp.9-12.
[33] 1576 Lok Accounts, pp.9-12.
[34] PRO HCA 24/ 50-57, passim.
[35] 1576 Lok Accounts, pp.9-12.
[36] Rule 1983, pp.181: arrow spacers from sheaves found in the Mary Rose were made to hold 24 arrows apiece.
[37] PRO SP12/119, 32, f.1.
[38] PRO E351/2225, ff.4v-5.
[39] Howard 1987, pp.160-1.
[40] Collinson 1867, pp.266-70.
[41] Collinson 1867, pp.73-4, 130, 236, 246 and 279.
[42] Collinson 1867, pp. 80-1, 153-4, 236-7, 279.
[43] Collinson 1867, pp. 132-3, 154.
[44] PRO SP12/130, 10.
[45] Information courtesy of Jim McDermott.

Appendix 1

THE 1578 INVENTORIES OF THE *GABRIEL, JUDITH* AND *MICHAEL*

The inventories do not necessarily list everything that made up the normal equipment of the ships: ship inventories were administrative or legal records that recorded what was present on a given date, not what should have been there to ensure the efficient running of the vessel. That said, comparative studies of surviving contemporary inventories and appraisals for royal and merchant ships strongly suggest that the gear listed on board these four ships represented the bulk of their normal gear. Conversely, they show that these vessels had little in the way of equipment to differentiate them from other ships of their size and type in the 1570s and 1580s.

See the Key, p.343 for an explanation of the notation.

Sources: SP12/129, ff.37/81 to f.87v

Item	*Gabriel*	*Judith*	*Michael*
Bowsprit			
Lifts	2	1 pr	2
Lift blocks	-	1 pr	-
False tye	1	1	-
Clewlines	-	1 pr	2
Sheets	-	-	2
Braces	-	1 pr	-
Spritsail halyard & 2 pulleys	1	-	-
Halyards		#	
Spritsail halyard with tye	-	-	1
Spritsail course	1	1	1
Bonnets	-	1	1
Yard	1	1	1

Appendix 1 cont'd

Fore topmast

Braces	2	2	2
Clewlines	-	2	2
Pair shrouds	2	-	-
Shrouds	-	-	6
Shrouds per side	-	3	-
Tackles	-	-	-
Swifters	-	-	-
Stay	-	1	1
Bowlines	2	2	2
Sheets	-	-	-
Halyards with the tye	-	#	1 pr
Tye	-		
Lifts	2	2	2
Lift blocks	-	2	-
Martnets	-	-	-
Parral	1	1	-
Truss	-	-	-
Halyards	1 pr	-	-
Sail	1	1	1^
Yards	-	1	-
Puttocks	2	-	-
Winding ropes	-	1	-
Top	-	-	1

Appendix 1 cont'd

Foremast

Braces	2 & 2	2 pr	-
Lifts	2	2	2
Lift blocks	-	2	-
Martnets	-	#	-
Tye with halyards	1	-	-
Halyards	-	#	-
Halyards with the tye	-	#	-
Bowlines	2	2 pr	-
Swifters	-	2	-
Parral	1	1	1
Truss	-	1	1
Tacks	-	-	2
Stay	-	1	1
Sheets with pulleys	2	-	-
Sheets	-	2	2
Sail course	1	1	1
Bonnets	1	1	1
Shrouds per side	4	-	-
Shrouds	-	6	8
Yard	1	1	-

Appendix 1 cont'd

Main topmast

Backstays	2	4	2
Braces	-	2	2
Pendants	2	2	
Bowlines	2	-	2
Bowlines with double blocks	-	2	-
Halyards	1 pr	-	-
Halyards with their tye	-	#	1 pr
Shrouds	2 pr	-	8
Shrouds per side	-	4	-
Tackles	-	2	-
Stay	-	1	1
Lifts	-	-	2
Lifts with lift blocks	-	2	-
Parral	1	1	-
Truss	1	-	-
Sail	1	1	1^
Sheets	2	2	2
Clewlines	-	2	2
Winding rope	-	1	-
Girding to wind up the topmast	-	-	1
Top	-	1	1
Flag	-	-	1
Flagstaff	-	-	1

Appendix 1 cont'd

Mainmast

Truss	1	1	-
Shrouds	5	-	8
Shrouds per side	-	6	-
Tackles	-	4	-
Swifters	-	2	-
Halyards with tyes	-	2	1
Tye	1	-	-
Halyards	1 pr	-	-
Lifts with their blocks	-	#	-
Stay	-	-	1
Sheets	2	2	2
Bowlines	2 & 2 (sic)	2	2 (1+)
Martnets	-	2	-
Parral	1	1	1
Tacks	2	2	2 & 2
Braces	-	2	-
Pendants of braces-	-	-	2
Sail course	1	1	1
Bonnets	1	2	1^
Drablers	1	-	-
Pendant	1	-	-
Yard	1	1+	-

Appendix 1 cont'd

Mizzenmast

Shrouds	-	-	6
Shrouds per side	-	4	-
Tackles with 1 fale(?)	-	2	-
Stay	-	-	1 old
Halyards	2 pr	-	-
Halyards with the tye	-	1	1 pr
Sheets	-	1	1
Lift	1	1	1
Bowline	-	1	2
Truss	-	1	
Sail	1	-	-
Pulleys	6	-	-
Parral	-	1	-
Yard	1	-	-

Appendix 1 cont'd

Implements

Cables	-	3	3.5
New cables	2	-	-
Old cables	2	-	-
Anchors	-	-	4
Anchors with stocks	3	3	-
Anchors without stocks	-	1	
Buoys	2	-	3
Buoyropes	2 & 2 (sic)	1	3
Boat ropes	-	1	-
Old junk*	1	1	-
Hawser	1	1~	2
Sounding leads with lines	1	-	-
Boat hooks (?)2			
Fish hooks	1	-	1
Fish hooks with lines	-	1	-
Blocks with hooks	-	3	-
Lofe hooks	-	-	1
Cate(?) ropes	-	2	-
Grapnel	-	1	-
Can hooks	-	2 pr	2 pr
Lasthooks with a rope	-	2	-
Barrels of tar	-	1	-
Half anchor stocks	-	2	-
New sounding lines	-	1	-
Deep sea leads	-	-	1
Deep sea lines	-	4	-
Sounding leads	-	8	2 old
Marlyn skeins	3	-	-
Scupper leathers	2	-	-
Single pulleys	10	-	-
Small pulleys	4	-	-
Irons (?) for the pump	2	-	-
Slings	1 pr	-	-

Appendix 1 cont'd

Pumpboxes	1	-	-
Shet (?) boxes for the pump	-	-	2
Flags	1	-	-
Pendants (flags)	1	-	-
Compasses	4	5	4 old
Compass of variation, old	-	1	-
Running glasses	5	-	3
Iron chains (broken)	2	-	-
Shovels	3	-	3
Lanthornes	-	5	-
Pitch pots	-	1	-
Iron fids	-	1	-
Fids	-	-	2
Fid hammers	-	-	1
Marlyn spikes	-	-	1
Top bolts	-	-	7
Scoops	-	-	2
Small barrels	-	-	1
Skiff with 4 oars	-	-	1

Appendix 1 cont'd

Ordnance

Brass robinets with carriages	1	1	-
Cast iron minions with carriages	-	4	-
Iron falcons with carriages	2	2	2
Iron fowlers	-	2	-
Fowler chambers	-	4	-
"Murderers pece"	-	2	-
Bases	-	-	4
Chambers for bases	-	-	8
Forelocks	-	-	4
Minion sponges	-	2	-
Minion ladles	-	4	-
Falcon sponges	-	2	-
Falcon ladles	-	3	2@
Robinet sponges	-	1	-
Robinet ladle	-	1	-
Falconet ladles	2	-	-
Falconet sponges	1	-	-
Minion roundshot	-	52	-
Minion crossbar shot	-	21	-
Minion chain shot	-	2	-
Falcon shot	-	42	-
Falcon crossbar shot	-	14	-
Falconet shot	26	-	-
Falconet crossbar shot	5	-	-
Falconet chain shot	2	-	-
Robinet shot	-	3	-
Fowler shot	-	16	-

Appendix 1 cont'd

Formers for minion, falcon & robinet	-	3	-
Staff with a wadhook	-	-	1
Calivers	6	12	5
Flasks	-	9	-
Touchboxes	4	9	-
Charges for calivers	-	56	-
Crows	-	-	2
Bows	-	-	8
Yew bows	-	10	-
Sheaves of arrows	-	20	12
Long pikes	-	12	-
Pikes	5	-	-
Pikes with wildfire	-	12	-
Balls of wildfire	-	9	-
Bills	-	-	2
Black bills	-	2	-
Borespeares	-	-	3
Bowge barrels	-	3	2
Sheepskins	-	-	1
Rolls of match	11	-	-
Merches of iron for the busses (bases) (iron miches or mikes?)	-	-	2

Appendix 1 cont'd

Cook room implements

Great kettles	-	1	-
Latten kettles	1	-	1
Iron spits	1	-	-
Spits	-	1	-
Gridirons	1	1	-
Pair of bellows	-	1	-
Iron pots	1	-	1
Frying pans	1	1	1
Flesh hooks	-	1	-
Ladles	2	2	-
Wooden platters	4	-	5
Trays	-	2	2
Lanthornes	1	-	1
Iron hooks for kettle	-	2	-
Chain & hook for kettle	1	-	-
Hatchets	1		
Old axes	-	1	-
Black juc...(?)	-	-	1

Appendix 2

THE 1578 INVENTORY OF THE *AID*

Source: SP12/129, 36

Bowsprit	No. of items	Pulleys	Double blocks	Pendants
Yard	1			
Sail	1x			
Halyards	#	2a		
Lifts	#	4		
Braces	#	2		
Sheet	1			#
Shank painters with chains	2			
Bolt,	1			
Collar	1			
and iron chains	#			
Davit with iron clasp	1			
Brass sheaves to the davit	2			
Grapnel with chain	1b			
Cats	#			
False tyre for the spritsail	1			
Clewlines	1			

Appendix 2 cont'd

Foremast	No. of items	Pulleys	Double blocks	Pendants
Mast	1			
Sheave of brass in the masthead	1			
Fore top not	1			
Yard with gromets	1			
Swifters on each side	1	4x		
Sail course	1c			
Sail bonnet	1c			
Pendants on each side	2	4d		
Tackles on each side	2	4e		
Shrouds on each side	6			
Stay	1			
Lifts	#	4		
Tye	1x			
Halyards with one sheave of brass in the ramshead and two coaked in the ramshead	#			
Parral with lanyards and breast ropes	1			
2 trusses		2		
Bowlines	2x		1f	
Braces	#x	4		
Sheets	#	2a		
Sheaves of brass in the ship's side	none			
Tacks	#g			
Martnets	#			
Boat's tackle with 3 brass sheaves	1			

Appendix 2 cont'd

Fore topmast	No. of items	Pulleys	Double blocks	Pendants
Topmast	1			
Brass coak in the masthead	1			
Yard	1			
Sail	1c			
Tackles on each side	1	4		
Shrouds on each side	4			
Puttocks on each side	4			
Stay	1			
Backstay	1			
Tye and halyards	#	2h		
Lifts	#	4		
Sheets	#			
Parral, lanyards and breast ropes	1+			
Truss		2		
Bowlines	#		1	
Braces	#	4		
Clewlines	#	2		
Craneline	1			
Pendant pulley	1			

Appendix 2 cont'd

Mainmast	No. of items	Pulley	Double blocks	Pendants
Mast	1			
Brass sheaves in the masthead	2			
Maintop	j			
Yard with gromets and staples	1+ and j			
Sail course	1k			
Sail bonnet	1k			
Drabler	1m			
Swifter on each side	1c	4		
Pendants on each side	3	6n		
Boat's tackles	#x			
Sheaves of brass for boat's tackle	2			
Tackles on each side	3	12e		
Shouds on each side	8			
Stay	1			
Lifts	#	4		
Sheets	#x	2h		
Sheaves of brass in the ship's side	2			
Tacks	#			
Knight with two sheaves of brass	1			
Halyards with 3 sheaves of brass in the knight and ramshead	#			
Parral with lanyards and breast ropes	1			
Truss	1j	4		
Martnets	#x	6		
Garnet	1	20		
Braces	#	2		
Clewlines	#			

Appendix 2 cont'd

Main topmast	No. of items	Pulleys	Double blocks	Pendants
Top	1			
Mast	1			
Brass sheave in the masthead	1			
Sail	1m			
Tackles on each side	1	3		
Shrouds on each side	1			
Puttocks on each side	5			
Stay	1			
Backstay	1			
Lifts	#	4		
Sheets	#	4p		
Brass sheaves in the "bubbridge" head (none of brass)???	2			
Tye and halyards	#	2h		
Bowlines	#		1	
Braces	#	4		
Clewlines	#	2		
Clewline (sic)				
Rane bagge (prob. crane bag)	1			
Pendant pulley	1			

Appendix 2 cont'd

Mizzenmast	No. of items	Pulleys	Double blocks	Pendants
Mast	1			
Sheave of brass in the masthead	1			
Yard	1			
Sail course	j			
Sail bonnet	j			
Swifter on each side	1j	4		
Shrouds on each side	5			
Stay	1			
Tye and halyards with a brass sheave and breast ropes	#			
Truss	1	2		
Bowlines	none			
Smiting line	none			
Mizzen martnets	#			

Mizzen topmast	No. of items	Pulleys	Double blocks	Pendants
Top	1			
Mast	1			
Shrouds on each side	3			
Puttocks on each side	4			
Stay	1			

Appendix 2 cont'd

Implements

	No. of items
Main capstan with collar and pawl of iron	1
Capstan bars	8
(note: no pawl or bars)	
Fore capstan with iron pawl	1
Fore capstan bars	2
State pump with a bracke (brake?)	1
Bedstead in the captain's cabin	1
Table in the captain's cabin	1+
Pair of bilbowes with 6 shackles	1
Grindstone with an iron winch and spindle	1
Copper kettle	1
Meat kettle	1
Very small meat kettle	1
Bar with a chain and 3 hooks in the cook room to hang the kettle on	1
but iii anchors (sic)	
Great anchors	4
12-inch cables that the ship is moored by	2
Cables of 11 inches	3r
Cables of 10 inches	1s
Cables of 8 inches for a boat rope	1s
Cables of 6 inches	1t
Geste ropes of 5 inches	1s
Condinge (sic) hawsers of 5 inches	1
Hawsers of 5 inches	1
Fathoms of a hawser of 5 inches	10
Breton tackle, with 4 sheaves of brass and one of iron coaked with 3 blocks and one 1 pendant tackle	1

Appendix 2 cont'd

Buoyropes	1
Cat ropes	2x
Fathoms of sacks of coil of 3 inches	10
Pieces of coil of one inch and one inch and a half	3
Flags of St George	1x
Compasses	2
Running glasses	1j
Sounding lines	2
Sounding leads	3
Buckets	2
Bowls	4
Shovels	4
Scoops (skoppes)	2
Spare pulleys great and small, 2 coaked with brass	6
Bundles of marlines	2
Ratline, shives (sic)	
Pounds of twine	10
Bolts of middremaxe	4
Calappes(?)	5
Pitch pots	1j
Fish hooks	2
Leech hooks	2/1 (sic)
Luff hooks	4
Ballast baskets	2
Pair of can hooks	1
Buoys	4/3 (sic)
Cat hooks sheaved with brass	2

Appendix 2 cont'd

Ordnance and munitions

"Ordnances and munitions put into the ship, after she was brought, which dide cost as followeth"

Brass ordnance	No.	Total wt. (lb)	Cwt. per gun	Total cost
Minions	2	2524	11.25	£67. 13s. 4d
Falcons	1	854	7.5	£22. 17s. 6d
Falcons	2	1680	7.5	£35. 0s. 0d
Carriages	5			£6. 13s. 4d
TOTALS	5	5058		£132. 4s. 2d

Iron ordnance	No.	Total wt. (lb)	Cwt. per gun	Total cost
Sakers	8	12544	14.0}	
Minions	1	1232	11.0}	£99. 0s. 0d
Falcons	5	4704	8.4}	
TOTALS	14	18480	33.4	£99. 0s. 0d
Carriages	14			£17. 13s. 4d
Fowlers	6 } stocked			£30. 0s. 0d
Fowler chambers	12 }			

Munitions	No.	Total wt.	Lb. per shot	Value
Roundshot				
Saker	207	1148	5.5	
Falcon	69	172	2.5	
Culverin	19	172	9.0	
Minion	17	70	4.1	
TOTALS	312	1562		£6. 18s. 0d (10s per cwt)
Crossbar shot				
Saker	69	364	5.25	
Falcon	27	140	5.2	
Minion	11	70	6.4	
TOTALS	107	574		£5. 18s. 0d
(23s per cwt)				
Chain shot				
Saker	14	112	8.0	
Falcon	7	28	4.0	
TOTALS	21	140		£1. 8s. 6d
Stone shot Fowlers		53		£1. 13s. 0d

Appendix 2 cont'd

Gun furniture

	No. of items
Ladles with staves for falcons and minions	15
Sponges and staves for sakers, minions and falcons	12
Rammer staves	20
Formers for sakers, minions and falcons	3
Iron crows	9
Drill	1
Tampions	29
Gouge	1
Chisels	4
Peckers for stone shot	1
Sledge	1
Spare truckles	9

Armour, weapons and munitions (some items in this section here transferred to "Gun furniture")

	No. of items
Stocked calivers	32
Calivers without stocks	6
(Powder) flasks	16
Touch boxes	10
Moulds (for shot)	20
Match skins	2 cwt
Ewe bows	25
Sheaves of arrows	45
Bowstrings	7 dozen
Partezans	4
Black bills	16
Pikes	5
Trunks of wildfire	2
Wildfire balls	2
Wildfire arrows	11
Wildfire pikes	5

Appendix 2 cont'd

Ship's boat

	No. of items
Brass sheave in the (mast)head	1
Painter chain	1
Davit with an iron sheave	1
Windlass	1
Mast with a sail	1
Rudder with spindle and caps	1b

Ship's skiff

Oars	12
Rudder with ironwork	none

Key

* containing 28 fathoms
\# listed, but without number
\+ broken
~ of 3 inches (circumference)
^ new
@ one with a staff
x worn

a	with brass coaks
b	lost
c	three parts worn
d	"one shevered and one cocked"
e	"three cocked with brass"
f	with 2 brass sheaves
g	one of them new
h	"one shevered and one cocked with brasse" (ie sheave and coak were of brass: cf main sheet listing in text)
j	"nawght" (seemingly means "worthless")
k	good
m	new
n	one with a brass sheave
o	with 3 brass sheaves
p	with 2 sheaves, one brass, and 2 coaked with brass
r	"one of the ii of 13 inches, one of them a juncke and cut"
s	half worn
t	"new, spent and gone"

Appendix 3

VALUATIONS OF THE *AID*, *GABRIEL*, *JUDITH* AND *MICHAEL*, 1578

Aid:

Value of ship, rigging and gear:	£850
Value of ordnance and munitions:	£345
Total:	£1195

Value given by William Winter and William Holstok:

Ship, rigging and gear:	£700 (23 February 1578)
Value of 5 guns and carriages:	£132. 2s. 11d*
Other ordnance in the inventory thought "not mete for her highness"	
Total:	£832. 2s. 11d

*valued at £138. 16s. 8d earlier

1578:

Gabriel: £150
Judith: £250
Michael: £150

Appendix 4

COMPARATIVE DATA ON THE AGE AND ORIGINS OF ELIZABETHAN MERCHANT SHIPPING

Information about Tudor merchantmen is not easily available. Inventories and other information relating to merchant vessels can be found in the naval and other records, but the most comprehensive source of information is in the archives of the High Court of Admiralty. The HCA had jurisdiction over legal matters connected with the sea, and regularly arrested ships in cases of piracy, contested ownership and other disputes. The ships were appraised by experts (generally shipwrights and mariners), who usually listed the tonnage, the gear on board and the value of the ship and its equipment. They also often made comments about a ship's condition, and on occasion gave estimations of the ages of particular vessels. One hundred and fifteen ship appraisals have been examined for the period 1579-1590: these vary in the amounts of detail given, so it is not possible to find complete inventories for each of these vessels, but taken together they give us an unrivalled insight into the nature of English, and to an extent, north European merchant shipping at the time (1). They also give us context for the ships used on the north-western voyages. References below to the "HCA Survey" refer to these documents.

Out of the 115 vessels, 97 were complete ships: the rest were unrigged, or in some cases, completely derelict. The tonnages of 49 are known: 22 (44.9%) were of 49 tons or less, while the remaining 25 (55.1%) were of 50 tons burden or more. Age estimates of varying degrees of vagueness were given for 66 of the 97, as Table 8 shows:

Table 8:   **Age estimates for ships appraised by the HCA, 1579-90**

Age range (years)	Number
3-6	7
7-10	5
11-15	8
16-20	14
21-25	2
50	1
"Old"	13
"Very old"	15

As the table shows, 54 (82%) of the 66 vessels were described as either "old," "very old" or more than 10 years old, suggesting that it was not uncommon for merchant vessels to remain in service for many years.

Appendix 4 cont'd

The ships were also of varied origins. This is important, because ships were regularly exchanged between countries, by means of sale, abandonment or capture. The origins of 112 of the ships were noted:

Table 9:   Origins of ships appraised by the HCA, 1579-90

Country of origin	Number
England	68 (60.7%)
Holland	19 (17.0%)
France	8 (7.1%)
Spain	6 (5.4%)
Germany	4 (3.6%)
Flanders	3 (2.7%)
Denmark	1 (0.9%)
Foreign, but country unknown	1 (0.9%)

Whilst we know very little about the majority of the ships used in Frobisher's voyages, this comparative data does suggest the possibility that some of the vessels were foreign-built, and some were of appreciable age.

Notes

1. HCA 24/50-57, passim

Appendix 5

THE QUEEN'S SHIP *AID*: A BRIEF HISTORICAL NOTE

The *Aid* was launched in October 1562, as ship of 250 tons, with a crew of 150 (1). The ship took part in the siege of a Hispano-Papal fort in Smerwick Bay, Ireland, in 1580, and was at sea in 1588 as part of the anti-Armada fleet. The *Aid* was finally disposed of by the navy in about 1599, after nearly 40 years in service.

(1).   Glasgow 1970; NMM 1988, p.156.

Appendix 6

GLOSSARY OF TECHNICAL TERMS

General descriptions of nautical gear are based on Kemp 1979 or OED. Other sources are given in brackets.

Rigging

Backstay	A rope giving longitudinal support to a mast, led aft
Block	A pulley
Bonnet	An extra strip of canvas, laced to the bottom of the course, or main body of a square sail to increase the sail area
Bowlines	Ropes attached to the vertical edges, or leeches, of a square sail, and led forward; when the ship is sailing to windward, the bowline on the weather side of the sail is pulled tight to keep that side of the sail taut
Braces	Ropes attached to each end of a yard, and used to move it round
Breton tackle	A type of tackle involving a multiple arrangement of pulleys
Clewlines	Lines used to haul up the clews, or lower corners of a square sail
Craneline	Line used to haul ammunition and other items up to a top in a crane bag
Coak	Brass bearing in the centre of a pulley sheave, used to reduce wear on the sheave as it turns, and to prevent it from splitting
Course	The main body (Latin: corpus) of a sail
Drabler	A secondary bonnet, that could be laced to the foot of a bonnet
False	In nautical terms, used to denote a temporary fitting
Forestay	Rope giving longitudinal support to a mast, led forward
Garnet	Tackle used for hoisting barrels
Girding	Seemingly, a rope used to raise a topmast (topmasts were detachable)

Appendix 6 cont'd

Halyard	Rope used to haul up a yard, in conjunction with a tye
Knight	Upright block of wood, containing pulley sheaves, fixed to the deck, and used with the ramshead to help raise and lower the yard
Leech	Vertical edge of a sail
Lift	A rope that lifts or supports a yard
Martnets	Lines used to haul the leeches of a sail up to the yard when the sail was being furled, or the sail area shortened
Parral	A rope or series of ropes threaded through wooden balls, and used to keep a yard against a mast whilst giving it freedom of movement
Pendant	A short rope made fast at one end to the head of mast or the end of a yard, with a pulley at the other end, through which a rope can be passed
Puttocks	Small shrouds at the top of a mast, used to give access to the top (q.v.)
Ramshead	Heavy block used to help raise and lower a yard
Ratlines	Ropes tied across shrouds to enable mariners to climb up a yard or top
Sheets	Ropes used to control the clews of a sail, led aft
Shrouds	Ropes used to give lateral support to a mast
Swifters	Ropes used to help keep the shrouds taut, and thus to help support the mast (Manwaring and Perrin 1921, p.240)
Tacks	Ropes used to control the clews of a sail, led forward
Top	Originally, a topcastle, a small fighting or lookout platform at the top of a mast
Truss	Rope used to haul the yard back against the mast; also used to help haul it down
Tye	A rope used to hoist a yard and sail

Appendix 6 cont'd

Winding rope Rope attached to a windlass or other type of winding gear

General equipment

Bilbow   Long iron bar used to secure prisoners

Buoyrope   Rope attaching a small buoy to an anchor: the buoy is used to
              mark the anchor's position when it is on the sea-bed

Can hooks   Hooks used to help hoist barrels

Fid   Wooden bar used to connect a topmast to a lower mast

Junk   Old rope or cable cut into short pieces and used for fenders, etc.

Lanthorne   Lantern: originally, the flame was enclosed by thin strips of horn

Lasthooks   Possibly hooks used to help lift large barrels, or lasts

Lofe/luff   Possibly rigging gear
hooks

Marline   Light, general-purpose line

Marline spike Wooden or metal spike used to help untie knots

Pump-box   Part of a ship's pump

Scuppers   Drain-holes in the sides of open, or weather, decks; leather valves
              could be used to close them under external water pressure

Shank   The part of an anchor connecting the arms with the stock

Shank painter Rope used with the shank of an anchor

Shovels   Probably used the shift ballast into or out of a ship

Stock   Removable wooden arm attached to an anchor

Appendix 6 cont'd

Weaponry

Base	Small breach-loading gun
Bill	Pole-arm with a blade
Borespear	Short pole-arm
Bowge barrel	Small barrel used to bring powder from the magazine to the gun
Caliver	Type of musket
Chamber	Removable metal cylinder, containing the gunpowder charge for a breach-loading gun
Chainshot	Two cannon balls linked by a length of chain: used to destroy rigging
Crossbar shot	Two cannon balls linked by an iron bar
Crow	Metal lever
Falcon	Cannon firing a shot of about 2½-3 lb (NMM 1988, p.175)
Flask	Powder flask
Forelock	Iron wedge used to keep part of a gun or carriage in position (Blackmore 1976, p.231)
Former	Round piece of wood used to make powder cartridges for guns (Blackmore 1976, p.230)
Fowler	Small breach-loading gun mounted on a swivel (Manwaring and Perrin 1921, p.228)
Ladle	Ladle with a long handle, used to load gunpowder into a muzzle-loading gun
Merche/ miche/mike	Possibly the swivel for a swivel gun
Minion	Cannon firing a shot of about 4 lb (NMM 1988, p.175)

Appendix 6 cont'd

Murderer   Small gun used to fire anti-personnel shot (NMM 1988, pp..175-6)

Robinet   Small cannon, firing a shot of less than 1 lb weight (NMM 1988, p.175)

Roundshot   Spherical cannon balls

Sponge   Wetted sheepskin mop on a long handle, used to dowse any sparks left in a gun barrel after it has been fired, to prevent them from igniting the next charge

Touch-box   Tinder-box for a musket

Wadhook   Hook on a pole used to remove charges or wads (plugs to keep charges in position)

Wildfire   Incendiary material

Cathay and the Way Thither:
the Navigation of the Frobisher Voyages

J. McDermott and D.W. Waters

THE ARTE OF NAVIGATION, demonstrateth how, by the shortest good way, by the aptest Direction, & in the shortest time, a sufficient Ship, betwene any two places (in passage Nauigable) assigned: may be conducted: and in all stormes, & naturall disturbances chauncyng, how, to vse the best possible meanes, whereby to recouer the place first assigned.[1]

To the modern eye, the self-evidence of the quotation from John Dee's renowned preface to Billingsley's *Euclid* would appear to render it almost superfluous. Writing in 1570, however, Dee was not addressing an audience to whom either the art or practice of oceanic navigation was a commonplace. To the contrary, the purpose of the text he introduced was to illustrate and correct the relative ignorance of contemporary Englishmen in all branches of the applied sciences, and in the "nautical" sciences in particular. The latter half of the sixteenth century was a period of striking transition in the nature and significance of England's maritime activities; one in which intention was not always matched by capability. The flux of novel circumstance and perceived opportunity was to create reputations — even fortunes — for some men, disasters and ignominy for many more; a process that was characterised by enthusiasm, energy and, undoubtedly, over-confidence. Yet by the end of the century, notwithstanding the misconceptions and errors which had confounded countless dreams of empire, English and Dutch achievements had begun to challenge — albeit tentatively — the Iberian Nations' absolute superiority in maritime technology and expertise. This transformation of English abilities, and the conditions which allowed it, forms a perspective into which the technical assessment of any contemporary English maritime project should be placed.[2]

Introduction: Leaving the Known World

The development of any applied discipline requires the stimulus of a cause; that of oceanic navigation was contingent upon the need for solutions to problems specific to long-range voyages. The geographical situation of the Iberian peninsula, and the southern drift of the Atlantic current down the North African coast, made it logical that Portugal and Spain should have led the European search for these solutions, and that the English should have come relatively late to this process.[3] Prior to the first north-eastern voyages of the 1550s, English "oceanic" experience — that is, of voyages off the continental shelf — had been largely the preserve of those Bristol, Hull and Newcastle men who, since the early fifteenth century, had plied the short passage to Iceland to buy dried cod and return, sometimes via Galway (where they may have traded with Portuguese ships putting in there).[4] The few, unnamed fishermen who made the more arduous passage to the Newfoundland Banks from the late fifteenth century onwards did so by following the prevailing winds with little more scientific method than the gulls in their wakes. They simply sailed due west until their "dipsie" (or deep sea) sounding line told them that they had reached the Banks, and then cast their nets into the water. And whilst Englishmen had long made voyages to Portugal, Spain and the Mediterranean, these required only the expertise which a literate Pilot gleaned from his rutter,[5] rather than from celestial observation, because sight of land was rarely lost (other than during the brief south-westerly passage across the abyssal depths of the Bay of Biscay).

There is, however, evidence that English long-range voyages were being planned with increasing frequency throughout the first half of the sixteenth century, without necessarily indicating that this represented a deliberate and sustained policy of expansion. John Cabot (of Genoese birth but in pay at least, an Englishman) crossed the Atlantic to Newfoundland in 1497, possibly using a simple westing course taken from Dursey Head on the Irish coast.[6] Other, English-born seamen had also made the trans-Atlantic passage in lower latitudes. In 1526, Roger Barlow (a Bristol merchant who had previously traded in Spain and Morocco) entered the River Plate, and in 1530 William Hawkins explored the coast of Brazil; yet it is almost certain that Barlow sailed in a Spanish ship, and that Hawkins employed a foreign, probably Portuguese pilot. Other, half glimpses of projects intended — probably — to seek passages to the east emerge from various sources, to confirm both a growing awareness of the possibilities of reconnaissance, and the inability on the part of Englishmen, unaided, to realise them.[7]

In contrast, the Portuguese, with their gradual push southwards into the Atlantic from the early fourteenth century and, more particularly, with the crossing of the equator in 1471, began to encounter navigational problems which required the amplification of a system based upon pilotage lore. Observation of the Sun and stars might allow the navigator to find his way, but scientific instruments and astronomical tables needed to be developed which would enable such observation, and the methods of calculation to utilise it. These innovations stand as the great achievement of the Portuguese navigators. Establishing a north-south position by observation of the altitude of the Pole Star became impossible as they moved southwards and progressively lost sight of that guide in the skies. The work of a Royal Commission established in 1484 by King John II resulted in the adaptation of the solar tables of the Jewish astronomer Zacuto of Salamanca for the use of the navigator, both in the northern and southern hemispheres. The new system was first tested off the coast of Guinea in 1485; with it, the Portuguese had devised the means to determine the daily declination of the Sun itself, and thus to establish latitude.[8] In 1487, the Portuguese rounded the Cape of Good Hope and entered the Indian Ocean, and the problem of oceanic navigation then became one of how to measure an east-west passage (a problem also to be encountered by Columbus in the Atlantic just five years later).

This, in contrast to the determination of latitude, remained beyond the abilities of fifteenth- and sixteenth- century science to resolve.[9] It was one thing to make the conceptual leap to regard oceanic navigation in a spherical context, and another to resolve the problems which such a perception brought. Celestial observation was not in itself of sufficient accuracy (at least not based upon contemporary data and instruments) to provide the solution; nor could an instrument to measure time be constructed with the necessary degree of precision (sixteenth-century timepieces tended to lose at the rate of about fifteen minutes per day). This lack of adequate technology consequently made the calculation of longitude impossible, even under "ideal" circumstances — for example, along an east-west course at or near the equator. Any variation from such a course swiftly exacerbated the problem of establishing longitude and of representing the same upon charts. By the early sixteenth century, it was appreciated that meridional lines of longitude — unlike parallels of latitude — inevitably converged (that is, towards the poles). However, the navigators of Spain and Portugal, whose strategic interests were largely confined to lands and oceans between latitudes 35° north and 35° south (and thus not exposed to the worst errors of calculation caused by ignoring meridional convergence) continued to use a "standard" measurement of length for one degree of longitude, thus adding the burden of conceptual inaccuracy to the mechanical difficulties of establishing longitude.[10]

The problem of depicting longitude had at least one advantage; it made clear the inherent inaccuracies of the plane chart, which had become the principal hydrographical tool of the pilot and navigator. On such a chart, meridians of longitude were drawn equidistantly and the same length as the equatorial line. The further from the equator, the greater the distortion from the true relationship of one meridian of longitude from another, which not only threw out the relative position of landmasses, but also the bearing of north-south coastlines. Plotting an accurate course upon such a chart, particularly one which crossed lines of longitude, was almost impossible. For example, a course drawn upon a plane chart as a straight line north-west from the equator would in reality take a vessel to a location significantly south-west of an expected landfall, as the plotted course would traverse "parallel" meridians of longitude at a point increasingly south from the true course.[11] It was to the navigators of nations whose areas of concern lay far to the north or, less likely, south of the Equator, that such problems fell most urgently to be resolved. In this respect, the geo-political limitations imposed by the Treaty of Tordesillas were in some ways fortuitous, in bestowing an additional incentive to innovate upon the North European states that wished to gain access to new markets without encroaching overtly upon Spanish or Portuguese possessions.

It was the work carried out in the Spanish Netherlands (under Imperial auspices) by men such as Gemma Frisius and Gerard Mercator that began to address problems which the Portuguese and Spanish had little further incentive to solve themselves. In particular, Mercator sought to overcome the errors of the plane chart with his terrestrial globe of 1541, which was not only of sufficient compactness to carry in a ship — though large enough to take a course from — but contained sufficient information (parallels of latitude, longitude properly drawn, tropics, rhumbs lines represented as a spiral, scales of distance and an adjustable quarter circle to allow courses to be taken from the curved surface) to enable those calculations to be fairly accurate — always subject, of course, to the flawed cosmographical assumptions upon which they were based.

Mercator produced a companion, celestial globe in 1551 for observation and plotting of the night sky. In Spain the same year, Martin Cortes published his *Arte de Navegar*, which, though not generally innovative in content, was undoubtedly the most comprehensive compendium of instruction and empirical observation available to the contemporary navigator. These developments, together with increasingly precise standards in the manufacture of instruments (which will be discussed with particular reference to the Frobisher voyages), brought increasing levels of sophistication to the practical application of navigational theory. They were principally Continental advances, however, and in this respect, England stood very much apart from the Continent.

What contemporaneous efforts were being made to correct England's relative technical backwardness? The first stirring of an appreciation of the problem came with the accession of Henry VIII, a sovereign with European ambitions. The work of the Corporation of Trinity House (established in 1514) eventually led to the end of English reliance upon foreign pilots, whilst that of the Navy Board brought great technical improvements to the construction and maintenance of the King's ships. By the end of Henry's reign, it was possible to conduct a well-built, efficient English fleet against that of the French without foreign expertise.[12] These, however, were largely structural improvements which supported a policy based around European waters. They did not, in themselves, provide a grounding upon which England might become an oceanic power. That was to be determined under the influence of the most powerful of national imperatives — economic necessity.

The religious upheavals of the mid-sixteenth century coincided with the near collapse (after a number of very disappointing years) of England's traditional markets in the Low Countries; a blow which carried at least one fortuitous repercussion in encouraging a general breakdown of commercially conservative attitudes. What had previously been the preoccupation of a few adventurous merchants and courtiers — the search for new markets outside Europe — became an increasingly important component of English commercial activity. In an early example of "head-hunting," the Pilot-Major of Spain, Sebastian Cabot, returned to England in 1548 and was persuaded (that is to say, bribed) to stay as a royal pensioner, meanwhile divulging the latest Spanish techniques of navigation and, vitally, the financial and organisational minutiae required to organise and set out a long-range voyage.[13] Cabot's influence was probably paramount in dispatching what amounted to an English training voyage for would-be navigators in 1553 under Roger Bodenham;[14] that of the bark *Aucher*, to the eastern Mediterranean. The vessel was crewed by approximately seventy men and boys, most of whom, according to Bodenham, were to become qualified to take charge as masters of their own vessels within six years of the voyage.[15]

It is clear, therefore, that if much of the new direction in English maritime activity was — inevitably — channelled into "piggy-backing" existing Spanish and Portuguese overseas markets,[16] the beginning of a significant and independent expertise was already discernible prior to the north-eastern voyage of Willoughby and Chancellor in 1553. Yet even acknowledging this point, it should be recognised that the amount and quality of subsidiary work carried out specifically in relation to the voyage was striking. John Dee, recently returned from Paris (where he had lectured on the geometry of Euclid), produced his *Astronomicall and Logisticall Rules* for use on the voyage. Dee also worked closely with Richard Chancellor, who independently invented a diagonal scale for the giant quadrant, with which he and Dee produced new solar declination tables.[17] Richard Eden produced a translation of Sebastian Munster's 1536 *A treatyse of the New India ...* to promote the aims of the venture, and Sebastian Cabot himself drew up ordinances for the conduct of the voyage which subsequently became a model for English expeditions of the period.[18]

The attention lavished upon — and generated by — the 1553 voyage is at once a strong indication of the relative dearth of expertise prior to that year and of the clear contemporary perception of that failing. The subsequent establishment of the Muscovy Company to exploit the new contacts with Russia, the almost simultaneous extension of the Barbary trade down the West African coast to "Guinea," and the myriad half-baked, speculative and sometimes grandiose schemes which characterised almost every avenue of English overseas expansion in the following two decades, were activities which would not have been possible without the growing expertise of the masters and pilots in whose vessels such schemes were tested. The Muscovy Company in particular ensured to itself a supply of the right men by appointing Sebastian Cabot and, following his death, John Dee, to oversee the training of Company crews. Of those who first learned their trade under "Company" tuition, several men stand out in the further development of English hydrographic expertise. As apprentice seamen, the Borough brothers, Stephen and William, received their theory from the hands of Cabot, Chancellor and Dee, and their practice upon the early voyages to Muscovy.[19] Christopher Hall, who was to figure prominently in the Frobisher voyages, was also a Muscovy boy and man, and may well have received some tuition from Dee prior to their first known association in 1576. These growing skills were by no means confined to the Company's men (who in any case had ample other employments through which to exercise and disseminate their skills), but rather reflected the broader contemporary English appreciation of the need to develop an expertise to challenge the activities of the new empires of Spain and Portugal.

Broadly speaking, however, if the rate of improvement in the practical skills of English mariners during the 1550s and 1560s seems striking, it is principally because standards had far to rise. Individuals may have transcended the abilities of their fellows, but anecdotal and documentary evidence suggests that the overall standard of pilotage and navigation remained unsatisfactory, even into the 1570s.[20] It is to their credit, however, that in learning a little of these necessary arts, English navigators realised the depth of their ignorance and worked to bring both practical and theoretical knowledge into the public domain. Returning from a visit to Seville in 1558, Stephen Borough brought home a copy of Cortes' *Arte de Navegar*, and persuaded the Muscovy Company to pay for its translation by Richard Eden. As *The Art of Navigation*, published in 1561, it was to be one of the most influential texts ever to appear in the English language.[21] On a more immediately practical level, Eden included narratives of English voyages in his 1555 translation of Martyr's *Decades of the new Worlde ...*, including the first two voyages to Guinea in 1553 and 1554 — in effect providing the first English rutter of the Atlantic.

Other Englishmen had already begun to fill the gaps in English understanding of the applied sciences. As early as 1551, Robert Recorde published an elementary textbook on geometry and the use of the quadrant, *The Pathway to Knowledge*; five years later, his treatise on the sphere, *The Castle of Knowledge* was printed specifically for Muscovy Company use. William Cuningham's *Cosmographical Glasse*, published in 1559 at the start of Elizabeth's reign, provided the first vernacular compendium of cosmographical data. Neither Recorde nor Cuningham could (or did) lay claim to originality of content or expression, but their works provided the first expositions on mathematics, navigation and cosmography that could be read by the educated layman, and thus were powerful tools in the creation of a broader expertise.[22]

Successive editions of a seaman's almanac, one of the basic tools of pilotage, were produced in increasingly sophisticated formats from 1555 by Leonard Digges, a mathematician like John Dee, whose interests crossed the indistinct contemporary delineation of science and the occult. Amongst the largely useless *prognostications* or astrological forecasts, these almanacs contained much valuable information on tides, constellations, the establishment of time at night, and even how to make a sun-dial. Another producer of almanac and prognostication was William Bourne, who issued editions in 1567 and 1571. However, his third publication was fundamentally more valuable; the *Regiment for the Sea* (1574) gave the English their first home-grown manual of navigation, one which was intentionally "written down" to a level which the literate master could understand. In it, and of particular relevance to those sailing to high latitudes, was an English innovation: how to take a latitude reading in regions where the sun does not set; that is, a reading at midnight, rather than at noon. Invaluable to those who would visit such regions in the future, it was undoubtedly drawn from the prior experience of the Muscovy men during their voyages to St Nicholas in the White Sea.[23]

One further area of English activity worthy of mention is that of the instrument maker's art. Until the accession of Henry VIII, this was almost entirely a European industry; but with the increasing sophistication of domestic metal-working needed to outfit the new Navy with guns and sighting mechanisms (largely utilising the skills of religious refugees from the Low Countries), a home-grown expertise in the production of scientifically precise instruments had come into existence by mid-century. With the work of Thomas Gemini from c.1550, and Humphrey Cole some years later, England had instrument makers to rival any on the Continent (as we shall note, Cole's craft was to be well represented in the Frobisher voyages).[24]

In his introduction to the *Regiment for the Sea*, William Bourne acknowledged his debt to Dee's preface to Billingsley's *Euclid*, but added his own definition of the good Master:

> *As touching those persons that are meete ... to be as maisters of ships in*
> *Nauigation, he ought to be sober and wise ... one as can wel gouern himselfe,*

for else it is not possible for him to gouerne his company ... And furthermore, the Maister ought to be suche a one, as dothe knowe the Moones course, wherby he doth knowe at what time it is a full Sea, or a lowe water ... and ... ought to be expert, how the tydegates or currentes doe set from place vnto place: and also not to bee ignorant of such daungers as lyeth by the way. ... and also most principally he ought to bee such a one, as can very well directe his courses vnto any place assigned. ... And also he that taketh charge for long voyages, ought to haue knowledge in plats or cardes, and also in such instrumentes as be meet to take the heigth of the Sunne or any Starre, and to haue capacitie to correcte those instrumentes, and also he ought to be such a one, that can calculate the Sunnes declination, or else to haue some true regiment, and ... knowe howe to handle the Sunnes declination when he hath taken the heigth of the Sunne.[25]

At the time that Bourne set down this definition of the complete navigator or, more accurately perhaps, his wish-list for the same, how far could his expectations be considered realistic? As we have seen, the tools with which the master-navigator might learn his trade were in place, if imperfectly; a body of empirical data was slowly gathering in the wake of the first Muscovy and Guinea ventures and, more recently, the Atlantic voyages of men such as Hawkins and Drake; and the imperatives of expansion were being confronted enthusiastically by a generation of propagandists, adventurers and speculators, many of whom were prepared to put up lawful money to realise their ambitions. There is certainly much evidence that the lessons acquired by these advances had yet to be fully absorbed across the broad profession of educated seamen — hence the worthy attempt of Billingsley's *Euclid* to provide an accessible grounding in the applied sciences. To what extent, then, was it possible for the execution of these increasingly ambitious voyages to match the vision of the intellectual promoters of English expansion? The following discussion will attempt to address this question by analysing the application of the new skills during one enterprise: the northwest voyages of Martin Frobisher.

Cathay and Meta Incognita

As early as 1555, Richard Eden had urged that the feasibility of a way to the Far East via the north-west be established. Humphrey Gilbert had taken up this theme in his *A Discourse of a Discoverie for a new Passage to Cataia* from 1566, although it did not appear in published form until a decade later — ironically, to publicise Frobisher's forthcoming attempt to realise the goal which Gilbert himself had failed to prosecute a decade before. The lure of the prospective Northwest Passage became more persistent as initial hopes for a readily-navigable north-eastern route faded (although interest in the latter revived briefly in the 1590s with the eclipse, in turn, of hopes for a northwest route), and thus Frobisher's self-confessed obsession with finding such a passage was the personal manifestation of a more-widely held interest — albeit one which he pursued more persistently than most of his contemporaries. However, it should also be noted that opinion on the existence of a Northwest Passage was not universally sanguine; nor, if it should exist, that such a navigation would be possible. Writing in 1574-5, an anonymous author (possibly Richard Grenville)[26] sounded a note of caution which, allowing for the gross errors inherent in his geographical assumptions, was entirely sensible:

> *The distante of the Straightes of Anian to the northweste course being 200 grades (ie. degrees) in longitude maketh 6000 myles, alowinge 30 miles to a grade, for suche is the quantitie of a grade in 60 of latitude. Herto if we maye adioyne 1200 myles, which is the quantitie of 10 grades ascendinge and 10 descendinge tofore mencioned, there amountethe 7200 myles. Nowe consideringe the seas and ayre vnder the Artike circle are so congeled that they are navigable only 3 monethes in the yeare, wherof it is requisite to reserve at the leaste one monethe to retorne, if the said passadge if the said passadge[sic] sholde not be mette withall. Then examyne howe farr in the moyetie of that quarter a man maie passe, and the possibilitie of the voiadge will soone apeare.*

Grenville concluded that the discovery of the Northwest Passage would therefore be "vtterly inpossible or not without extreme perills of liefe and expence of victualles, without any advauntage in the meane." Such a view, whilst sensibly cautious, does not seem to have deterred the proponents of the north-western route. Grenville's comments on high latitude were specifically refuted by an anonymous author, who pointed out that, although the passage north-eastwards to Muscovy lay in 72° at its most northerly point, it was navigable for up to five months in the year.[27] That such conflicting opinions of the feasibility of extreme northern voyaging found equally robust support only serves to emphasise the utter dearth of hard contemporary data. The fact was that no contemporary commentator could offer more definitive evidence to support his arguments than the writings of Pliny, Nicholas of Lynn and the Zeno brothers; yet while men such as Grenville showed an admirable degree of scepticism in refuting such "evidence," potential investors having before them the rich example of the Spanish and Portuguese discoveries did not tend to err towards circumspection. Had Frobisher and Davis not attempted to find the Northwest Passage, others inevitably would have done so.

The provenance of the 1575-6 project — Frobisher's initial association with the London mercer Michael Lok and their subsequent approach to the Court of Elizabeth I and Muscovy Company (whose exclusive charter rights to seek a Northwest Passage had first to be circumvented) — has been dealt with in detail elsewhere, and needs little reiteration.[28] However, it is instructive to note the degree to which Frobisher and Lok sought to utilise the technical expertise gained upon previous Muscovy Company voyages, once the requisite licence had been obtained. In addition to enjoying a near-obsessive interest in the expansion of England's overseas trade (and the technical library to feed it), Lok was the Company's London Agent,[29] and must have had direct experience of the practicalities of organizing northern voyages. If such experience did not allow him to provide the necessary technical input himself, he knew at the least where to seek it. From an early stage — perhaps even before the project was resurrected in the early months of 1576 — William Borough was assisting in preparations for the forthcoming voyage; choosing a master and men (all probably in current or former service with the Muscovy Company), advising on equipment for the two barks, and offering his opinion on the intended course of the expedition.[30] Nicholas Chancellor, son of Richard, was appointed as purser to the expedition, with the responsibility of that office for outfitting the vessels. Perhaps most significantly, Borough's old teacher and former technical adviser to the Muscovy Company, John Dee, approached the adventurers to offer his professional expertise and, in particular, to school the expedition's principal officers in the rudiments of the nautical sciences.

It is difficult to assess the practical value of Dee's assistance. As the friend and respected correspondent of men such as Gemma Frisius, Pedro Nuñez and Gerard Mercator, and as a noted mathematician in his own right, the relevance of Dee's abilities to the requirements of the adventurers needs no special pleading. However, he was a late-comer to the project, first hearing of it just sixteen days before the expedition sailed, according to Michael Lok.[31] Frobisher's appreciation of Dee's tuition, dispatched in a letter from the Shetland Islands some days following the departure of the 1576 expedition, is well known, but his tone hints at a last-minute "cramming" of concepts and techniques which he might have found difficult to absorb, even with months of preparation. Hall, on the other hand, was probably familiar (at least in a practical sense) with most of what he heard.[32]

Given the brief time-scale of Dee's involvement prior to the dispatch of the 1576 voyage, it is also unlikely that he provided significant advice on the purchase of instruments, charts and texts (but see below). These were itemised by Michael Lok in his account books — with the cautionary note "theis Instrumentes to be restored"[33] — and offer a valuable insight into what was considered appropriate for such a voyage of discovery. Before we look at these purchases in detail, however, it is necessary to sound our own cautionary note. The list of instruments taken is almost certainly incomplete. Experienced pilots and navigators would have owned at least some of the most necessary means with which to exercise their trade, particularly where variations in quality and accuracy were an issue — as was the case, for example, with magnetic compasses. Furthermore, there is no indication in Lok's accounts of the provision of such vital information as solar or Pole Star declination tables, without which no navigator could hope to establish latitude. Even setting aside these omissions, it is apparent that the provision of instruments in Lok's list could only be considered adequate for a single vessel. Unless the adventurers were exhibiting blind optimism in assuming that the *Gabriel* and *Michael* would maintain contact at all times, we must assume that other equipment was taken, either by individuals as part of their personal property, or "loaned" by un-named sources.

Lok's accounts make it clear that at least some of the instruments were purchased from Humphrey Cole.[34] Their total cost (with charts and texts) was slightly more than £50, a significant proportion of the total outlay upon ships' equipment. The first listed item of expenditure was a practical, if mundane inclusion for a voyage of discovery: "for ii paper bookes for Accomptes ... li 0. 9. 0." Observation was useless if not recorded, and clearly, it was the intention that such new knowledge became the intellectual property of the "Company of Cathay," rather than be confined to the personal rutters of Hall and Griffin. The most expensive item purchased was "a great globe of metall in blanke in a case of Leather," upon which to work out problems of navigation whilst at sea; most particularly by circumventing the previously discussed errors of the plane chart. A "great instrument of brasse named Armilla Tolomei, or hemispherium" — or armillary sphere — was a companion globe upon which the plotting of constellations might be effected.

Another instrument — a "Sphera Nautica" — presents some problems. It is not clear whether Lok was referring to a globe upon which rhumb (that is, direction) lines were drawn, or whether this was a device for finding the variation between true and magnetic North (as devised by Jean Rotz in the 1540s).[35] No such ambiguity surrounds a "great Instrument of brasse named Compassum Meridianum" for establishing variation. Another brass instrument, a "Holometrum Geometrum," was an early precursor of the theodolite; a bearing plate mounted upon an open sight with adjustments for bearings and elevations, designed to chart unknown coastlines. Two items, a "Horologium Universale," and an "Annalus Astronomicus," provide the only evidence of duplication; these were, respectively, a universal dial or ring and an astronomical ring. Both were designed, albeit employing slightly different methods, to find the time by the Sun's declination at a particular latitude, (the latter was either invented or popularised by Gemma Frisius).[36] It would seem that two such similar instruments were not intended to be used on the same ship, unless for the purposes of cross-checking. In another entry, Lok unconsciously illustrated either the influence of his years on the continent, or the conservatism of current terminology, in describing a cross-staff as a "Balistella" (cf. the Portuguese *balestilhã*); again, the provision of just one of these fundamental tools of navigation suggests that others were carried on the expedition.

An astrolabe — like the cross-staff, for taking the Sun's altitude — was purchased from William Borough for £3. 10s. 0d. Waters has suggested that this was probably a universal planispheric, as opposed to the simplified sea-astrolabe, and may have been employed to tutor Frobisher and Hall at Muscovy House prior to sailing.[37] Nevertheless, it seems that a sea-astrolabe — or "mariner's ring" — was subsequently taken on the voyages, as George Best implies that such an instrument was found to be inadequate for use during the 1577 voyage.[38] Finally with regard to instruments, the compass maker William Thomas supplied 20 compasses "of divers sortes" (presumably some meridional ones, and others of the "Flemish" design — that is, without off-set flies to adjust for variation), and 18 hour-glasses, for measuring distance/time elapsed.[39]

The nature of the charts and maps for the expedition clearly illustrates the lack of reliable contemporary intelligence regarding the region to which it would sail. The greatest expense here was upon "a very great carte of Navigacion." This, or one of "vi Cartes of navigacon written in blanke parchment wherof 4 ruled playne and 2 rounde" was prepared by William Borough himself, upon which either Frobisher or Hall were to meticulously record the degree of magnetic variation of the compass at several points upon their course; the earliest extant manuscript to be thus marked.[40] The data upon which Borough drew prior to Frobisher's departure was based upon the orthodoxies of the Zeno map, as was "a great mappe universall of Mercator in prente"; a copy of Mercator's world map of 1569, purchased for the expedition at a cost of £1. 6s. 8d. In an attempt to resolve the problem of reconciling the depiction of longitude, the map represented meridians in parallel (the common practise upon plane charts), but progressively increased the length of a degree of latitude further away from the equator to compensate for this. The practical experience of the Frobisher voyages later caused Borough to criticise Mercator's map for this and also — his personal preoccupation — for failing to recognize magnetic variation.[41] Finally, Lok's accounts included an entry — "for a carte of Ortelius, prynte," but gave no cost; this was a reference to Ortelius' world atlas of 1570, the *Theatrum Orbis Terrarum*, which would have been available in England by the mid 1570s both in its entirety and in sections; William Borough later praised the work in his *Discours of the Variation*, and may have owned a copy (perhaps lending it to the adventurers for the purposes of tuition, which is why no cost was shown).

The literature purchased for the expedition — or rather, the nature of that which was omitted — again suggests that Lok's accounts do not offer a complete picture. Cuningham's *Cosmographical Glasse* and Recorde's *Castle of Knowledge* were bought (for ten shillings the pair), but these were primarily works of tuition, not reference. Andre Thevet's *Cosmographie Universelle* (Paris, 1575) and *Les Singularitéz de la France Antarctique ...* (Paris 1558), and Thomas Hacket's English translation of the latter, *The New found World or Antarctike* (London, 1568), also purchased by Lok, were devoted to the cosmography of North America, and again of limited use at sea. Another volume, Sir John Mandeville's *Voyages*, was useless for any purpose save as a paperweight (but fortunately cheap, at just one shilling). Only Pedro de Medina's *Regimiento de Navegaciõ* (Seville, 1552 or 1563 edition) could be described as a practical tool of the navigator (and an excellent one); but it was, of course, written in Spanish, and thus not likely to have been purchased to take on the voyage. Where, then, were the almanacs and Regiments (in English translation or, like that of Bourne, produced specifically for the benefit of English seamen), which we would expect to have seen employed by the masters of the *Gabriel* and *Michael*? From these apparent omissions we might deduce either such works were considered to be inadequate (which is highly unlikely) or that men such as Hall and Griffin possessed a small, representative selection already.

The two pages upon which Lok recorded these purchases constitutes almost all the evidence for instruments and literature utilised in the Frobisher voyages. A further entry in the accounts for the provisioning of the second voyage reveal that Humphrey Cole was paid for repairing certain instruments and for the supply of several more, none of which was specified.[42] In 1577, the ship *Ayde* was acquired from the Queen with all tackling, but no instruments.[43] The *Judith*, William Borough's own vessel, was bought for use in the third voyage; again, without mention of such items (the eleven further vessels hired to transport ore mined in 1578 came with all equipment ready supplied, and in their case, therefore, no incremental provision of instruments would have been required).

Lok's list of instruments accords broadly with what John Dee recommended to the accomplished master in his preface to Billingsley's *Euclid*, but in addition to these Dee also mentioned dividers or proportional compasses (probably owned personally by Hall and Griffin), circumpolar charts, and half- and three-hour glasses in addition to hour glasses, clocks and quadrants.[44] The dividers were vital, as we shall see, but the remaining items were probably mentioned by Dee for the sake of completeness, and not, in the light of other instruments already discussed, irreplaceable in themselves. Insofar as the judgment may be made on extant evidence, Frobisher's 1576 expedition appears to have been supplied with a broadly representative selection of the equipment available to contemporary seamen for long-range voyages. Whether this was adequate for their purpose, and that their employment of the technology matched the ideal promoted by Dee, Bourne and others are, of course, entirely distinct issues.

The Navigation of the Frobisher Voyages

The master's art

In examining the professional abilities of the seaman, our most valuable technical source is the master's log. All other accounts of the Frobisher voyages contain much detail which is of great supplementary value, but being written for the edification of a wider readership, they are largely unconcerned with the fundamentals of determining and following a course at sea. Owen Griffin's 1576 log for the *Michael* is not extant, which in view of his ignoble decision to abandon the voyage in the face of bad weather is hardly surprising (a more regrettable loss is the master's log of the *Michael* for the third voyage, in which the bark, separated from the rest of the fleet, spent almost three weeks ice-bound in Frobisher Bay, an ordeal reported from the *Judith*'s perspective by her captain, Edward Fenton). For the first voyage, therefore, Christopher Hall is our only first-hand technical authority. Unfortunately, his account is a drastically condensed version of his (no longer extant) ship's log, reduced and censored for reproduction by Hakluyt in the *Principall Navigations* of 1598-1600. In contrast, his log for the third voyage, extant but as yet unpublished,[45] offers abundant evidence of the master's craft.

Finally, Edward Fenton, though not a professional seaman, captained the ship *Judith* in 1578 and kept a log which offers sufficient evidence of the master's craft to constitute a valuable supplement to that of Hall.[46] Curiously, the extant fragment of the journal kept by Fenton's master, Charles Jackman, is clearly *not* a master's log, but rather a general account of the voyage, much in the manner of that written by George Best, although less detailed (why Jackman should have used such a format is unclear; the evidence of his performance in the latter two Frobisher voyage, and of his later north-eastern expedition with Arthur Pet, indicates that he was an accomplished mariner, although his written style is quite untutored).[47] There are no extant ship's logs for the second, 1577 voyage, although other material will be adduced, where relevant.

Why the master's log should be so important to the researcher is a function, at the most fundamental level, of his role within the ship's complement. He was, first, a pilot with practical experience of many harbours and coastlines of his own country. To bring his vessel into safe harbour, however, the master also needed to know the lie of the land (or rather, sea bed) that lay beneath him in shallow, tidal waters. His fundamental tool was the lead and line, an ancient device which allowed him not only to avoid treacherous reefs and shoals, but to judge his approximate position in known waters, even when out of sight of land. The lead was a hollow plummet "armed" with tallow or, sometimes, cloth. This would enable the master, in addition to determining the depth of water beneath him, to collect a sample which would describe the nature of the seabed or "ground"; again, the smell, texture — even taste of this sample — would provide evidence which allowed the master to know whether his course had been true. As a skill, it had necessarily predated any of those which were to allow oceanic voyages.

Then, as now, the handling of vessels in coastal waters was the pilot's responsibility. Christopher Hall's own expertise is evident from the frequency — particularly during the third voyage — with which he was called upon to take charge of vessels other than that to which he was appointed master. Thus, at Bristol on 2 May 1578, prior to the departure of the 1578 voyage, Hall's log reveals that he piloted the flagship *Ayde* out of King Road (the channel in the Severn Estuary immediately outside the mouth of Bristol's river, the Avon) and sailed her to Plymouth. From there, he took charge of the *Gabriel* to London, anchoring at Blackwall on 11 May. On 26 May, he took the *Gabriel* to Gravesend, and there the following day, took charge of the *Thomas Allen* to Harwich, where the fleet was to assemble. On 30 May, he was in charge of the *Ayde*, towing her from Harwich Haven into the "Rolling grownde," an anchorage between shoals outside the mouth of the river Orwell. Only on 3 June did he finally assume his place in the *Thomas Allen* for the voyage to Meta Incognita. Possibly to forestall his own confusion, his log contains marginalia recording his numerous transfers "in the Ayde" and "owt of the Gabriel." Clearly, Hall's expertise as a pilot was recognized and employed to the full by the adventurers, although his talent, as will be seen, was not always appreciated by Frobisher.

Hall's 1578 log in particular offers an excellent insight into the ceaseless spirit of enquiry which characterised the good master in an age when detailed and accurate charts of English coastal waters had yet to be drawn. On his journey down the river Severn in the *Ayde*, he took the opportunity of describing and sketching the navigable channel, with landmarks and fathom soundings shown clearly; although this passage was clearly of no more than marginal significance to his purpose in the coming expedition.[48] Three days later, off the Lizard in Cornwall, he recorded:

> *Note that the longest marke to go clere of the manickles,[49] is to kepe the* Lezard *a sayles bredth open of* Blackhed *to go clere withowt them & allso a sharp steple with a broche[50] to be kepte open over the land which serveth for the* Lecke ....

It requires no great leap of imagination to appreciate that similar data was finding its way into a hundred personal rutters, placed there by men whose trade depended upon skills acquired in empirical observation. The ship's log was not merely a record of events set down by reference to the division of the ship's watch; it was the means by which the master expanded his knowledge in a world in which there remained everything to learn.

In 1576, and again in 1578, Hall conscientiously marked the commencement of a voyage by taking the latitude of his point of departure from English waters. In 1576, he merely noted:

> *...being ouer against Grauesend, by the castle or blockhouse, we obserued the latitude, which was 51. degrees 33. min<u>ute</u>s. And in that place the variation of the Compasse is 11. degrees and a halfe.*[51]

Two years later, he set out a similar observation in a far more precise manner, almost as if it were intended to instruct others in the art, or perhaps as a self-conscious acknowledgement of the skill with which the good master plied his trade:

> *The 6. day, Tusday ... at that present beinge a Sowth sun<u>n</u> I did observe my Latitude one myle from the* Lezard
> *And fownd my elevation to be* _____ *49. grad.*
> *my aquinoctiall* _____ *41.*
> *my declination* _____ *09.*
> *my Latitude to be* _____ *50.*[52]

Hall's observation of latitude is correct, although the equinoctial is mis-stated (it should have read 40 degrees). To take the elevation of the Sun, he would have used a cross-staff,[53] dexterity with which came only as a result of long practise. Firstly, the Sun would have to be "taken" at its highest point; that is, at noon (more probably, the measurement would commence shortly before the estimated time, and several readings taken to straddle the correct moment). The end of the staff would be placed against the cheek-bone directly underneath the observing eye, and the horizon and Sun's upper edge (its body being shielded from the eye)[54] observed simultaneously — achieved by rapid blinking of the eye — whilst the crosspiece of the staff was maintained in the vertical plane and slid backward until Sun and horizon could just be seen at the edges thereof (the experienced master would know when noon had passed, as the cross-section would be moved away from the body for each successive reading, the Sun and horizon slowly converging).[55] The altitude of the Sun was then read from a scale upon the long axis of the staff. The fact that this arm-numbing and potentially blinding operation was usually carried out on a rolling deck did not add to its potential accuracy; the frequency with which observations were noted as "truely observed" indicates that they were subject to much verification.

Once at sea, the master was of necessity much busier than his modern counterpart. Had he the means of establishing longitude as closely as latitude, and possessed accurate charts of the entire surface of the Earth, finding his position on a certain day would not have been difficult. This was not possible, however, and meticulous observation of speed and direction needed to be made upon each watch, to allow even the roughest approximation of a ship's longitudinal passage. A typical day's entry from Hall's 1578 log gives some indication of how onerous this could be:

> *The 9. of June Monday from 4. to 8. in the forenone the winde at S.S.E a fayre gale the ship sailed N.W. & by W._____ 6.L.*
>
> *from 8. to 12. at None the winde at S.S.E. a good gale the ship sayled N.W. & by West_____ 6.L.*
>
> *from 12. to 4. of clock at afternone the winde at S.S.E. a fayre gale, the ship sailed N.W. & by W. _____ 6.L.*
>
> *from 4. to 8. of clock the winde at S.S.E. litle winde, the ship sayled North West & by West _____ 4.L.*
>
> *from 8. to mydnight, the winde at S.E. a fayre gale, the ship sayled N.W. & by W. _____ 4.L.*
>
> *from mydnight to 4. of clock in the morning, the winde at S.E. a fayre gale, the ship sayled North West & by West _____ 4.L.*[56]

Each of the above observations would have been recorded on a traverse board: a piece of wood in which a series of holes allowed the insertion of pegs to show the direction of a course over each watch. At the end of each day, a mean course could be drawn, and that course committed to the chart (Waters considers it likely that the traverse board was used only on English ships during this period). It is, however, difficult to over-emphasise how approximate these measurements were. Setting aside the variable quality of the instruments used, the inevitable failings of contemporary theoretical science made a true plot almost impossible. By the 1570s, English seamen appreciated that the proximity of metal would have an effect upon the magnetic compass. Yet having gone so far as to replace the metal pins of compass binnacles with wood, they ignored the presence of other, larger sources of variation such as ordnance. Whilst, therefore, the compass card was divided into quarter points (and therefore ostensibly accurate to within 0.3 of a degree), an observation within 5 degrees of true was probably the best of which they were capable.

Direction was of course determined by compass, but distance had to be calculated by monitoring the ship's speed. This was done with the seaman's log and line. William Bourne described their use in his *Regiment for the Sea*:

> *And to know the ships way, some do vse this which (as I take it) is very good: they haue a pece of wood & a line to vere out ouer borde, with a small line of a great lengthe whiche they make fast at one ende, and at the other ende and middle, they haue a piece of a line which they make fast with a small thred to stande like vnto a crowfoote: for this purpose, that it should driue a sterne as fast as the shippe doth go away from it, always hauing the line so ready that it goeth out as fast as the ship goeth. In like manner they haue either a minute of an houre glasse, or else a knowne part of an hour by some number of wordes, or suche other like, so that the line being vered out and stopt iuste with that time that the glasse is out, or the number of wordes spoken, which done, they*

hale in the logge or piece of woode againe, and loke howe many fadome the shippe hath gone in the time: that being knowne, what part of a league soeuer it be, they multiplie the number of fadome, by the portion of tyme or part of an houre. Whereby you may knowe iustly howe many leagues and partes of a league the ship goeth in an houre.[57]

Once more, it may be imagined how difficult this process must have been when conducted in poor weather. The absence of any "minute of an hour" glasses in Lok's list of purchases suggests either that Hall and other masters carried their own glasses, or that they used a phrase or series of words, long-practised to be spoken at a precise rhythm, as the line was played out astern.

When the estimation of direction and speed had been made, the master "pricked" his chart to find the ship's position relative to the previous mark. This was also known as "keeping the account," and required the use of two pairs of dividers. The point of one pair would be placed upon his approximate position, the other upon the "line" or direction in which the ship had sailed. One point of the second pair of dividers would be placed upon the latitude scale of his chart at the currently-observed latitude, and the other on the East-West line closest to the observed latitude. The dividers were drawn together, and where the estimated course and point of observed latitude met, there was the ship's observed position, to be "pricked" by the end of the dividers, and a note made of estimated distance sailed[58] (occasionally, Hall's log testifies to the frustrations of calm weather; for 15 June 1578, and again two days later, a margin note recorded "pricked 0"). As with estimation of course, conceptual errors made the observation of ship's speed something of a "shot in the dark." Contemporary navigators had little understanding of the effect of the ocean current's velocity, and thus could not factor this important brake or accelerator into their calculations.[59] Also, English seamen used a "mile" of 5000 feet in determining speed with the log and line, with a further adjustment required to compensate for this (eventually, by using a "half-minute" glass of about 28 seconds' duration!).

Thus, the good navigator made his way in the sea, and committed it to the log. However, Bourne had also recommended that he not only understand the use of his instruments, but that he be able to correct their defects or, more appropriately, their inadequacies. We have already noted the uncertainties inherent in the use of the cross-staff. These might be dealt with adequately, if the master were sufficiently assiduous. In contrast, several of the items purchased for the voyages were fundamentally flawed (though executed with great craftsmanship), and provided little practical assistance. Instruments for establishing time, such as astronomical and universal rings, were completely inadequate for their intended purpose. A modern attempt by Waters to take the time of day using the universal ring (Lok's "Horologium Universale") gave, at best, an error of fifteen minutes, a margin of inaccuracy which rendered any calculation of distance sailed unfeasible.[60]

The cartographical errors of chart and map were, if possible, even more pronounced than their technical defects, particularly as any contemporary representation of the north-western Atlantic north of 60° was, at best, speculation and, at worst, the uncritical repetition of a deliberate deceit. To that extent, the most useful charts provided for Frobisher were blank; at least using these, he was not burdened with the further problem of reconciling his discoveries and observations with existing data. Nevertheless, the potential for error, encouraged by the limitations of instrumentation and the lack of understanding of the region to which they sailed, can hardly be overstated. Under these difficult circumstances, the mistakes and intelligent improvisations which characterised the performance of Frobisher and his men offers much valuable evidence of how English voyages in this period built English expertise.

The Way to Meta Incognita

Despite its association with the disastrous gold-mining project which superseded the original aims of the enterprise, Frobisher's 1576 expedition was a genuine voyage of discovery. The Norsemen who had previously made the passage to north-eastern America left no technical literature from which lessons could be drawn, and thus the blank charts prepared in 1576 symbolised more than just an English ignorance of the area, despite the assumptions set out upon the Mercator and Ortelius maps. What, then, determined the course which Frobisher set for the unknown region?

The easiest option — from a purely practical perspective — would have been to sail due west until they made the coast of America, and then to pass to the north, surveying the coastline and exploring potential straits. This, however, was not possible, given the need not only to avoid potential clashes with Spanish interests in the western hemisphere, but also to ensure that the expedition and its ultimate goal remained unknown to other nations. Furthermore, the available intelligence suggested that they would find a passage, if at all, somewhere above the latitude of 60° (where the "Strait of Anian" supposedly separated the continents of America and Asia). With these preoccupations, Frobisher, emerging into the North Sea from Harwich on 12 June, made a course as near to due north as possible, until he reached 60° (south-east of the island of "Fowley" or Foula, western-most of the Shetland Islands), before setting his tiny fleet west and by north.[61]

Neither Hall nor George Best (whose account of the first voyage must have been drawn from Hall and other sources) have much to report concerning the outward voyage until they reached the south-east coast of Greenland,[62] other than in one important respect: the recording of magnetic variation of the compass. We have noted already that the chart prepared by William Borough for the 1576 voyage contains the earliest extant markings of magnetic variation, for which Frobisher has been given credit. It is unlikely, however, that Frobisher himself carried out these observations (despite George Best's claim)[63] or, if he did, he was almost certainly duplicating measurements taken by Christopher Hall, as recorded in his log.[64]

In his *Regiment for the Sea*, Bourne explained the method of establishing variation:

> to finde the true Meridian do this. Set the Sunne with your compasse at hir rising or appearing aboue ye horizon, & then (knowing what point & part the

Sunne doth rise at) set the Sun with your compas at hir setting or departing vnder ye horizon & (that being known) you shal perfitly know, whether the compas be varied, & how much.[65]

The sun not always being conveniently visible at dawn or sunset, Bourne went on to propose a more flexible method:

at any time in the fore noone, first set the Sunne with your compas, and then take the true heigth of the Sunne. Now you (knowing how many degrees ye Sun was high at that point of the compas) may in like maner obserue the Sunne in the afternoon, vntill you do find the Sun iust at that heigth that it was in the forenoone, marking at what point of the compas the Sunne is, and so shall you see perfitely whether the compas be varied or no, and also howe much.

The evidence of Hall's log entry for 18 July 1576 does not suggest that he was performing an unfamiliar measurement; again, an indication of experience probably gained in his former employment with the Muscovy Company:

The 18. day at a Southeast sunne I found the sunne to be eleuated 33. deg. And at a Southsoutheast sunne 40. deg. So I obserued it till I found it at the highest, and then it was eleuated 52. deg. I iudged the variation of the Compasse to be 2. points and a halfe to the Westward.[66]

Insofar as it is possible to judge from the distance of three centuries, the magnetic variations noted by Hall and/or Frobisher appear to have been accurately measured. We have no information for the 1577 voyage, but neither Hall nor Edward Fenton appear to have recorded variation during the final expedition of 1578, probably because readings taken only two years later would not have been measurably different from the earlier observations.

Lack of other detailed information concerning the outward voyage in 1576 does not prevent us from drawing certain conclusions regarding Frobisher's motives. The course described so imperfectly in Hall's account (and not at all in Best's) took the expedition well south of Iceland, to a point on the south-east coast of Greenland somewhere in the region of what is now known as Danell Fjord (Hall noted their latitude off "Friesland" as 61° exactly). It is clear, therefore, that since losing sight of Foula some 30 days before, Frobisher's course had been almost due west. Acknowledging the political necessity of the initial northward passage to the Shetland Islands, therefore, his course thereafter had been prudent; seeking to go to an unknown region by the simplest navigable route; that is, east to west. For eight days from 30 June, the two barks had been unable to bear sail for all but fleeting periods, being carried somewhat to the south of their course by a storm which took the lives of either three or four men in a pinnace.[67] At each opportunity to raise their sails, the course of the *Gabriel* and *Michael* had been corrected to west and by north — back to approximately 60°. This technique of latitude sailing had been employed by Columbus in his 1492 voyage westwards, and in 1576 it served Frobisher equally well: both men wanted to find Cathay, yet neither wanted to lose the way back. Frobisher's was the more acute problem, in sailing through regions where he might expect — and indeed suffered — visibility poor enough to prevent latitude observations and the effect of currents for days at a time. Under such circumstances, the chances of correcting leeward drift, and thus plotting an accurate course, were extremely poor; yet if — at each break in the weather — they could return to a pre-determined latitude and continue west, they effectively ensured that their "ball of string" was played out behind.

Once off the coast of "Friesland," the *Gabriel* and *Michael* became separated. According to what appears to have been a collectively-agreed justification of their actions, the mariners of the *Michael* took their own counsel thereafter and sailed west for a further four days, until they had sight of what they took to be the coast of Labrador; at which, fearing danger from the large ice-floes which screened them from the shore, they turned about and returned to England.[68]

The *Gabriel*, under the more resolute command of Frobisher himself, explored the coast of the supposed Friesland but, finding the waters immediately offshore to be too deep to anchor, and the prevalence of ice too hazardous to attempt a landing via the ship's boats, turned south along the coastline. We do not know if Hall made sketches of what he saw during this first reconnaissance, but two years later, he drew what is probably the earliest extant pictorial representation of Greenland in his log entry for 20 June 1578:

> *And at that present being 2. of the clock in the morning, I had sight of Friseland, being from me 5. leages in this forme from Dee's Pinacles, being the Sowth hed to* Mount Edgcombe, *being the North point in sight, this Land by the S.S.W. & N.N.E. being the S.E. parte of Friseland. And note that from the Sowth Pinacles westerly, from the said* Dee's Pinacles to frobushers Cape, *the land lyeth S.W. and by W, N.E. and by E. 5L. And from* Frobushers Cape *to* Borowe's *point, is W. & by S, E. & by N. 5L / geving respect to* Hawles needels *by the way, wh<u>i</u>ch be certain Rocks, ther is 16. of them lyeth in sight / from* Master William Borowe's point, *to* Master Michael Locks foreland, *is N.W. & S.E, 5L, so that the land falleth & turneth Northerly /*

The contrast between this entry and the narrative of his 1576 account[69] is striking; the earlier description was reproduced for the edification of laymen, but the latter formed as fine an example of a surveyor's report as the limitations of the period allowed (although in mitigation of the brevity of the earlier account, it should be noted that in 1576 the region was only of secondary importance to the voyagers; their sole preoccupation was Cathay, and the way thereto). Another singular aspect of this and other observations made by Hall is the use of the personal names of prominent adventurers and patrons to name geographical features encountered in the new lands; possibly the earliest known example of what was to become a standard practice in the process of exploration.

The passage across what was later to be named Davis Strait, and the *Gabriel*'s initial reconnaissance of the coastline, revealed the first signs of what were to be pervading problems — the almost continuous presence of potentially lethal ice-floes and the persistence of coastal fogs. The first of these made any landfall a hazardous undertaking; the second rendered the majority of the ship's instruments redundant. Add to these complications the naturally hostile topography of south-eastern Baffin Island and its unusually swift tidal streams, and it becomes clear why the finer points of the navigator's art were necessarily abandoned in favour of conscientious pilotage. Hall's account for 28-29 July gives a flavour of their travails:

> *The 28. day in the morning was very foggie: but at the clearing vp of the fogge, we had sight of lande, which I supposed to be Labrador, with great store of yce about the land: I ranne in towards it, and sownded, but could get no ground at 100. fathom, and the yce being so thicke, I could not get to the shoare, and so lay off, and came cleare of the yce. Upon Monday we came within a mile of the shoare, and sought a harborowe: all the sownd was full of yce, and our boate rowing a shoare, could get no ground at a 100. fathom, within a Cables length of the shoare: then we sailed Eastnortheast along the shoare, for so the land lyeth, and the currant is there great, setting Northeast, and Southwest: and if we could haue gotten anker ground, wee would haue seene with what force it had runne, but I iudge a ship may driue a league and a halfe, in one houre, with that tide.*

This final observation was to have particular significance two years later, when Hall alone recalled this tidal current, and stood against Frobisher and all his officers on the position of the fleet after several days in fog.

Frobisher named this first discovery Queen Elizabeth's Foreland (the latter-day Resolution Island, at the southern entrance to Frobisher Bay).[70] For the next ten days, they explored the immediate coastline, attempting to secure a safe anchorage; each time they were denied either by ice or by shores which in effect formed the summit-edge of a cliff-face which dropped almost vertically into the deeps, thus making the use of the ship's anchor impossible. Only on 10 August were Hall and four other men able to land upon an island with one of their ship's boats; even then, the threat of fog and a tide which rose over a foot in minutes drove them swiftly back to the *Gabriel*. The discovery was allowed to the master, as Hall's Island. The following day, he noted their latitude to be 63° and 8′, and thereafter the *Gabriel* passed into the "strait."[71]

The bark sailed Northwest along the southern coastline of Frobisher Bay (with a brief detour to Gabriel Island in the middle passage) as far as "Burcher's Island" and "Five Men's Sound" (named after the unfortunate boat's crew lost to the Inuit on 20 August);[72] at that point, Frobisher seems to have reached a point some twelve miles from the head of the bay, but was not within sight of it. One of the authors has previously speculated that once the loss of a quarter of his remaining company made it impossible to continue to Cathay, Frobisher may intentionally have allowed the western exit of the "strait" to remain an open question; recognising that the prospects for a second expedition (and thus for his own future reputation) were far greater if he did not disprove the passage that year.[73] Whether this was indeed the case, or that the clash with the Inuit had emphasised his vulnerability, Frobisher was obliged to make a definite decision on the expedition's future the following day when, according to Hall, "the snow lay a foote thicke vpon our hatches." They spent a further forty-eight hours searching for their missing party, and then turned about to the south-east, departing from the mouth of Frobisher Bay on 27 August.

By 1 September they had sight of Friesland once more, yet contrary winds forced them to stay off that coast for a further six days. Equinoctial storms seem to have been an almost continuous problem on the return passage, but with broadly favourable winds. On 25 September, Hall reported that they had sight of Orkney, which suggests that their homeward route was as close to that of the outward passage as the weather would allow (the observation of latitude was made extremely difficult by these conditions). The *Gabriel* anchored at Harwich on 2 October 1576.

Whatever Frobisher's private opinion of his discoveries, he made an effective show to the Commission newly-appointed to examine and assess their significance:[74]

> *at which tyme he vowched to them absolutlye with vehement wordes, speches and Oathes; that he had founde and discoverid the Straights, and open passadge by Sea into the South Sea called* Mar de Sur *which goethe to Cathaj / and by the waye had founde diuers good ports and harbors for passadge of all the navye of her Maiesties Shipps, and affirmed the same by diuers arguments of the depthe and culler of the water, the sight of the heade landes one boathe the sides of the Straightes at the west end thereof openinge into the broade Sea, called* Mar de Sur, *and the setting of the tydes with a fludd from the west owt of the sayde sowthe sea / and by diuers other arguments by demonstracion in the Cartes and Mappes, which things the Commissioners beleued to be trewe.*[75]

His assurances (not contradicted, as far as we know, by Hall or any of the other mariners) were sufficient to bring promises of further investment; so much so that a preliminary plan for the second voyage, prepared sometime before March 1577, envisaged an expedition of two ships (of 140 and 120 tons burden) in addition to the barks *Gabriel* and *Michael*, with a total complement of 180 men. The cost was budgeted at £6,280.[76] A second estimate, dated 26 March 1577, was more modest. By that time, the Queen had become an investor and "sold" the ship *Ayde* to the enterprise as part of her stock. The new plan provided for this vessel and the two barks from the first voyage, with a total complement of 115 men, at a cost of £4,500.[77] This latter plan is particularly interesting: so similar was it to the eventual scale and character of the 1577 voyage that we must assume it to be the definitive blueprint for a second attempt to reach Cathay, had such an expedition sailed. Approximately four days after it was set to paper, however, news of the supposed value of ore returned from the 1576 voyage rendered this and previous plans redundant, and the discovery (and navigation) of a route to Cathay ceased to be the principal preoccupation of the adventurers — or at least of those adventurers who set the agenda.

The instructions for the second voyage reflected this shifted emphasis.[78] If any of the ore samples mined on Hall's Island or elsewhere proved to be promising, Frobisher was simply to take the *Gabriel* and *Michael* as far into the "strait" as was necessary to reach its western exit. Only if the ore was proved to be worthless on site were the two barks to proceed to Cathay, meanwhile sending home the *Ayde* with all the miners on board. The instructions did not specify the course of their outward route to Meta Incognita, only that, after leaving "England, Scotland, or Ireland" they should direct their course to Hall's Island. However, as Frobisher was also directed to set down six of ten convicts to be carried with the expedition upon the coast "Friesland" — either on the outward or return voyage — the Privy Council clearly envisaged the outward route of the 1577 voyage to mirror at least the later stages of that of the previous year.[79]

One aspect of the provisioning for the 1577 voyage illustrates something of the practicalities of navigation. We have noted and discussed the instruments carried with the 1576 expedition (which were subsequently sold to the account of the following year's expedition). Lok recorded an amount of £7. 11s. 0d. paid to Humphrey Cole "for reparinge and newe makinge divers Instrumentes of navigatione, for the voyage."[80] Clearly, therefore, the rigours of oceanic voyages took their toll upon the delicate technology employed by Frobisher and his masters. Perhaps in response to the lessons of the previous year, the adventurers hired a "soldiare Instrument maker," Anthony Rambridge, to accompany the new voyage; thereby ensuring that instruments damaged at sea should not be rendered useless until Humphrey Cole could perform major repairs once more.[81] Rambridge's dual occupation is an interesting reminder of the military necessities which had fostered the growth of a domestic industry in the production of scientific instruments, although his particular skills do not appear to have commanded much of a premium.[82]

As we have noted, there is no extant ship's log for the 1577 voyage. All the evidence is derived from Best's *Discourse* and the account of Dionyse Settle, one of a number of gentlemen soldiers who accompanied the expedition.[83] There is little technical information on the navigation of the voyage, therefore; although again, deductions may be drawn with some certainty. The expedition sailed from Harwich on 31 May 1577, and once more a course set was due north to the Orkney Islands. After taking in water there, the *Ayde*, *Gabriel* and *Michael* departed on 8 June and, according to Best, made a course west-north-west for two days, until the wind shifted. Thereafter, as in the previous year, the expedition attempted to keep as true to a westerly course as possible, steering north only to correct the drift caused by contrary winds. The weather remained fair, and on 4 July, the coast of "Friesland" was sighted. Christopher Hall, now master of the *Ayde*, was sent by Frobisher aboard the *Michael* to confirm the sighting (interestingly, the master of the *Michael* in 1577 was James Beare, son-in-law of William Bourne).[84] For the next four days, the expedition tracked the coastline north and then south again; both Settle and

Best noted the forbidding nature of its mountainous profile, yet speculated (from the abundance of birds observed) that the interior might be habitable. Curiously, in noting the supposed discovery of Friesland by the Zeno brothers, Best praised the accuracy of their representation of its coast.[85]

Although Best and Settle had neither the training nor inclination to dwell upon the technical intricacies of their navigation,[86] both men exhibited keen powers of observation; Best in apparently determining (by taste) that the ice floes they encountered, being almost free of salt, were not formed upon the sea about them, but came from elsewhere (he was not aware that sea-ice loses salt); Settle — like Frobisher and others before him — assumed from the strength and height of the tidal variation within the "strait" that a large volume of water must flow from the west, and that the ice which this flow carried with it was responsible for bestowing local temperatures much lower than those encountered in similar latitudes elsewhere. Both men's accounts, if flawed by the misconceptions of their age, are nevertheless characterised by an appreciation of their novel experience, and the corresponding imperative to inform. Settle in particular devoted considerable attention to the character and customs of the Inuit (a matter of paramount interest to his readers), and to the benefits of almost continuous daylight in dealing with the severe conditions they experienced:

> *(We) were forced to abide in a cruell tempest, chancing in the night, amongst and in the thickest of the yce, which was so monstrous, that euen the least of a thousand had beene of force sufficient, to haue shiuered oure shippe and barkes into small portions, if God (who in all necessities, hath care vpon the infirmitie of man) had not prouided for this our extremitie a sufficient remedie, through the light of the night, whereby we might well discerne to flee from such imminent daungers, which wee auoyded with 14. bordes in one watch the space of 4. houres.[87]*

And again, summarizing his memories of the voyage in an extremely pertinent way:

> *'Who so maketh Navigations to these contries, hath not only extreme winds, and furious Seas, to encounter withall, but also many monstrous and great Islandes of yce: a thing both rare, wonderfull, and greatly to be regarded'* (a prudent margin note to this statement concludes: *'Yce needefull to be regarded by seafaring men.'*)[88]

The 1577 voyage did not extend the bounds of the previous year's hydrographical discoveries appreciably. Frobisher's priorities, even in the light of his heavily-weighted instructions, were clearly focused upon locating seams of potentially rich ore and coming to terms with the local inhabitants. Such observations that were made, of inlets and harbours on both sides of the "strait," were for the purpose of securing adequate shelter for mining operations. In describing Warwick's Sound, the most promising harbour on the northern shore, Best acknowledged it to be their furthest penetration of the supposed passage in that year; a distance, he calculated, of no more than 30 leagues from the eastern mouth of the "strait."[89]

The most promising ore-seams were discovered on the Countess of Warwick's Island on 29 July; by 23 August, almost 160 tons of ore had been mined and loaded, mainly into the *Ayde*. Mindful of the speed with which weather conditions turned for the worse, Frobisher did not pause; the following day, the small fleet sailed clear of Queen Elizabeth's Foreland with its ore and three Inuit captives, and into the Atlantic Ocean. This time, however, the expedition did not retrace its outward course. According to Best: "we bare further into the mayne ocean, keeping our course more southerly, to bring our selves the sooner under the latitude of oure owne climate."[90] The inference is clear: as much as their growing confidence upon the ocean may have allowed Frobisher and his men to consider the unfamiliar southern passage feasible, it was the need for warmth in their bones, after several weeks of back-breaking toil in lethally cold conditions, which provided the immediate spur.[91] Even so, they encountered snow storms on their passage south south-east; they were severe enough for Best to add an incredulous margin note in his *Discourse*: "Snow half a foot deepe in August." On 29 August, they lost the company of the *Michael*, which, speculated Best, "shaped hir course towardes Orkney as we supposed, bycause that way was better known unto them."[92] Given the *Michael*'s well-deserved reputation as an unlucky ship (she had lost her mast upon at least two occasions on the outward passage), her captain, Gilbert Yorke,[93] and master, James Beare, might be considered to have displayed commendable prudence in seeking the comfort of a familiar passage, cold though that comfort undoubtedly was.

Two days later, the *Gabriel* also became separated from the *Ayde*, and returned to England without the benefit of a master, having fortuitously met with a Bristol merchantman at sea (probably en route from Iceland) which led her home.[94] The *Ayde* herself came into Milford Haven in Wales on 23 September, having previously attempted and failed to enter Padstow Harbour in Cornwall. The *Ayde*'s return passage cries out for the hand of Christopher Hall to describe it in detail, but failing that, it seems likely that much of Best's commentary derived from conversations with the master of the *Ayde*. His statement on the inadequacy of the astrolabe, and his observations on taking latitude and soundings, indicate an expertise not normally displayed by gentlemen-soldiers. Where Best discusses the navigation of the return voyage, therefore, we may assume he is speaking with borrowed authority.

The outward passage from Harwich had described two sides of a rectangle; that of the homeward passage completed it. Best makes it clear that Frobisher's intention, having passed into the Atlantic, was to sail to the south until the latitude of the Scilly Isles was achieved, and then to set a course due east thereafter. The intention was disrupted by "contrarye" winds which took them to the east prematurely, but at each opportunity, they adjusted their course southward towards 50° with as much assiduity as they had sought 60° on the outward passage. It was an unadventurous, sensible strategy which served them admirably. By 16 September, they were within the Soundings, and the following day between Land's End and Scilly. Best's account of that day's sailing bears the unmistakable imprint of the master's preoccupations, so much so that we may assume it was lifted directly from the log of the *Ayde*:

> *The seaventeenth of September we sounded, and had fortie fadome, and were not farre off the landes end, branded sand with small worms and cockle shells, and were shotte betweene Sylley and the landes end, and being within the baye, we were not able to double the point wyth a south and by east way, but were fayne to make another boorde,[95] the wynde beeyng at southweast, and by weast, and yet could not double the poynte, to come cleere of the landes end, to beare along the Channell.[96]*

The safe return of the 1577 expedition (there had been only two mortalities at sea, including the regrettably clairvoyant Smith) marked what was probably the highpoint of Frobisher's brief reputation as England's Columbus. This fame, enhanced by the swift publication of Settle's account of the second voyage, gained a wider currency than perhaps even Frobisher desired. Word of his exploits began to circulate through Europe; as early as 25 June that year, Philip II had been made aware of Frobisher's expedition (and subsequently managed to secure an informer — possibly the English assayer Robert Denham — on the third expedition),[97] and the French Court was receiving information from its Ambassador to England, Castelnau de la Mauvissière, that Frobisher had discovered gold mines.[98] Even the Tsar's Court received news of the voyage; he wrote to Elizabeth, asking for the return of "their" three subjects, abducted from the Yugorskii region of Siberia; a claim which indicates that the Tsar's understanding of the wilder regions of his own domains was no greater than that of the English.[99]

The tortuous course of technically imperfect assays and subsequent professional back-stabbing which muddied any attempt to determine the true value of the ore brought home by Frobisher is not part of this paper's brief. However, the uncertainty created by this failure of the assayers' technology, rather than introducing a degree of circumspection amongst the adventurers, resulted in a far greater commitment of resources. The new expedition was to be significantly larger than those which had preceded it, for several reasons.

First, the estimated value of the ore had been revised progressively downwards following each assay; from an initial figure of £240 per ton (claimed by Lok following his early association with the Italian assayer John Baptista Agnello)[100] to just £23. 15s. per ton by 8 March 1578.[101] To secure an adequate return on the latter basis, large amounts of ore would need to be mined and transported in 1578. Secondly, the growing awareness of this potentially vast source of revenue may have inclined the Queen and Council to seek to establish *de facto* rights of ownership — by establishing a large scale operation in Meta Incognita before foreign intervention could be made (this was almost certainly the principal reason for further burdening the company's purse with a proposed 100-man colony). This latter motivation may have been given further impetus by Frobisher himself who, according to Michael Lok — not, admittedly, an impartial source — deceived the Commissioners as to the imminence of French interference.[102]

The definitive proposals for the 1578 expedition allowed for the four "company" vessels (including the *Judith*, recently purchased from William Borough), and six further ships chartered from private owners to be employed as freight ships for the ore. Additionally, Lok and a business partner, Richard Fairbrother the elder, despatched a ship which they privately chartered (or possibly owned jointly), the *Beare Leicester*; and Frobisher himself arranged for a further three ships and a bark, again without official permission. In total, twelve ships and three barks assembled in Harwich haven in the final week of May, 1578.

The documentary sources for the 1578 voyage are numerous, and require a degree of critical analysis in reconciling their respective versions of events. As we have noted previously, the major technical sources are the logs of Christopher Hall (in the *Thomas Allen* and then the *Ayde*) and Edward Fenton, captain of the *Judith*, "vice-generall" of the expedition and commander of the intended colony. More general accounts were supplied by George Best and Thomas Ellis (who claimed to be a sailor "more studied and vsed in my Charde and Compasse, and other thinges belonging to Nauigation, than trayned vp in *Mineruas* Court..."),[103] and a hybrid journal/log by a merchant, Edward Selman, who accompanied the expedition in the capacity of Michael Lok's "eyes."[104] Finally, Charles Jackman's fragmentary journal offers some detail of the outward voyage, albeit in a markedly simple style.

Christopher Hall, who had good reason to consider himself the leading mariner employed, was not appointed master of the flagship *Ayde* (although he was later to take charge of the vessel upon her return passage). He was not even designated master of the *Thomas Allen*, the vessel to which he was appointed merely as "pilot." However, what appeared to be a serious demotion was in fact entirely logical. The *Thomas Allen* was the "vice-Admiral" of the fleet, and the largest vessel other than the *Ayde*. She was, furthermore, a privately-owned vessel whose crew had no experience of the passage to Meta Incognita. Her titular master, a man named Gibbes, no doubt represented the interests of his employer, the merchant Thomas Allen; yet there can be little doubt that Hall had effective control over the ship whilst at sea. Thus, the two leading ships of the fleet carried the best expertise — a prudent strategy, should the fleet be separated.[105]

The fleet left Harwich on 31 May 1578, but rather than follow the course of the two previous voyages, a course was set south, then west along the English Channel, and across the Soundings to Dursey Head, in Ireland. Edward Selman offers a clue as to why this was done:

> *I Iudge this vyage is better to be attempted, followed & vsed by the West parts, then by the North parts, as well for the avoyding of much cold within the North Passage we had, as allso redyer windes to follow our said vyage, as by the falling owt of this passage doth appere.*[106]

Selman was correct in his latter assumption; the fleet sighted "Friesland" after only 18 days at sea (the first voyage had taken over thirty days to reach the same point from Harwich; the second, 26 days from as far out as Orkney). Given the known brief span of the Meta Incognita summer, the need for a speedier passage than in the previous voyages was clearly established, particularly if the expedition were to fill the holds of the freight ships before conditions became unbearable. Furthermore, one of the few advantages of the growing awareness of Frobisher's project throughout Europe was that secrecy no longer need confine their route across the Atlantic to one in an uncomfortably high latitude.

The fleet took its point of departure from Dursey Head in Western Ireland on 7 June. Both Fenton and Hall record the sighting, the former also observing his latitude at 52°.[107] Thereafter the ships, assisted also by the direction of the prevailing surface currents,[108] made very good way, save for brief periods of calm. It appears that the fleet managed to keep together on the passage across the Atlantic, although as early as 15 June, Fenton noted that the *Michael* — almost inevitably — was "farr to the Leawardes." The coast of "Friesland" was sighted by Hall in the *Thomas Allen* at 2am on 20 June, and by Fenton in the *Judith* at about the same time. Hall's first sight of the land has been preserved; it is probably the earliest extant pictorial representation of the Greenland coast. The drawing appears to represent the eastern side of the southern extremity of the island (the latter-day Kap Farvel), thus making their landfall precisely at 60°; an admirable example of accurate navigation along an unfamiliar course.   In contrast to the previous two years' explorations, the fleet sailed about the cape to the western coastline, where the *Ayde* and *Judith* were able to launch their boats and put a party (including Frobisher, Fenton, Hall and Jackman) onshore.[109] Their observations, particularly those of Jackman, indicate the general surprise that the flimsy craft of the local inhabitants were capable of navigating the treacherous waters between "Friesland" and Meta Incognita.[110]

The following day, the fleet moved north-west into what would become known as Davis Strait. On 22 June, the *Michael* went off on her traditional absence. By 27 June, the prevalence of ice floes suggested to both Hall and Fenton that they were nearing land. At that point, Fenton gave his latitude as 63° - 3′. However, on 1 July, Hall — having since 27 June sailed 17 leagues south-east and then 20 leagues north-west, observed his latitude at only 62° - 14′. The discrepancy suggests either that one man had wrongly observed his latitude, or that the fleet was unable to keep visible contact in the midst of the ice.

The *Judith* had become separated from the rest of the fleet. In his log entry for that day, Fenton records that at 6 o'clock in the evening, the *Judith* made the North Foreland, at the northern entrance to Frobisher Bay. At the same time he noted:

> *we fell with much ize and were environed all to the southe, being a good gale of winde north northest. Woulde faine have borne with the other shipps, but coulde not for thize.[111]*

With ice all about them to the South, and the wind north northeast (thereby driving them onto the ice), Fenton would no doubt have been doing his best to sail away, rather than towards, his General. By the early hours of the morning of 2 July, the two elements of the fleet were approximately ten to fifteen miles apart; Fenton's *Judith* still managing to stay off the North Foreland, whilst Frobisher and his remaining vessels lay to the south, at approximately the centre-most point of the Bay's mouth. All accounts speak of the great volume of ice which lay to the West, between the Fleet and its goal. However, Jackman also records that the weather was "very fayre and the wynd prosperous" (ie. south south west). These apparently favourable conditions had two evil consequences; both Frobisher and Fenton were lulled into disregarding the great incidence of ice before them and thus attempted to enter into the Bay, and the same favourable wind which carried the fleet more quickly into the Bay also brought the ice which lay to their stern in after them.

The events of 2/3 July are worth examining in some detail. This paper has analysed the techniques of contemporary seamen at length, yet the practical difficulties of navigation, particularly in novel climatic conditions, have never been portrayed as graphically as by the eye-witnesses in Frobisher's fleet. The attempted passage into Frobisher Bay on the evening of 2 July 1578 was a mistake, one of near-fatal proportions for every one of the 350 sailors, miners and soldiers who fearfully rode out the storms that beset them throughout what was undoubtedly their longest night.

Chistopher Hall, as usual, emerges from the episode in the most favourable light. The *Thomas Allen*, had arrived at the mouth of Frobisher Bay early in the morning of 2 July, and thus several hours before the rest of the fleet. According to his journal entry for that day, Hall immediately judged the conditions to be unsuitable for any attempt to be made to reach their landfall. He tried desperately to head off his Admiral:

> *I had byn hard aborde the yse, and cam of to tell my Amberall & the rest of the flete, that there was no way into the straightes, bycause the yse was so thick, so at my comming of, I met first with the Master of the Barke Dennis, whose name was Dabney, & told him, and he was partely perswaded, and so from him I spoke with Androw Diar, Master of the Hopewell, and perswaded him, so that the rest of the ships were to windeward, that I coulde not speake with them, so that Richard Cockes came sayling vp being to windewardes, and I could not speake to him, he presently set vp his Mainetop sayle, and fortop sayle, and sayled in among the yse, and the bark Dennis after him, the Salamon after him, the Fraunces of Foye after him, and one after another, to yt came to the 11. sayle and that was the Amrall, I next to him, and the Hopewell last of all, so that we ronne so far in among them (ie. the ice) that we were inclosed of every side, that we could neither get out nor in no way.[112]*

Prudently, Hall did not record his feelings as he was obliged to follow his Admiral into the ice. Moving into the bay, the fleet and the *Judith* remained in touch, if barely. From the *Ayde* Thomas Ellis noted:

> *Being in amongst it (ie. the ice), we sawe the Michael ... accompanied with The Iudith, whose Captaine was Maister Fenton, the Maister Charles Iackman, bearing into the foresaid yce, farre distant from us ... .*[113]

By about ten o clock that night, taking the opportunity afforded by the fair weather, Frobisher's ships had passed beyond the entrance to the Bay some ten leagues, or thirty miles, northwest of their position earlier in the evening, to a point at which they were confronted by an impenetrable density of ice. At about that time, the weather turned suddenly and violently against them, bringing an unusual combination of high winds (still from the southeast) and thick fog. Too late, Frobisher attempted to put the Fleet about, and weather the storm outside the mouth of the Bay; yet only the four vessels furthest astern managed to force their way clear again, to ride out the night in relatively clear water: the *Moon*, *Frances of Foy*, the *Anne Frances* (Best's ship) and the *Gabriell*. The remaining nine ships (including Hall's *Thomas Allen*), trapped within the closing ice floes, were left to fend as best they could.

Somewhere amongst the ice, in this middle passage of the Bay, the *Ayde* and her remaining eight escorts found a relatively clear polynya, sufficient to allow the smaller vessels to maintain sail and manoeuvre throughout the course of the night. However, the two largest vessels — the *Ayde* and *Thomas Allen* — were too long to turn in the channel (which gives some indication of its size), and therefore obliged to fend all night.

Though none make the point explicitly, the narratives of Best, Ellis and Selman give the strong impression of increasing congestion within this channel, created by the gathering storm, the closing ice, and from the confusion created by so many vessels within their treacherous confinement; a confusion increased by the decision to despatch the ships' boats — despite the severity of the storm about them — in order that their crews might hack at the edges of the icepack and thus prevent its complete sealing.

As Captain of one of the ships which had escaped this ordeal, George Best is not strictly an eyewitness to these dramatic events, yet his is the most comprehensive and satisfying description of something approaching panic amongst the enclosed Fleet (we must assume that Hall, Ellis and Selman were too busy in their extremity to note the finer detail of the experience):

> *And againe some (ships) were so fast shut vp, and compassed in amongst an infinite number of great Countreys and Ilandes of Ise, that they were fayne to submit themselves, & their Ships, to the mercie of the vnmercifull Ise, and strengthned the sides of their Ships with junckes of cables, beds, Mastes, planckes, and such like, whiche being hanged ouerboard, on the sides of their Shippes, might the better defende them from the outragious sway and strokes of the saide Ise.*[114]

These precautions, haphazard and makeshift, were nevertheless vital; with all hands set to fending the ice with spars, cables and even topmasts, the *Ayde* and *Thomas Allen* came close to disaster:

> *And yet (that whiche is more) it is faythfully and playnely to be proued, and that by many substantiall witnesses, that our Shippes, euen those of the greatest burdens, with the meeting of contrary waues of the Sea, were heaued vp betweene Ilandes of Ise, a foote welneere out of the Sea, aboue their watermarke, hauing their knees and timbers within boorde, both bowed, and broken therewith.*[115]

It should be remembered that had these fragile vessels been breached, the freezing and turbulent waters of the Bay would have swiftly destroyed Frobisher and his men. Even if some of them had managed to make the short but near-impossible passage to the shore, the land itself was well known to be too hostile to support European castaways. In every sense, there was but a single option available: somehow to survive the night and hope for a turn in the wind and tide. Christopher Hall's anxiety for his own vessel, the *Thomas Allen*, is palpable; though he had some experience of pack ice from the previous two voyages to the area (and from earlier voyages to Russia), his log entry for the evening clearly describes something beyond his expectations:

> *and the yse cam so thick vppon vs, that we could not sayle, but drive among the yse, ready to sink vs, yf the mighty power of God had not bin great, for we put a whole cable all abowt the side as thick as yt wold lye of the one syde of the ship, and for all that cable, the sea was so growne, that yt was like to beat in the ships sydes, yf he had not byn a strong ship, nor none of the rest of the ships that there was, but were in as great danger as we were.*[116]

In the face of these hazards it was inevitable that the relatively good fortune so far experienced by the Fleet had to fail. Captain Dabney and his crew paid the price for ignoring Hall's earlier warning when the *Dennis* lost the wind in her foresail and struck an iceberg. Her side was torn open, a mortal wound, but a fortunate effect of the ships' general crowding within the polynya was that adequate assistance was close at hand. According to Jackman (not an eyewitness), boats from the *Beare Leicester* managed to take off all the crew of the stricken vessel, which sank within a half hour of the collision (Hall disagreed, and identified the rescuers as being from the *Ayde*). Perhaps even more fortunately, the *Dennis* had been carrying the major proportion of the frame of a prefabricated blockhouse in which the intended colony was to winter in Meta Incognita (Fenton, *log*; 9 August). This loss, together with the spoilage of stores in other vessels, effectively ended any chance of establishing the first English colony in North America that year (a colony that must surely have been wiped out in the coming winter).

Hall's appreciation of Divine assistance has been noted. The other narrators also stress the efficacy of His intervention at vital moments, particularly Best, whose play upon his English readership's heartstrings was entirely unabashed:

> *But as in greatest distresse, men of best value are best to be discerned, so it is
> greatly worthy (of) commendation and noting, with what inuincible minde
> euery Captayne encouraged his company, and with what incredible labour,
> the paynefull Mariners, and poore Miners (vnaquainted with suche
> extremities) to the everlasting renowne of our nation, dyd ouercome the brunt
> of these so greate and extreame daungers.*

In fact, their "overcoming" of these dangers was due principally to a change in wind
direction at about mid-morning of 3 July, from southeast to southwest, simultaneously
breaking up the local concentrations of ice and enabling the battered fleet to lay off and
on — or tack — towards the southeast. This is, however, to anticipate the chronology of
events. By the early hours of 3 July, the ships of the Fleet, even at moments of greatest
danger, were managing to keep their channel sufficiently clear to maintain some hope of
eventual deliverance.

The four vessels which had managed to regain the mouth of the bay some hours earlier
had not escaped all of the hazards experienced by their fellow mariners. Best (this time
as an eyewitness) claimed that:

> *(we) were broughte manye times to the extreamest poynte of perill,
> Mountaynes of Ise tenne thousande tymes scaping them scarce one ynch,
> whiche to haue stricken, had byn theyr presente destruction, considering the
> swifte course and way of the Shippes, and the vnwildynesse (ie. inability,
> refusal) of them to stay and turn as a ma<u>n</u> would wish.*

Yet as desperate as their situation appeared, an even greater crisis was being enacted
some twenty miles to the north. The *Judith*, forcibly prevented from moving towards the
illusory succour of the fleet, was having even more of a night of it.

Charles Jackman's account of the *Judith*'s movements during the evening of 2 July,
though fragmentary, is in some respects more revealing than the more composed log of
Edward Fenton. Whether this was mere bravado on Fenton's part or a reflection of his
character is difficult to determine; but even he gives more credit to God for their lives
than his own skills as a seaman.

For all his known competence, Jackman offers not the least pretence that he bore himself
with calm efficiency during those hours (though ironically, his skills were never put to
better use); yet in some ways, he is the most informative on the reasons for the errors of
judgement which led to the crises of that day. It is Jackman alone who points out that the
same — apparently favourable — conditions which had lured the fleet into the Bay
during the afternoon of 2 July encouraged Fenton to attempt the same. Standing far to the
northwards of Frobisher's Fleet, the *Judith* was much closer to their eventual destination,
the Countess of Warwick's Sound; given steady conditions, she had every chance of
navigating through the ice and reaching safe harbour before midnight. Unfortunately, this
illusory proximity to their goal may have inclined Fenton and his Master to continue to

push into the Bay long after the worsening weather should have brought them fleeing out again. Jackman reports that the *Judith* penetrated some five leagues — or fifteen miles — further into the bay than the Fleet, before the gathering ice brought them to a halt.

Like Frobisher some hours before, Fenton realised his error too late. Yet in going about to retrace their former course, the storm threw the ice about the *Judith* so severely that they could not bear sail; and so "under hull" they went, "whether wynd and tyde wold carry vs abydinge for that night (in) furious and stormes of Ise."[117]

By three o'clock in the morning the ship was completely "environed" by ice floes, an extreme predicament in the calmest conditions, and those of that particular evening were anything but calm. Fortunately, the *Judith* carried with her the chaplain who had volunteered to winter with the colony in Meta Incognita; a man whose particular talents found ample opportunity for expression in this extremity:

> *... then the storm again growinge then the Ise so vehement (ag)ainst the side of the shipp that notwithstandinge all defences aforesaid was so brused (and) crused that we supposed ourself lost forlorn hope then Master Woolfall a good godly precher who for his zelowes and godly lyffe was chosen to haue remained with vs the (pre)cher moved vs to prayer layinge before vs our present danger and how we ought to behave (our)selues to godward in this distres to whom as it semed from this woorld we ware redy (se)singe this his comfortable exhortation so quitned and reviued our present estate that the dangers wherin we ware was therby relented and made the more tollerable in ye hope (we) had in godes mersis.*[118]

As may be imagined, this dramatic and impeccably Protestant intervention had an immediate bearing upon the fortunes of the seemingly lost company:

> *This his exortation fynished our captayn and master by god apoynted our safegard incoraged ye gentelmen and soldiers with pikes and owers to beare ye Ise (from) the side of the shipp, the other with lyke diligenc chered his saylors with great currage (and) manlynes to stand to ther labor and taklinge. then every man imployed hymself to labore he cold best skyll of and as the spech goeth we laboringe for lyffe it (ples)ed god to send by .9. aclocke to apeas the storme and open a glad in ye Ise and therwith (the) myst clered vp that we might see in what parte of the strates we ware in.*

For six hours, therefore (ignoring the important but necessarily brief exhortation of Master Wolfall), the crew of the *Judith* had fended large ice floes which — seemingly at every moment during that time — had threatened to crush their small ship, in the midst of an arctic storm and fog which further reduced their capacity to make any effective manoeuvre. Fenton's own account of the evening is more succinct, yet his brevity complements his master's account effectively:

And abowte 4 of the clock in the morninge we were in great daunger to loose Shipp and ourselves (if god of his great mercie and providence had not wonnderfullie delivered us) after lying thus tossed and shutt vpp in the ize with muche winde and a greate fogg, after our hartie prayers made to god, he opened vnto us (as to the children of Israell in the brode sea) a litle cleare to the northwestwardes, wherinto we forced our shipp with vyolence. And thus having given our selves to the mercifull handes of god, he of his greate goodnes sente us presentlie faire weather.[119]

The "litle cleare" which Fenton mentions was a local symptom of a more general easing of conditions in Frobisher's Bay that morning; from which — as we have noted — the fleet derived similar benefit; there was clear weather and a strong wind at west south-west which dispersed the ice sufficiently to allow the battered ships to make their way slowly south-eastwards — towards the Queen's Foreland, and the mouth of the Bay. Either coincidentally, or in obedience to a pre-arranged plan, the *Judith* was also making her way towards the Foreland that day; Fenton having judged that the volume of ice remaining in the mouth of the Bay made it far too dangerous to attempt a further entry. By the evening, his vessel was within fifteen miles of the Foreland, though without sight of the Fleet.

Almost certainly, the events of the night of 2/3 July had brought each of the three battered sections of the expedition to believe that the other two were lost. Separately, the fleet and the four ships which had escaped from the bay earlier spent the remainder of that day and the following morning in carrying out essential repairs to their ships:

Some in mending the sides of theyr Shyppes, some in setting vp their toppe Mastes, and mending theyr Sayles and tacklings. Agayne, some complayning of theyr false Stemme borne away, some in stopping their Leakes, some in recounting their daungers past, spent no small time and labour, and I dare well auouche, there were neuer men more daungerously distressed, nor more mercifully by Gods Prouidence deliuered.[120]

These two elements of the expedition were reunited during the evening of 4 July at a point — they believed — some 20 leagues southwest of the Queen's Foreland (Selman). The *Judith*, ironically, had reached that area several hours before, but had then turned to the north-west, to go in and behind the Queen's Foreland, and at the time of the others' rendezvous, her mariners were discovering that the "foreland" was in fact an island.[121]

Even then, it was possible — perhaps even likely — that the Fleet and the *Judith* would have met the following day. Both Frobisher and Fenton had but one goal, and that was to re-enter the Bay and make their prearranged landfall within the Countess of Warwick's Sound. Again, however, the weather's malign influence was decisive. Best and Ellis disagree as to the precise events of that day; the first blames the continuing prevalence of ice, whilst the other speaks of a great and thick fog, which descended in the morning and did not disperse for some fourteen days thereafter. Whatever the cause, Frobisher ordered the Fleet to put out further to seaward and lower their sails; he was content to drift until the weather improved sufficiently to allow them to re-enter the Bay. By that time, the *Judith* had already re-entered the bay; she was to spend the next three weeks alone, attempting to make a landfall that was never more than forty miles distant.

We have discussed the theoretical limitations of contemporary equipment and techniques of navigation in some detail. The repercussions of an imperfect science imperfectly implemented may be seen at its most profound in the events which followed the reunion of the fleet on 3 July. The following day was spent making urgent repairs to most of the ships, but on 5 July, and for four days thereafter, the fleet attempted to move north-westwards, to regain the mouth of the "strait." Their efforts were not aided by a thick coastal mist, nor by the strong south-westerly current which Hall had noted two years before.[122] On 9 July, they had sight of a coastline and open water before them, which Frobisher immediately took to be the entrance to his eponymous strait. His opinion was confirmed by most of his captains and masters (Best commented that the opinion of James Beare was considered particularly weighty in this respect); only Christopher Hall, trusting to the evidence of his eyes and former observations, disagreed:

> ... and I stode against them all, and sayd yt was not yt, And then I toke my Pinas, & rowed abord my generall, I told him that yt was not the streits, and told him all the marks of both the lands, that yt was not the Streicts, and he presently was in a great rage & sware by Gods wounds that yt was yt, or els take his life, so I see him in such a rage, I toke my pinas & came abord the Thomas Allin againe.[123]

Hall's expertise was to prove superior to that of Beare and the others (at least upon this occasion), but their error, insofar as we may judge, appears to have been one of temperament as much as of skill. Hall's logs and other writings often hint at a certain pedantry; yet this was perhaps the natural consequence of his diligent nature. The cloudy skies which prevented observation of latitude on 9 July 1578 hung equally over his own head, but Hall compensated for the limitations of his science by other observations of coastlines, currents, and, no doubt, of anything else which might allow him to establish his position. In contrast, James Beare may have been as adept, perhaps even more so, in using the technology of the day (particularly with the expertise of his father-in-law to draw upon), but he and the other masters appear to have neglected the most mundane requirement of the pilot's craft, to know his coasts.[124] Such necessary assiduity was, of course, completely at odds with their Admiral's temperament, which made their own failure the more damaging. In the midst of fog the following morning, Gilbert Yorke, Vice-Admiral of the fleet and captain of the *Thomas Allen*, formed his own opinion as to who was the better judge of their position, and slipped away from the fleet in the company of the *Anne Frances*, *Frances of Foy*, and the *Emanuel* (or "Busse") of Bridgewater, to seek the true course to their designated landfall.

The eight remaining vessels continued to sail north-westwards into what Frobisher assumed to be his strait, but which was rather the latter-day Hudson Strait. Best (although no longer present), stated that they sailed 60 leagues into the Strait before turning about, which would put them in the vicinity of Big Island (a few mariners claimed to have seen land on their larboard — that is port, side — which, if true, could only have been that landmass). He claimed that Frobisher soon knew himself to be in a mistaken strait, but that he continued to persuade his captains otherwise, hoping — in these broad, ice-free waters — to find the passage to the South Sea. This does not seem to be an entirely improbable interpretation. If Frobisher appeared to be convinced that he was in the correct strait, and argued that conviction with his usual force, then the wisest heads may have considered it prudent not to argue the point. Conversely, it is not inconceivable that the masters who accompanied Frobisher continued to believe that they were in the correct strait, as the fog and mists continued to hide both the features of the coastline and the sun from their view. Their ignorance became unsustainable on 17 July, however, when the clouds parted to allow latitude to be observed.[125] On the same day, Frobisher turned about to the south-east, leaving the location of the true Northwest Passage apparently even further from resolution than had previously been the case.[126]

By 21 July, the fleet was off the western side of Queen Elizabeth's Foreland once more, and having noticed a deep sound therein which tended to the north, Frobisher sent in the *Gabriel* to ascertain whether Frobisher Strait lay at its opposite extremity. This short passage was hazardous; as we have noted, Fenton had already examined the area and baulked at the attempt ("so that I iudge certeinlie the Quenes forelande but an ilande: But the ize being manie coulde not goo thorow"). The *Gabriel*, not having the luxury of choosing to avoid its dangers, encountered a tide of such strength that the passage was barely forced. Emerging from the northern exit into the mouth of Frobisher Bay, the bark immediately encountered the *Thomas Allen* which, since abandoning the fleet eleven days before, had borne tides, fog and ice off the foreland, attempting to regain the passage first attempted on 2 July.

Perhaps understandably, neither Yorke nor his pilot Hall seemed overwhelmed by the news that their Admiral would soon be with them once more; indeed, the following day, the *Thomas Allen* risked the ice within the bay to sail north-west — away from the fleet — and anchor in Jackman's Sound. It was only a week later, after snow storms and high winds had almost entombed his ship within its "safe" harbour, that Hall transferred from the *Thomas Allen* to the *Gabriel*, and went to seek his Commander.[127] On 2 August, having crossed the bay to the northern shore, and the designated rendezvous in the Countess of Warwick Sound, Hall found the fleet, newly reunited with the *Judith* and *Michael* (which had reached the sound on 21 July after many moments of near-disaster amongst the ice). We have no record of Hall's reunion with Frobisher, but perhaps the uncharacteristic brevity of the master's log for that day (and the reference to the presence of his sometime protector, Edward Fenton) is sufficiently eloquent in itself.[128]

From the moment that the fleet achieved its harbour, all the efforts of Frobisher and his men were devoted to securing ore from a dozen sites at and around the Countess of Warwick's Sound. Ostensibly, the search for a route to Cathay had ended on 16 July, when Frobisher admitted his error and turned the fleet back out of the "Mistaken Strait";

yet it should be noted that even this limited and imperfect reconnaissance had been carried out entirely upon his own initiative, and not upon that of his paymasters, the adventurers.

The Privy Council's instructions for the voyage had made it clear that an attempt to reach Cathay was not even a second, fall-back option in 1578. The barks *Gabriel* and *Michael* were to sail up the strait as far as Five Men Sound to search for further potential mining sites, and from there as far west as was necessary to find the western exit of the "strait," but thereafter to rejoin the rest of the fleet. Even this half-effort was only to be undertaken "yf leisure and tyme permit."[129] The explicit abandonment of any serious commitment to force the passage — at a time when the value of ore returned from the second voyage had yet to be proven — may have provided a motive for Frobisher's extended "misapprehension" regarding his position between the 9 and 15 July. Michael Lok later claimed that Frobisher prevented Hall and Jackman from exploring the western extremity of his "strait" because he wanted the credit for that achievement,[130] yet this interpretation seems unduly harsh. Hall's log suggests that the master himself was far more preoccupied with arranging the transportation of miners and ore to — and from — the scattered sites, than with any further exploration of the area. There is also evidence to suggest that Frobisher and the officers of his council[131] discussed a further attempt to navigate to the western extremity of Frobisher "Strait," but — for several sound reasons — it was agreed to be unfeasible.[132]

With the abandonment of the scheme for a 100-man colony (again, blamed by Lok upon Frobisher's vainglory, yet agreed unanimously by his council), the only implicit commitment to a future English presence in Meta Incognita — and perhaps a further attempt to force a western exit into the "Mare de Sur" — was Fenton's construction of a watch tower on 24 August, to test the winter climate should they return.[133]

By 31 August, almost 1200 tons of ore had been mined and largely transported to the collection point at the Countess of Warwick Sound. On that morning, the weather was uncharacteristically calm (although extremely cold, with ice forming thickly upon the decks of the ships in the sound), and on the following day, Frobisher and Hall went to Beare's Sound to supervise the final lading of ore into the barks *Gabriel* and *Michael*, and to pick up miners from the site. A wind arose, and Frobisher told Hall to return to the *Ayde*, saying (according to Hall) that he would return before nightfall. For the next thirty-six hours, Hall vainly awaited the return of his Admiral, at first removing the *Ayde* from a dangerous anchorage upon a lee shore, then hanging out a light to guide in Frobisher's pinnace. One by one, the ships and boats of the fleet passed him, reporting that they had not seen Frobisher, or that he was coming after in the *Gabriel*. Unfortunately, Hall took this to mean rather more than Frobisher had intended, and on the morning of 3 September, he led the *Thomas Allen* and *Moon* out of the mouth of Frobisher Bay. He had, finally, secured the undisputed command of the *Ayde* whilst Frobisher was obliged to return to England in the *Gabriel*, having allocated a further twenty-six miners (who should have been recalled to one of the larger ships) between his own small bark and the *Judith*.[134]

The return passage to England commenced in atrocious weather. At least five ships' pinnaces and boats — including those of the *Ayde* and *Thomas Allen* — were lost in collisions; fortunately, with the loss of only one man. Storms followed the scattered fleet as the ships — save one, the *Emanuel* of Bridgewater — raced for lower latitudes. The *Ayde* was in 55° and 42′ by 9 September, the *Judith* in 55° and 15′ two days later.[135] By 19 September (in 52°), the *Ayde* had news from the *Hopewell* that the *Beare Leicester* and *Salomon* were ahead, and on the following day made brief contact with the *Ann Frances*. Before they separated once more, George Best managed to send word across to Hall that Frobisher was "in great coller" against him for not awaiting his return to the *Ayde*, and also that they feared the "Busse" of Bridgewater lost in Meta Incognita, having been forced onto a lee shore.

In fact, the Busse, or *Emanuel*, had escaped this potential disaster. The story of her homeward voyage was set down by one of her crew, the boatswain Thomas Wiars; his *Relation* was published by Hakluyt in the *Principall Navigations* (1589).[136] The *Emanuel* was beached as a wreck in Smerwick Harbour on the west coast of Ireland on 26 September, but her claim to a more enduring fame lay in the supposed discovery of an "island" in mid-Atlantic approximately 50 leagues south-east of "Friesland." Subsequent attempts to find this land have proved unavailing, and it must be assumed either that the navigational skills of the *Emanuel*'s master were lamentably poor, or that the crew as a whole were positioning themselves for potential future employment.[137]

In the *Ayde*, meanwhile, Hall appears to have spent his time as *de facto* captain to some profit. His log for the homeward voyage — particularly upon days in which they encountered storms — contains a level of detail which can only have been intended as an *aide memoire* for his future use. On 10 September, the day that his main yard broke in a gale, Hall recorded every combination of sails he had set at each watch;[138] either because he had nothing better to do with his time (which seems extremely unlikely), or because he wanted to know what to do — or *not* to do — to prevent a recurrence of the incident.

On 25 September, the *Ayde* was within the Soundings, eight leagues south-east of the Scillies. Two days later, the *Judith* met with the *Salomon* and *Ann Frances* to the south-west (but not yet in sight) of the islands, and Fenton was obliged to persuade Best to sail north-east in his company (Best believed that he had already passed the Scillies). On 30 September, two days after the *Ayde* had anchored at Portsmouth, Fenton brought the *Judith* "into the grasse" (possibly a shallow beach without berthing) at Weymouth. Most of his swollen complement of 67 men, he reported, were "infected with the skirvie and other gingerfull diseases." Fenton's is the only specific comment upon the general health of the mariners and miners, but the physical hardships endured during the voyage and the weeks devoted to mining ore must have lowered their physical resistance considerably. The implied dietary deficiencies which exacerbated this problem suggests that a more protracted return passage, for example through the latitude taken by the returning 1576 expedition, would have resulted in many more men being "heaued ouerbord" than the five unfortunates recorded in Hall's log for the *Ayde*.[139]

Frobisher began and ended his hoped-for "high Admiral-shipp by sea"[140] on the deck of the *Gabriel*, which came into Portsmouth on or about 1 October 1578. His first interview thereafter with Christopher Hall, who awaited him in that town, has not been recorded, but we may assume that it took the form of what has since come to be known as a frank exchange of views. Two days later, Frobisher left for the Court in London, to report on the "success" of his voyage. It is not known whether he and Hall ever met again, although they may have had some contact during the early stages of preparations for the 1582 voyage which Edward Fenton eventually commanded (and to which Hall was appointed as master of the "Admiral," the *Galleon Leicester*). It is not likely that either man regretted their subsequent estrangement.

A few months later, the "Company of Cathay," never to be burdened by the sordid embarrassment of income, ceased to exist even in the imagination of its stockholders. The outstanding debts of its adventurers, and the hundreds of tons of worthless ore which represented the only tangible achievement of three years' endeavour, ensured that no fourth voyage would be made. Furthermore, the failure of the enterprise was seen by contemporaries as having a significance beyond the specific errors of temperament and assumption. The return of Drake's fabulously profitable circumnavigation appeared to provide a sound lesson for future speculators — that it was far more economical of time and money to allow others to find gold, and then to take it from them, either by acts of piracy (often the favoured option), or in lawful trade. The tensions which characterised future projects largely resulted from conflicting priorities concerning existing gold; in contrast, the prospect of prospecting — after the demise of Frobisher's enterprise — appeared to have little to recommend it.

Conclusion: The Significance of the Frobisher Voyages

Inevitably, any impartial assessment of Frobisher's three voyages to Baffin Island is obliged to acknowledge the financial disaster which attended the brief life and messy demise of the so-called "Company of Cathay." In the search to emulate the Spanish and Portuguese successes of the early sixteenth century, Englishmen had once more allowed desire to override prudence, their fertile imaginations to suppose that the rich promise of the New World lay covered by only the thinnest topsoil. Indeed, Frobisher's failure was probably the defining example of this uncritical trait, an exemplar of such striking clarity that the modest scale of future voyages to the north-west appears to represent his only positive influence upon the history of navigation.

From a cartographical perspective also, the voyages had an almost wholly negative legacy, though this could hardly have been foreseen. Continuing faith in the "orthodox" cartology of the north-western Atlantic (as established by the Zeno Brothers) could not be reconciled with the data provided by those who had sailed with Frobisher. It therefore became necessary to place the new discoveries upon the south-eastern coast of Greenland (thereby preserving the supposed position of "Friesland" at 60°); a fallacy which endured, albeit increasingly weakly, into the early years of the nineteenth century (cartographers had no similar conceptual difficulty with "Busse Island," which became a regular feature in contemporary charts).

Yet a positive navigational legacy is not wholly wanting. Insofar as the enterprise broadened the experience of English masters and mariners in an unfamiliar region, they provided lessons which were no less valid for being associated with economic failure. Nor should that failure disguise the fact that these three voyages, by comparison to the earliest north-eastern expeditions, were technically impressive. The tortuous course of the true Northwest Passage is of course an extremely difficult navigation, even for modern vessels carrying preserved foodstuffs; for wooden-hulled vessels, in an era which had no adequate charts of the area, a resolute attempt to force the passage would inevitably have proved fatal. Nevertheless, it must be allowed that the second and third voyages achieved their primary goals in every respect save that of establishing the first English colony in North America. In successive years, hundreds of men were transported to perform heavy manual labour in bitterly hostile conditions, and succeeded in returning to England with approximately thirteen hundred tons of ore for the loss of between 25 and 35 lives (including those lost in the 1576 voyage). In 1578, the largest fleet of ships to visit Baffin Island prior to the twentieth century — not all of which would be considered ocean-worthy by modern standards — made the crossing to Greenland in an unfamiliar latitude, yet achieved a landfall of pin-point accuracy only thirteen days after leaving the coast of Ireland. Their subsequent difficulty in making the pre-arranged rendezvous in Frobisher Bay was largely due to poor weather and the judgement of one man, their leader (a man who was notoriously incapable of accepting unpalatable or contrary opinions); yet even in this relative failure of skills and technology, there is heartening evidence that men such as Hall, Jackman and even the "amateur," Edward Fenton, overcame the limitations of their craft with great intelligence and resource. The burden of blame for the fiasco which attended the supposed discovery of gold should be placed elsewhere than upon the masters, mariners and miners who fulfilled their orders with admirable assiduity.

Frobisher did not discover a passage to Cathay via the north-west, a failure for which he can hardly be held to account. Conversely, he can — and should — be criticised for not disproving the Passage via his own "strait." In every tangible sense, the northwest enterprise of 1576-8 was a dead-end in the history of English maritime exploration; an episode whose lessons were considered by Frobisher's contemporaries to be wholly cautionary. Yet the experiences of these voyages provided the most rigorous training for men of a nation which had come late to oceanic voyaging. They allowed William Borough and Robert Norman to prove the inequality of magnetic variation, the first exclusively English contribution to the science of navigation. At the most fundamental level, they — like Drake's almost-concurrent circumnavigation — added to a growing self-confidence which would allow Englishmen to believe they could challenge the power of Portugal and, more pertinently, Spain in a global arena. The majority of seamen who provided the Queen's ships with manpower and leadership during the years of the Spanish War were first tested in private ventures, some of them as ill-advised as that which occupied the efforts of the fleeting "Company of Cathay." Acknowledging this fact, we must also acknowledge the place of the Frobisher voyages in the developing British naval tradition.

Notes

---

[1] H. Billingsley, *The Elements of Geometrie of the most auncient Philosopher Evclide* (London, 1570); reproduced in D.W.Waters, *The Art of Navigation in England in Elizabethan and Early Stuart Times*, (H.M.S.O. 1978), 3rd edition., p. 521 (hereafter cited as Waters).

[2] It is not the authors' intention to examine the cosmographical significance of the Frobisher voyages in detail, nor to assess the impact of contemporary ship-building technology. These matters are dealt with elsewhere in this volume.

[3] This bald statement undoubtedly belittles the singular contribution of Genoese pilots to the history of discovery. It is, however, fair to conclude that the experience of earlier Genoese voyages outside the Mediterranean left no permanent mark, other than in the practical knowledge subsequently transmitted by Genoese pilots hired by other nations with fledgling navies (the construction of a Genoese fortress in the Canary Islands in the thirteenth century was an exception, but it had been abandoned long before the islands were permanently settled in the early fifteenth century).

[4] Bristol men had already acquired a reputation which spread far beyond the confines of their profession; Raimondo de Raimondi de Soncino, ambassador to England of the Duke of Milan, wrote to his master on 18 December 1497, referring to them as "great seamen" (J.A. Williamson, *The Voyages of the Cabots and the Discovery of North America* (Argonaut Press ed. 1970), p. 31).

[5] Printed versions of rutters — small, proto-almanacs containing magnetic compass courses between ports and capes, distance tables, depth of water in the Soundings and strengths of tidal flows — began to appear in north-western Europe in the first years of the sixteenth century (printed in Rouen by Pierre Garcie), although the oldest known English rutter in manuscript form may have dated from 1408 (Waters, I, p.12).

[6] A precise assessment of Cabot's abilities as a navigator is not possible from extant documentary sources. However, Soncino (*op. cit.*) stated that Cabot was careful to keep the Pole Star to his starboard on the outward passage, which suggests that he was familiar with the principles of latitude observation. Furthermore, John Day, in his letter to Christopher Columbus (English translation reproduced in J.A. Williamson, *The Cabot Voyages and Bristol Discovery under Henry VII, with the Cartography of the Voyages by R.A. Skelton*, Cambridge, 1962, p.213) stated that Cabot also noted magnetic variation of the compass.

[7] Most original sources for projected English voyages in 1517 and 1521 are reproduced by J.A.Williamson, *op.cit.*

[8] Waters, I, p. 47. The sun's declination upon a particular day — that is, its distance in degrees from the "equinoctiall" or celestial equator — was established from solar tables ("The Regiment of the Sun") and subtracted from the observed meridian altitude (measured by astrolabe or, more often, by cross-staff). The resulting figure represented the altitude of the equinoctial and was deducted from the theoretical Zenith at 90 degrees to give the correct latitude. For an illustration of this measurement by Christopher Hall, see his log for 6 May 1578; British Library, Harleian MS 167/42, f. 184r.

[9] Measurement of longitude at sea was achieved only in the mid-eighteenth century, with the pioneering work of the clock-maker John Harrison.

[10] Waters, I, pp. 64-5.

[11] This inherent error of the plane chart was not overcome until 1599, when Edward Wright devised a table for delineating meridians of longitude upon a chart using Mercator's projection.

[12] Waters, I, p. 83. Possible, but apparently not yet customary. In 1540, the French Ambassador in London reported that English ships were full of Ragusans, Genoans, Normans and Bretons; although he did not mention whether this applied specifically to Royal ships (E.G.R. Taylor, *The Haven-Finding Art. A History of Navigation from Odysseus to Captain Cook*, London, 1971, p. 194. Hereafter cited as Taylor, *Haven-Finding Art*).

[13] Waters, I, pp. 82-3.

[14] A Bristol mariner and later founder member of the Spanish Company (1577).

[15] Waters, I, p. 85. Amongst Bodenham's crew were Richard Chancellor and Matthew Baker, who became one of the leading Elizabethan shipwrights (he built the bark *Gabriel* for Frobisher's 1576 voyage). Their pilot from Cadiz into the Mediterranean was a Spaniard named Nobiezia, who apparently served without wages — a charity which must have recommended him even less to his own people.

[16] See the discussion on Michael Lok earlier in this volume for one English family's activities in Portugal and Spain during the 1550s.

[17] Taylor, *Haven-Finding Art*, p. 196.

[18] Waters, I, p. 90.

[19] Stephen Borough offered evidence — perhaps unwittingly — of the difficulties of learning the techniques of navigation. Both he and William had sailed with Willoughby and Chancellor in 1553, in Stephen's case as master of the *Edward Bonaventure*. Yet it was only in 1556 that he could claim (in his journal) that they had learned to take the Sun and find variations of the needle (Taylor, *Haven-Finding Art*, p.196). By 1558, however, Stephen had been appointed Chief Pilot of the Muscovy Company and, remarkably, admitted as an honorary guest of Spain's prestigious academy of the sea, the Casa de Contratación in Seville (Waters, I, p. 103).

[20] Infra.

[21] Waters, I, p. 104.

[22] Despite their limitations, it is significant that *The Castle of Knowledge* and *Cosmographical Glasse* were considered suitable texts for the elementary tuition of Frobisher and, to a lesser extent, Christopher Hall, prior to their first north-west voyage some two decades later.

[23] Waters, I, p.134.

[24] Ibid., p. 96; see also S. Ackermann, ed., *Humphrey Cole: Mint, Measurement and Maps in Elizabethan England* (British Museum Occasional Paper no. 126, British Museum Press, 1998).

[25] *What maner of persons be meetest to take charge of Shippes in Nauigation*; William Bourne's introduction to *A Regiment for the Sea*, London, 1574: Quoted in E.G.R. Taylor, *A Regiment for the Sea*; Hakluyt Society, Second Series, vol. 121 (1961), pp. 170-1 (hereafter cited as Taylor, *Regiment*).

[26] BL Lansdowne MS 100/4: "A Discourse concerninge a Straighte to be discovered towarde the Northweste, passinge to Cathaia and the Orientall indians, with a confutacion of their errour that thinke the Discoverye therof to be moste convenientlye attempted to the Northe of Baccalaos." The outer leaf of the manuscript is annotated : "M*aster* Grynfoldes voyadg/Discovery of a Streight in ye N.W. Passage to Cathay & ye E.Indies."

[27] BL Cotton MS, Otho E VIII, f 239.

[28] For these events, see Jim McDermott "The Company of Cathay: the Financing and Organization of the Frobisher Voyages," in this volume.

[29] Lok was the Company's London Agent in 1571 and 1575-6 (T.S. Willan, *Early History of the Russia Company* (Manchester, 1956, p. 287)). It is not known whether he held the post continually between these dates.

[30] BL Cotton MS; Otho E VIII, f 41; Michael Lok's account of the initial preparations. The master to whom Lok refers was probably Christopher Hall, a known Muscovy man. Borough's interest in the new project did not extend to risking his money therein, until he succumbed to the gold-fever which followed the return of the 1577 voyage (Lok's list of adventurers for the 1578 voyage; Henry E. Huntington Library, HM 715, f 2; hereafter cited as HM 715).

[31] BL Cotton MS; Otho E VIII, f 41. Inevitably, in describing his meeting with Dee, Lok made much of his own studies, particularly in consideration of the north-west route: "...freely and playnly I layd open to him at large my whole purpose in the traffike of merchandise by those new partes of the world for the benefit of the realm ..... And allso declared such coniectures and probabilities as I had conceved of a passage by sea into the same sea of East India by that way of the north-west from England. And for the proof of these two matters I layd before him my bokes and authors, my cardes and instrumentes, and my notes thereof made in writing, as I had made them of many yeres study before. Which matters, when he had thus hard and sene, he answered that he was right glad to know of me thus much of this matter, and that he was greatly

satisfyed in his desyre about his expectation, and that I was so well grounded in this (good pur)pose he sh(o)wed me all(so) his own."

[32] Frobisher's apparent diligence in recording variation suggests that Dee's tuition was not entirely wasted. Dee's reward for his association with the enterprise was to be included as an adventurer in the second voyage, with £25 of stock, provided — in the first instance — from the pocket of Michael Lok. With subsequent assessments, Dee's eventual stock stood at £100, of which fifty shillings remained unpaid in May 1581; even at this late date, it was still listed as due from Lok, and not Dee himself (PRO EKR E164/36, 322; HM 715, f 29).

[33] Ibid.; E164/35, 16-17.

[34] Ibid.

[35] Waters, III, p. 531.

[36] Ibid.

[37] Ibid.

[38] George Best, *A True Discourse of the Late Voyages of Discoverie for finding of a Passage to Cathaya by the North-Weast, under the Conduct of Martin Frobisher General* (London, 1578), in R.Collinson, *The Three Voyages of Martin Frobisher* (London, 1867), p. 155 (hereafter Best in Collinson): "And here (ie. at c. 61 degrees north) the north starre is so muché elevated above the horizon, that with the staffe it is hardly to be wel observed, and the degrees in the Astrolabe are too small to observe minutes. Therefore we alwaies used the staffe and the sunne, as fittest instruments for this use."

[39] Some of these items may have resembled the integrated compass and sundial of the type recovered from the wreck of the *Mary Rose*; a design which thus had been in use for a number of decades prior to the Frobisher voyages.

[40] The chart is preserved in Hatfield House. For a detailed discussion of its content, see Waters, III, Appendix no. 10. Using the evidence of the chart in 1581, Robert Norman proved the inequality of magnetic variation in his work *The Newe Attractive*: "Goyng to *Meta Incognita*, it varieth more in 1/3 parte of the last of the way then in 2/3 of the first; and in those partes is found to be sudden." Norman also invented a "double-fly" compass which could be adjusted to account for local variation.

[41] William Borough, *A Discours of the Variation*, in *The Newe Attractive*: "defectes of the latitudes have been verie well reformed by the famous and learned Gerardus Mercator (whom I honour and esteem as the chief Cosmographer of the World) in his universall mapp, which though he have made with sayling lines, and dedicated to the use of seamen, yet for want of consideration of the Variation, and partly by augmentyng his degrees of latitude towards the Poles, the same is more fitte for such to beholde, as studie in Cosmographie, by readyng authors upon the lande, then to bee used in Navigation at the sea" (quoted in Waters, II, p. 160).

[42] EKR 164/35, 102: "paid to humfrye Cole, for reparinge and newe makinge divers Instrumentes of navigatione, for the voyage....li. 7. 11. 10." The instruments returned from the first voyage were sold to the account of the second, valued at £40 (ibid).

[43] Inventory of the *Ayde*, SP/12/129, 36.

[44] Waters, II, p. 144.

[45] BL, Harleian MS 167, 42, ff. 184-200

[46] Magdelene College Library, Cambridge, Pepys MS 2133, ff. 17-75 (hereafter Pepys MS). All the ships' logs discussed here are set in a linear format, with the entire width of the page employed (save for a left hand margin — usually ruled — into which memoranda, summaries of daily sailing distances and, occasionally, sketches were placed). D.W. Waters has recently established that John Davis was almost certainly the first European navigator to use the columnar form in making log entries; a more economical style which eventually was to become the norm.

[47] BL, Harleian MS 167/42, ff. 181-2.

[48] Ibid., f 184.

[49] A reef.

[50] A rock formation.

[51] Richard Hakluyt, *The Principal Navigations Voyages Traffiques & Discoveries of the English Nation* (1598-1600), III, p. 58. (hereafter Hakluyt, *PN*). However, two weeks later, on 26 June, Hall set out his calculation more fully, although there was some confusion of terms. He claimed to have added the sun's

declination to the "elevation" to establish his latitude, but a margin note stated "By elevation he meaneth the distance of the sunne from the zenith"; this was a clear indication that, whilst the theory was understood (Hall's observation of latitude was correct), the scientific terminology remained elastic.

[52] The calculation is annotated: "truely observed being a myle from the *Lezard*."

[53] At an elevation of 49 degrees, the Sun was just low enough to allow the measurement to be taken by cross-staff; above 50 degrees, and the distance between Sun and horizon would have obliged Hall to use a mariner's ring, or astrolabe (however, see n. 38 above).

[54] Approximately 5' would be deducted from the observation to deem it to be made from the Sun's centre, (from which the true reading should be taken).

[55] Waters, I, p. 54.

[56] BL, Harleian MS 167/42, f. 186r. Curiously, unlike other experienced mariners, Hall commenced the day in his 1578 log with the first watch, from 4 to 8 o'clock in the morning; whilst the landsman, Fenton, recorded his log from midday in the accepted manner.

[57] Taylor, *Regiment*, pp. 237-8. Waters believes that log and line measurements were not recorded with direction on the traverse board until the introduction of the knotted line, c.1600 (Waters, I, p. 37).

[58] Additionally, Bourne recommended that latitude observations be made as often as possible to correct errors of calculation created by a leeward drift of the ship.

[59] But see n. 108 below.

[60] Waters, I, p. 60.

[61] Hall (27 June 1576); Hakluyt, *PN*, III, p. 59.

[62] Mistakenly believed to be the mythical island of "Friesland" because their copy of Mercator's world map using the evidence of the Zeno brothers, placed that landmass across 60°.

[63] Best, *Frobisher*, p. 30: "...our worthy Captaine *Martine Frobisher*, who ... hath diligentlye observed the variation of the needle."

[64] The inference of his account is that Hall recorded his "reference" variation in his log at Gravesend at the commencement of the voyage, and upon three later occasions. The chart itself was marked more often, of course, because that is where the variation needed to be observed.

[65] Taylor, *Regiment*, p. 210.

[66] Hakluyt, *PN*, III; 59.

[67] Michael Lok's account of the first voyage (BL Cotton MS, Otho E VIII; f 46) claimed three; Best's four.

[68] BL Cotton MS, Otho E VIII, f 46.

[69] Hakluyt, *PN*, V; 133. "...we had sight of the land of Friseland bearing from vs West northwest 16 leagues, and rising like pinacles of steeples, and all couered with snow."

[70] It was only discovered to be an island — by Fenton in the *Judith* — in 1578 (Pepys MS 2133, f 27).

[71] Best's account is wildly inaccurate at this point, claiming that the Gabriel entered the "strait" on 21 July. At that date, according to Hall, the coast of Meta Incognita had not yet been sighted.

[72] Neither location has been identified definitively; Burcher's Island is possibly the modern "Frobisher's Farthest" (although the latter name was itself bestowed speculatively).

[73] See Jim McDermott, "A right Heroicall heart: Sir Martin Frobisher," in this volume. It should be noted also that the *Gabriel* was hardly in a fit state to go further; Hall stated that on 14 August they had anchored near Prior's Sound and re-caulked her hull "being weak from the wales vpward."

[74] The Commission comprised Sir William Winter, Thomas Randolph, Edward Dyer, Anthony Jenkinson, Edmund Hogan, Matthew Field, Andrew Palmer and Michael Lok.

[75] Michael Lok, "The doinges of Captaine Furbisher / amongest the Companyes busynes"; BL Lansdowne MS, 100/1, f 2v.

[76] SP/12/111, 49.

[77] SP/12/111, 48 (i).

[78] There are at least three extant versions of these instructions, refs. SP/12/113, 12; BL Add. MS 35831 & BL Sloane MS 2442. There are certain differences between these drafts, and it is not known which represent the definitive instructions of the Privy Council as issued to Frobisher and his men. The latter document omits any reference to the further search for the western exit to the "strait."

[79] All the condemned men were set ashore at Harwich before the expedition sailed, in order to reduce Frobisher's swollen complement of men.

[80] E164/35, 102.

[81] Ibid., 112.

[82] Ibid., 142. Rambridge received £5. 11s. 1d. upon the return of the expedition, whilst the basic rate for other, non-ranked soldiers was £5. Edmund English, presumably their sergeant, received £7. 06s. 8d.

[83] Dionyse Settle, *A true reporte of the last voyage into the west and northwest regions, &c, 1577, worthily atchieved by Capteine Frobisher of the said voyage the first finder and generall* (London, Henry Middleton, 1577), in V. Stefansson & E. McCaskill, *The Three Voyages of Martin Frobisher* (London, 1938), II, pp.5 - 25 (hereafter Settle : SM).

[84] EKR E164/35, 145. Beare was master of the *Ann Frances* in the 1578 voyage.

[85] Best in Collinson, p. 125: "...they have in their sea cardes set out everie part thereof ..... And for so much of this land as we have sayled alongst, comparing their carde with ye coast, we find it very agreeable."

[86] Best did note — or at least reproduce — latitude observations, particularly on the homeward voyage, but these were excised by his publisher (possibly at the order of the Privy Council).

[87] Settle: SM, pp. 14 - 15.

[88] Ibid., p. 15.

[89] One interpretation of Frobisher's reasons for not seeking the passage was put by Best thus: "Now, had the generall altered his determination for going any further into the straights at this time, for any further discoverie of the passage, having taken a man and a woman of that countrey, whiche he thought sufficiente for the use of language; and having also mette wyth these people heere, which intercepted his men the last yeare (as the apparell and English furniture whiche was found in their tentes very well declared), he knewe it was but labour lost to seeke them further off, when he had found them there at hand. And considering, also the shorte time he had in hande, he thoughte it best to bend his whole endevour for the getting of myne, and to leave the passage further to be discovered hereafter. For his commission directed hym in this voyage only for the searching of the gold ore, and to deferre the further discoverie of the passage untill another tyme" (Best in Collinson, pp. 147-8) The last statement is clearly inaccurate, unless the document designated BL Sloane MS 2442 was the final version of Frobisher's instructions.

[90] Best in Collinson, p. 153.

[91] The *Ayde*, laden to almost double her normal tonnage, must have sat extremely low in the water — another urgent reason for avoiding the higher, stormier passage at 60°. The official instructions for the voyage had anticipated the problems of severe weather, and had suggested a more southerly course: "...you shall make yor retorne homewardes by the west partes of *Ireland* and so by the narrowe seas of *England* to London for that we doo take the same to be yor safest course because we doo not knowe what other matters maye happen to you in the tyme of yor iorney and therefore cannot prescribe what is to be don for yor releife in suche a case. We doo therfore referr the the consideracion thereof to yor good discrecion not doubting but that the order which you will take therein shalbe agreeable with the good expectacion that is conceaved of you." (BL Sloane MS 2442).

[92] This was later confirmed by Settle, who stated that the *Michael* came into Yarmouth via Scotland.

[93] Vice-Admiral of the 1578 expedition.

[94] William Smith, master of the *Gabriel* in 1577, was swept overboard and drowned on 30 August, immediately after revealing a premonition of drowning to his captain, Edward Fenton (Best in Collinson, p.153).

[95] In other words, to tack.

[96] Best in Collinson, p. 156.

[97] See Bernard Allaire and Donald Hogarth,"Martin Frobisher, the Spaniards and a Sixteenth Century Northern Spy," in this volume.

[98] Conyers Read," Despatches of Castelnau de la Mauvissiere 1577-81," *American Historical Review*, vol 31 (1926), p.286.

[99] SP/91/1/1a.

[100] SP/12/112, 25: "Mr Lockes Discoors Touching the Ewre 1577."

[101] SP/12/123, 5. Assay carried out by Jonas Schutz, Humphrey Cole, Robert Denham and John Brode at Muscovy House.

[102] See McDermott, "Michael Lok," in this volume.

[103] Thomas Ellis, *A true report of the third and last voyage into Meta Incognita* (London, Thomas Dawson, 1578).

[104] BL Harleian MS 167, 40, ff. 166-180. Selman, like his "master" Lok, appears to have had previous experience of foreign travel, and thus may have commented upon matters of navigation from an informed layman's perspective. Best states that Selman was appointed "Notarie" to the expedition, with responsibility to provide the official account, should the Queen require it (Best in Collinson, p.255). The fact that the journal was delivered instead to Lok suggests that Elizabeth was happier to have the executive summary.

[105] Best referred to Hall as the "chiefe pylot of the Voyage" (Best in Collinson, p.255). Hall's appointment to the *Thomas Allen* may also have reflected the tension of his relationship with Frobisher. He was eventually to express a rather raw opinion of his Admiral's abilities, a disillusionment which appears to have dated from the previous year. According to Michael Lok, Frobisher had threatened Hall with hanging for no more than failing to remove his cap when addressing his Commander. Whether this was another example of Lok's hyperbole is difficult to assess; Lok claimed he heard the story from Fenton (who seems to have defended Hall during the episode), but if there is some truth to the story, it is clear that it was merely one of a number of occasions upon which they clashed. There can be little doubt that Hall came to consider Frobisher's skills both as a navigator and commander in a very unfavourable light, and with good reason.

[106] BL, Harleian MS 167, 40, f.166r.

[107] Fenton made numerous observations of latitude on both the outward and return passages, although referring to them as readings of "altitude," until (presumably) corrected by Charles Jackman on 7 September; after which he noted his observations as "latitude" (Pepys MS 2133, f.62).

[108] In the summer months, the North Atlantic surface currents at c.55° run almost directly north westwards, whereas at 60° the prevailing current runs north-eastwards towards the Norwegian coast. It was the southern extremity of this current, clipping the Irish continental shelf, which was commented upon by George Best, who reckoned that it carried them a full point off course at the start of the 1578 voyage (Best in Collinson, p.232).

[109] The depth of water there meant that the ships could not anchor. Frobisher put his ship's pinnace into the water on his lee side, and the *Thomas Allen* came up to allow Hall to board the pinnance whilst it lay in the lee calm. When the boats returned to their ships later in the day, the heavy seas made it difficult for Fenton to re-board *Judith*, and he was forced to spend most of the rest of the day and night "at hull" (that is, hoved to) until he could be picked up (Pepys MS 2133, f. 21).

[110] "...it passeth manes reasone for asmuch as yet (we can not) desern how they cam (to) haue skill to conducte them selues (across) so large and wyde a passage or therfrom (be) able to brooke such hyswellinge seas which we haue founde very dangerous to our gr(eat shi)ps...." (BL Harleian MS 167, 41, f 181r).

[111] Pepys MS 2133, f 25.

[112] Hall's log for 2 July; BL Harleian MS 167, 42, f 190r.

[113] Thomas Ellis, *A True Reporte of the third and last voyage into Meta Incognita: atchieved by the worthie Capteine M. Martine Frobisher Espquire, Anno 1578* (London, Thomas Dawson, 1578), in Stefansson & McCaskill, *Three Voyages*, II, p. 37.

[114] Best in Collinson, pp. 236 - 7.

[115] Ibid., p. 237.

[116] BL Harleian MS 167/42, f. 190v.

[117] Ibid., 167/41, f. 181r.

[118] Ibid.

[119] Pepys MS 2133, ff. 25 - 26.

[120] Best in Collinson, p. 239.

[121] Pepys MS 2133, f 27.

[122] "And truly it was wonderfull to heare and see the rushing and noyse that the tydes do make in thys place with so violente a force, that oure Shippes lying ahull, were turned sometimes rounde aboute euen in a moment, after the manner of a whirlepoole..." (Best in Collinson, p. 240).

[123] Edward Selman claimed that the previous day, Robert Davis — master of the *Ayde* — had also disagreed with the general consensus (BL Harleian MS 167, 40, f 169r).

[124] In mitigation, Best pointed out that snowfalls had obscured many of the features of the coastline, and that the north-west trend of this new coast was very similar to that of the northern shore of the strait. Whether it was so similar "that the best Mariners ... may be deceyued" is difficult to judge in retrospect.

[125] "The 17 said we toke the Altitude of the sunne & found vs but in the latitude of 62. & 10. minuts, and therevppon found the error which we were in, then knowing that we were vppon the S. side of the S. shore called the Queens foreland, and with the winde at W. we did beare owt agayne....." (Selman; BL Harleian MS 167, 40, ff. 169r - 170v).

[126] Best's *True Discourse* analysed the potential of the "mistaken" strait in some depth, commenting upon the strength and volume of the tidal flow, the great width of the passage, and even the evidence of several mariners on the *Gabriel* that the western exit to Frobisher's "strait" emptied into the larger body of water (Best in Collinson, pp. 242 - 5).

[127] Frobisher's ships had reached the Countess of Warwick's Sound on 29 July, after Frobisher himself had first mistaken Gabriel Island for his intended landfall; an error noted with some exasperation by Edward Selman (BL Harleian MS 167, 40; f 172r).

[128] "The 3. of August sonday callme & no winde, I went a shore to my generall, & to Captayn fenton, vppon the Countes Iland."

[129] For a more detailed discussion of the instructions for the third voyage, see McDermott, "The Company of Cathay," in this volume.

[130] BL. Lansdowne 100/1, f.8r: "..which service he did putt of from tyme to tyme, sayenge that he woold fynde a tyme for yt, but he employed all his tyme onely to the seakinge and digginge of mynes.... And his mind beinge so vayne glorious, that he will not suffer anye discouerye to bee made without his owne presens...."

[131] Frobisher's "council," appointed by the Privy Council, were captains Fenton, Yorke, Carew, Best and Philpot (Best in Collinson, p. 255).

[132] "Whiche, after long debating, was found a thing verye impossible, and that rather consultation was to bee had of returning homewarde, especiallye for these causes following. First, the dark foggy mistes, the continuall fallyng snowe and stormy weather which they commonly were vexed with, and nowe dalye ever more and more encreased, have no small argument of the winters drawing neare. And also the froste everye nighte was so harde congealed within the sounde, that if by evill happe they shoulde be long kepte in wyth contrarye windes, it was greatly to be feared that they should be shutte uppe there faste the whole yeare, whych being utterly unprovided, would be their utter destruction." (Best in Collinson, p. 273).

[133] Pepys MS 2133 f. 55: "...this I did to prove what the vehemencie of winde and weather would do therwith this winter, to thende, that if the nexte yere habitacion shoulde be performed there, that then by this litle begynninge, a iuste occasion and experiment should given how we shoulde deale in building greater howses."

[134] Ibid., ff.59-60 (2 September): "..in the afternoone we cam to the Quenes foreland, and there founde the Gabriell and the Generall aborde her, being commed that daie from Beares sownde with a Pynnass and 26 men in her like to be caste awaie...." fo 60; 3 September: "And afterwardes we bare into the straites againe to see if we could meete the Ayde or any other of the shipps (which failing of) the Generall determyned to passe home in the Gabriell." To Frobisher's credit, he took considerable personal risks to recover all of the miners from their scattered sites. His decision to return home in the overladen *Gabriel*, when he might have transferred to one of a number of larger vessels, was one of his more inspired acts of leadership by personal example.

[135] The *Ayde* had lost the company of the *Moon* on 5 September, and the *Thomas Allen* parted from the *Ayde* on 10 September when a broken yardarm forced Hall to heave to for repairs. The *Judith* had departed from Meta Incognita in the company of the *Anne Frances*, *Gabriel* and *Michael*, but lost sight of these ships on 8 September.

[136] For a comprehensive modern discussion of the *Emanuel*'s eventful return passage, see D.D. Hogarth, P.W. Boreham & J.G. Mitchell, *Mines, Minerals, Metallurgy* (Canadian Museum of Civilization, Mercury Series, 1994), pp. 60-72.

[137] Hogarth, Boreham and Mitchell, *op. cit.*, suggests that the crew of the Emanuel had in fact sighted Cape Farewell, and that their mis-observation of latitude caused the error. This interpretation must rely upon significant professional incompetence on the part of *Emanuel*'s captain and master, one or both of whom, in fair weather, observed the southernmost point of their "island" to lie in 57° and 1' (Cape Farewell lies in 60°).

[138] On the first watch, "a fayre gale," the main sail, 2 top sails and the sprit; then "all the sayles attaint" except the foretop sail; third watch, "all the sayles attaint to the hard top"; sixth watch, "a good hard gayle my foresaill & Maynsayle & topsaile & spritt sayle abroade, being but a reasonable gale of winde at the end of this sterbord watche I broke my mayn yard 2 howres afore day..." (BL Harleian MS 167, 42, f 197v).

[139] "...drincke was so scant throughout al the Fleete, by meanes of the greate leakage, that not onely the prouision whiche was layde in for the habitation (ie. for the proposed colony) was wanting and wasted, but also eache Shippes seuerall prouision spent and lost, which many of oure companye, to their greate griefe, founde in their returne since, for al the way homewards they dranke nothing but water." (Best in Collinson, p. 273-4).

[140] Frobisher's petition to the Queen, SP/12/119, 31.

Speculative Ambitions and the Reputations of Frobisher's Metallurgists

Robert Baldwin

Introduction

The English voyages made in 1577 and 1578 to the Frobisher Bay region of Baffin Island were the product of an extraordinary, even fevered, anxiety to exploit at once two major and distinctive new technologies: oceanic navigation and non-ferrous metallurgy. The former seems to modern eyes to have been much the more reliably exploited, despite the dangers and difficulties of ice and massive changes in compass variation in the vicinity of Meta Incognita. Yet the voyages did not prove that Frobisher had found the Northwest Passage from Europe to China as he had claimed after his first voyage there in 1576. By 1579 the attempt to exploit new metallurgical knowledge in Meta Incognita had failed badly.

This was despite the fact that Frobisher's metallurgists could draw on their successful regional experiences throughout England and Wales. Some of the most important practitioners were denizens from central Europe, and brought their ideas directly from European practice. By 1576-77 their industry could be seen as enjoying unprecedented growth, for the number of men employed in it in England and Wales grew hugely between 1566 and 1576. It has been estimated the Company of Mines Royal and the Company of Mineral and Battery Works together created new employment for 10,000 men over that decade.[1] This success was a reflection of the particular strategic priority that had been given by Elizabeth I's Privy Council to the sourcing of native copper because of the importance of copper alloys in the making of ordnance. Similar growth was evident within the smaller operations that characterised the iron and steel making industry. All this contrasts starkly with the otherwise lacklustre performance of the English economy from 1561 to 1574, but underlies the misplaced confidence of speculative investors in Frobisher's plans in 1577-78.

Until 1575-76 most of Thomas Gresham's efforts on behalf of the English Crown to borrow abroad to finance its strategic priorities were frustrated by trading and money market conditions. Consequently many of Gresham's efforts in Antwerp were directed to timely repayments of earlier Marian borrowings and to defensive purchases of weapons and ordnance. In consequence, ambitious and expensive foreign policy ambitions were impossible and the Crown was forced into extensive land sales to make ends meet. But the years from 1576 to 1578 saw the opening of a window of financial opportunity for the Crown, and concurrently the growth of what can only be described as a speculative bubble in Privy Council and City of London circles based on Frobisher's alleged discoveries. As the Crown's credit rating improved, and the management of Parliamentary subsidies and Crown property sales became less pressing priorities,

Elizabeth I's large speculative investment in Frobisher's voyages became possible, beginning with the £1,000 Adventurer's share taken up in 1577.[2] Having advised her, many of her Privy Councillors followed Burghley and themselves took up shares as Adventurers.

Somewhat similar events characterised the private sector of the English economy. In 1576 the Company of Mines Royal had followed the Company of Mineral and Battery Works into profit, and the Muscovy Company had succeeded in opening up a new trade route from Persia via the Caspian Sea and the Volga, which proved profitable from 1573 to 1581, as well as expanding trade to Narva. Speculative success also accompanied privateering voyages to Africa, while a revival in the Levant trade completed the broader commercial context in which the Adventurers who invested in the unincorporated Cathay venture lost so much, but where quite as much was concurrently recouped in the booty and profits from Drake's circumnavigation that began in 1577.[3]

The Politics Of Seizing And Defending American Mineral Wealth

Elizabeth I and her Privy Council longed for the freedom of strategic action which would come from mineral resources matching those of Philip II, especially his American ones. As a teenager living at Hatfield House she may have heard tell of the Duke of Northumberland's plan to attack Peru's silver mines, a plan leaked to Charles V by Sebastian Cabot in November 1553.[4] Thereafter Spain was wary of a repetition of the attempt, or the attempting of anything similar by Protestant corsairs like the seizure of shipping carrying the wealth of those mines to Seville. That would have entailed a naval war Elizabeth could ill-afford. Her Lord Treasurer, William Cecil wrote:

> *The realms of England cannot be assayled from Spayn or the Low Countries but by sea. Therefor hir Majesty's speciall and most proper defence agaynst the Enemy's Navy must be by shipps. ... [but] if also in tyme of yere convenient, shipping may be ready to pass to the Islands to intercept some of the Indian Flete, the execution thereof will be very profitable for the mayntenance of the chardges of the warres.*[5]

That strategic context was the making of Frobisher. Given his buccaneering outlook he was as ready to seize precious metal cargoes as to facilitate the lading of ores that offered similar prospects of wealth. Others had a much more sophisticated view of lands with metallurgical opportunity. In the Americas land was seen to be plentiful, unlike Europe, where land was a symbol of social prestige and complex systems of land law.

In 1573-4 Sir Richard Grenville had proposed a briefer strategic plan to the Queen[6] to "ascend from the Equinoctial in the Pacific" to discover the Northwest Passage. Grenville used the argument of "the likelihood of bringing in great treasure in gold, silver and pearls into this realm from those countries as other Princes have out of like regions," meaning the Americas or the Philippines.[7] But it was not, in mid-1574, diplomatically convenient for the Queen to sanction Grenville's plan.

Sr Martin Frobisher Knight.

The noble flames that glowd in his stout brest
Could ne're be quencht, nor by that Ice opprest
Of Northerne Seas; His praise let him not want
Whose worth deserves a print of Adamant,
That he may still guide ships whose fame let grow
So long as sea shall haue an Ebbe and flow. A.H.

Figure 1: Martin Frobisher wearing an up-to-date suit of armour while on campaign to France with Sir John Williams. This cut-down copper plate engraving was prepared about 1592 by Robert Boissard to show him in the context of the two major strategic targets of Williams' forces in North Western France, Croidon (or Crozon) and Brest. The lost right hand side of the plate with its land may well have represented Meta Incognita, and thus have included a matching pillar, suggestive of the pillars of Hercules and thus Frobisher's achievements. Reproduced by permission of the Bodleian Library, University of Oxford. 4° Rawl 170. *Baziliogia, a book of Kings, 1618*, folio 124.

Meanwhile Sir Warham St. Leger, an associate of Grenville and Humphrey Gilbert in southern Ireland, had entered into secret negotiations with Frobisher, negotiations of which Frobisher's wife clearly disapproved, as her betrayal of them to Sir Francis Walsingham, causing their separation, reveals. It was either insurrection or piracy that was planned, or part of an assignment for the Spanish Ambassador agreed in May 1573.[8] While St. Leger was arraigned and executed for it, high level influence extricated Frobisher for a strategic exploratory role. Lord Burghley and John Dee who had been in correspondence since 1563, if not from their Cambridge undergraduate days,[9] concerted their response with Lok from 3 February 1574, and brought Frobisher to heel because he badly needed powerful friends. George Best later wrote that Frobisher consulted with "friends" and "Merchants of our Country" about "the plot & summe of hys devise." Best recalls that next "he layde a playne platt unto them, [showing] that that voyage was not onely possible by the North Weast, but also as he could prove, easie to be performed." Best also confirms that he had relied on "Secret intelligence which heere for sundry causes I leave untouched" adding that for a "Long time he [Frobisher] conferred with his private friends of these secretes ... before he attempted the same," namely an attempt on the Northwest Passage.[10]

By mid-1576 the Queen was persuaded that she could support commercial reconnaissance, and even mineralogical exploration, but not license explicit colonisation or attempts on the transit of Peruvian silver. Frobisher's alleged discovery of a Northwest Passage on his first northern foray in 1576 fitted exactly this group of speculative quasi-political hopes. By 1577 the wider ambitions of Frobisher, Hawkins, Drake and Dee were being indulged with royal confidence. Dee's text, *Cotton Otho E.VIII*, written in the spring of 1577, reveals a strategic plan akin to Grenville's plan was broadly informing the plans laid for Drake and Frobisher to reach towards a Pacific presence.[11] The intoxicating prospect of using their navigational competence to strategic, trading and mineralogical gain was thus set before the Queen and her Privy Council to organise, along with good reasons to assemble mineralogical expertise for Frobisher's next voyage on which William Wynter could speak.

Teasing Abraham Ortelius on account of his earlier correspondence and fully aware that Humphrey Gilbert had only copied Ortelius in making his map in 1566 (published in 1576 showing the most northerly point as 'C. de Paramantia'), Dee wrote on 16 January 1577 to ask him "on what authority you have placed the Cape Paramantia and Los Jardines on the northern coast of the Atlantic, and of all the other things, which you are the first and only one to place in that region."[12] Dimly aware of a metallurgical reason for this inquiry, Ortelius visited his cousin in London in March 1577. After discursive meetings with William Camden and a young lecturer on geography, Richard Hakluyt, Ortelius visited Dee on 12 March 1577. Dee then helped finalise instructions for Frobisher's second voyage, using ideas derived from Mercator's letter of 20 April 1577.[13] In his *The Great Volume of famous and Riche Discoveries,* written late in 1577, Dee shows a misplaced confidence in rich mines in the far north of North America and along the route to Asia, which he expected the exploration of his pupils Martin Frobisher and Christopher Hall to vindicate, writing: "I trust with one or two complete surveys, after this to be performed by my travail ... that all the northern part of Asia, with the two principall cities thereof, Cambaia and Quinsay, will become to the British natural inhabitants of this Monarchy so well known as are the coasts of Denmark and Norway and their periplus."[14]

Meanwhile, in the 1570s and 1580s several major English landowners looked to the speculative opportunities of ores found within their lands. A momentous legal judgement in the case of The Queen v Thomas Percy, 7th Earl of Northumberland, launched in 1568, over whether all precious metallic ores and feedstocks were necessarily the Crown's accentuated the trend.[15] The Crown too took an active interest in the outcome.

Successive Tudor Privy Councils had tried to improve English mines and metallurgical practice, especially the manufacture of modern ordnance. Henry VIII gave a high priority to importing into England and Wales the processes which Kratzer,[16] Holbein,[17] Groff,[18] and Biringuccio[19] had illustrated by 1540. Georg Agricola's many systematic treatises printed between 1530 and 1556 made the subject much more accessible, and greatly enhanced the reputation of metallurgical practitioners from Saxony.[20] In 1550 a complete team of German experts, led by Joachim Kundelfinger,[21] was enticed with Privy Council approval to County Wexford to settle to silver and lead mining, although their success and that of the local mint was problematic.[22] Soon afterwards Burcot Kranich tried to do the same in Cornwall.[23] Metallurgical progress was fastest within the Royal Armouries where new casting techniques were perfected,[24] and notable in the Wealden iron industry where gun manufacture boomed,[25] and in Cumberland where copper mining and processing began on a large scale around Keswick.[26] In the Forest of Dean in the 1560s a new non-ferrous smelter was added to the well-established iron furnaces.[27] After successive setbacks and insolvency, business success in the non-ferrous sector would attend the Assay Master of the Royal Mint, William Humfrey, fully rewarding his decision to re-settle, at his own expense, a skilled master workman from Anaburg in Saxony, named Christopher Schutz.[28] Schutz settled first in the Angiddy valley near Tintern in 1564 [29] and was made a denizen using prerogative powers in 1568,[30] and soon acquired a reputation as the successful designer and operator of several English smelters for iron and non-ferrous metals.[31] After Schutz had found the calamine ores of the Mendip Hills with the help of Bevis Bulmer and some German associates in 1566,[32] and introduced sieving of those ores prior to smelting in 1568,[33] he enjoyed, as Humfrey's co-partner, over twenty years of commercial success working for the Company of Mines and Battery Works at Tintern and Beauchief near Sheffield. Significantly, it was after Schutz commissioned the building of a new furnace in 1576 for the Company of Mines Royal at Keswick that it too moved into profit. This was just before he was chosen to join the second of Frobisher's voyages to the North West.[34] Accounts preserved in Augsburg by Hans Loner and Ulrich Fross show that Schutz used the names Jonas and Christopher interchangeably when commissioning a furnace in Keswick for 17 weeks in early Spring 1576.[35]

These events show why Schutz was thought to be a sound choice for Frobisher's voyage in 1577 and then why, having "travailed greatly by land and sea," it was recommended to

Chancery that Jonas Schutz be employed as Master Workman for ores "of the North parts." The royal grant of letters patent on 11 January 1578 was based on his promise that in smelting Meta Incognita's ores he would extract half an ounce of gold from every hundredweight of Meta Incognita ores processed.[36] Despite Schutz's failures to match the terms of his own offers to extract gold from Canadian ores made on 25 November 1577,[37] the specialised knowledge, experience and patents held by Schutz and the Humfrey family ensured their financial security long past William Humfrey senior's death in 1584. With work at Tintern, Sheffield and Nottingham,[38] Schutz could afford a home in Cripplegate, London until his death in 1592.[39] His will, made in 1574, confirmed his origins in Anaburg and identified his few relatives and his legal advisors in London.[40] An obituary written in a Jacobean hand posthumously commended his many metallurgical skills.[41]

Before Schutz's arrival in England, Richard Eden in his *Decades of the New World*, 1555, and in the preface of his *Art of Navigation,* 1561, had extolled the advantages of English settlement in North America and the possibility of creating an empire to rival Spain's, and Spain's mineral wealth, given mastery of the alchemical theory of the "generation of metals" and of the skills of prospecting and smelting of appropriate ores.[42] Having translated Biringuccio's *Pirotechnia* (written by the head of the Papal foundry) Eden had noted in 1555 that "there is fewe or none in England that have any great skill thereof, or anything written in oure owne tounge, whereby men may be well instructed of that generation and finding of the same: as the lyke ignorance hath been among us touching Cosmographie and Navigation until I attempted according to the portion of my talent and simple learning to open the first doore to the entrance of this knowledge into owre language." [43]

That Meta Incognita might hold a mine site was suspected as early as January 1577. Hoping to prove this the Privy Council instructed Frobisher in May 1577 to concentrate on locating precious ores and the mine sites now recognisable on Baffin Island and the smaller Kodlunarn Island, rather than on exploring the Northwest Passage. Taking formal legal possession of the mines was to be his top priority. Significantly, one earlier draft of those instructions differs textually in requiring Frobisher's refiners and tryers of the ore *NOT* to discover the secrets of the riches of the mines in Meta Incognita.[44] It shows instead that Frobisher was to command the venture with the status of an Admiral of private fleets that would defend the mines from Spanish attacks. It is certainly plausible that Frobisher wanted the authority to control a fleet more than the task of shipping home mineral ores, but the Privy Council determined this was not a risk wisely taken. Nonetheless, Captain Edward Fenton's journal of Frobisher's 1578 voyage, records that he was required by his instructions from the Privy Council to fortify it "bothe for the defence of myners and also for possessing of the countrie and bringe home w[i]th you a perfecte platt and parfaicte notes thereof to be kept in cecreat; and so delivred unto us."[45]

Figure 2: Agricola in *De Re Metallica*, Basle, 1556, Book VIII illustrates the iron wired sieves which later made a major difference to the effective use of the furnaces at Tintern when Schutz adopted their use at Hechstetter's behest in 1567.

Figure 3: The title page of Biringuccio's *De La Pirotechnia*, Venice, 1540, showing assay techniques, the provision of blast assisted furnaces and gun founding on the left, and bell founding on the right.

Technical Roots for the Amalgam of Naval and Metallurgical Ambition

In constructing this well-developed amalgam of strategic, navigational and metallurgical ambition, replete with legal justification and defensive provisions, we have to look to the earlier work of Richard Eden, who died in 1576. Eden provided some of the crucial textual translations into English of texts relevant to the harnessing of the two principal technologies of navigation and metallurgy, and that common product of the two disciplines, the mapping needed for formally taking and fortifying distant lands, and subsequently returning to exploit their expected wealth. He envisaged creating a rival to the Spanish Empire by such means. Eden's translation into English in 1555 of Vanuccio Biringuccio's *Pirotechnia* made available hugely influential sections on: the most up-to-date European practice in metallurgy and furnace construction; the making and use of crucibles and cupells; several ways of assaying for precious and base metals; and making such copper based alloys as brass made with lead and zinc introduced through the use of calamine rich ores (i.e. those containing zinc carbonate — a technique which Biringuccio had first witnessed while touring foundries in Germany and Milan). This metallurgical theme was included towards the end of Eden's translations of Spanish and English voyages of exploration in his *Decades of the New World* when published in London by William Powell in 1555.

Much earlier on a heavily gilded wood and plaster ceiling painted for Henry VIII by Hans Holbein for the royal palace of Placentia at Greenwich the world's geography and (at the sides) mining scenes were associated together again. That ceiling encapsulated what the less discriminating investors among the Privy Councillors and courtiers thought they knew of the geographical grounds for Frobisher's voyages.[46] They would have known it because Elizabeth I's Privy Council regularly met at the riverside palace. Andrews suggests it was pride in this side of Frobisher's achievement which led to the display for such courtiers of a large brass globe (bought by Lok) at the bowsprit of the *Gabriel* on 9 October 1576 as she sailed past that Palace and into the Pool of London.[47] That globe was a careful copy punched onto brass by Humphrey Cole, so that its full detail was only visible by looking inside each half, much like Whitwell's much smaller silver globe still at Greenwich. Lok's accounts describe it as brass globe in blank. It probably followed a Venetian exemplar of about 30 inches in diameter whose outline in turn owed much to Abraham Ortelius's world maps. It would thus accord with the basic inventory data on the items purchased for the 1576 voyage and "the great globe of metal in blanke."[48]

Almost equally important to the events and equipment used on Frobisher's voyages from 1576 to 1578 was Eden's *Arte of Navigation,* first published by Richard Jugge in 1561 as a translation of Martin Cortés's *Arte de Navegar* written in 1545. In simply translating those texts and adding ambitious introductions, Eden gave insufficient thought to the barrier of cost which the need to import good latten or brass put on the initial practicability of his suggestions that astrolabes, quadrants, and various dials be made from it. He made virtually no changes for the 1572 reprint. He might have anticipated that many would by then have read his translation of Biringuccio's texts on latten or brass making, and he must have known that some like Humfrey Cole had taken his text's advice on instrument making. In fact latten was almost all imported from the Netherlands or Saxony prior to 1569. Most of the copper extracted in Cumberland was bought by the Crown as ingots for use in the Royal Armouries or the Royal Mint until, in the mid-1570s, Daniel Hechstetter began the large scale manufacture and marketing of copper utensils for domestic use, and sheet metal for the instrument makers and copper plate engravers of London. The discovery of indigenous English sources for calamine or zinc bearing ores was the other major pre-requisite to the making of hard, but readily engraved, latten or brass in England.[49] It was not yet a properly regulated trade, as the Founders Company petition to the Lord Mayor of London in 1584-5 showed, because there were no enforced standards for brass weights — despite their value in developing good assaying methods and as proper means of controlling traders in non-precious metals, like pewterers and tinners.

Metallurgists (excepting goldsmiths) operated within the type of trade Biringuccio had known where:

> *he who wishes to practice this art must not be of a weak nature, either age or constitution, but must be strong, young and vigorous, so as to bale to handle things, as you almost always have to, that are heavy and inconvenient because of their weight — things like bronze, iron tools, wood, water, clay, rocks, bricks and the like. Nor do I doubt that whoever considers this art well will fail to recognise a certain brutishness in it, for the founder is always like a chimney sweep, covered with charcoal and distasteful sooty smoke, his clothing dusty and half burned by the fire, his hands and face are all plastered with soft muddy earth. To this is added the fact that for this work a violent and continuous straining of all a man's strength is required, which brings great harm to his body and holds many definite dangers to his life. In addition holds the mind of the artificer in suspense and fear regarding its outcome and keeps his spirits disturbed and almost continually anxious. For this reason they called fanatics and are despised as fools.*[50]

As advancement of non-ferrous metallurgy became a matter for policy at the highest levels, success in its practice owed much to William Humfrey and Christopher Schutz. Thus Humfrey petitioned the Queen and her Privy Council knowing that Lord Burghley realised the significance of his request. On 16 July 1565 royal permission was forthcoming that Humfrey and Schutz should search for and mine calamine ores in England and within the English Pale in Ireland, and use them for making latten and other mixed metals, iron, cast work, steel, and battery works. They were empowered to erect buildings for that purpose on Royal lands, and to pay workmen as assistants.[51] More significantly, the Charter Roll copy of that grant shows exactly how the technology came to England. It reveals that William Humfrey, with only the personal resources and contacts of the Assay Master at the Tower, "by his great labour and charges" brought to England one Christopher Shutz (or Schutz) "an Alemayne born of Saint Annen Barghe" [i.e the modern Anaburg] describing him as under the obedience of the Elector of Saxony. It shows that Schutz, although then an alien, was already valued as a workman of great knowledge and experience, both in finding calamine stone and in its use in metallic alloys, especially in making latten, and in the reduction of it to soft and malleable forms; also in the mollifying and making of iron, and steel, and in drawing and finishing it into wire and plate useful in the making of armours.

Readily available latten was also needed to make many of the instruments which Eden's *Arte of Navigation* described. Ercker, writing in 1574, suggested that a good brass for such purposes would comprise 60% copper and 29% calamine or zinc.[52] Prior to that date most European brass came from the Meuse valley, and from Aachen which by 1559 had a hundred water powered foundries producing about 1,500 tons of brass. A few used methods first devised by Theophilus (Roger of Helmarhausen) around 1100 to produce "auricalcum" from which lead had to be removed by beating, but by 1559 most had adopted a much more complex mix involving copper-rich ores, calamine, and even some tin and charcoal additives in much hotter blast-assisted furnaces.[53] Whether or not they were aware of growing international competition to make it, all Eden's editors left those passages about latten unchanged, with later editors simply assuming its ready availability in the subsequent editions published after his death in 1576. Surprisingly Eden never referred to the particular achievement of Christopher Schutz and William Humfrey in locating and smelting calamine ores in the Mendip Hills in Somerset, or in locating new Cumbrian, Welsh and Cornish sources for copper, all of which had been accomplished by 1569. Yet it was the availability of those more local sources of copper and zinc which first enabled English instrument makers and copper plate engravers to make instruments and maps competitively, and to avoid the monopoly prices which European made brass had commanded until the early 1570s.[54] As late as 1565 Sir William Cecil had envisaged the extensive import of brass from Aachen as justification for the Society for Mineral and Battery Works to obviate this difficulty by locating domestic sources to make this vital metal alloy. The near monopoly accorded the Society of Mineral and Battery Works in England at Burghley's instance allowed it to see off the competition in lead and brass manufacture, but it could not avoid reducing the price of its output of brass, to compete with European brass from Aachen, and towns in Bohemia, Slovakia and Hungary.

Initially, Schutz had had a problem in producing enough because the Somerset calamine ores from Worle Hill in Somerset contained too much lead, a problem that recurred in using the Lake District ores and caused his presence to be sought there in 1576.[55] Only when those problems were solved did the processes, new to England, make brass instruments for navigation and mine survey work much cheaper. That in turn gave much encouragement to their manufacture and use in England and Wales. Thereafter the new availability of a hard yet sufficiently malleable brass with a reasonable zinc content made it suitable for industrial wool combs and for rolling prior to engraving on it to produce reliable and well graduated surveying and navigational instruments. That market would, in its turn, lie behind the family fortune subsequently made by the Humfrey family.

Apprenticeship through the well-established and rigorous supervision of the Goldsmith's Company, followed by practical experience as a goldfiner, was a guarantee that the skills would pass down a further generation by patrimony. Indeed, William Humfrey the younger who sailed with Frobisher in 1578 as a metallurgist and assayer had been trained by his more famous father. Lok's accounts for the 1578 voyage show payment to William Humfrey's son of the same name, who had learned the skill as an assistant to Schutz at Tintern from 1568. The payment appears as "To William Humfrey goldfyner, the 13 day of January 1579 in full of his waiges in the last day of November last past £8. 14s. 4d."[56]

It is also fair to conclude that the five brass instruments, including the globe mentioned above, and some of the printed maps bought for Frobisher's 1576 voyage illustrate reliance on the newest navigational technology. Other items containing brass parts, such as the various beam scale balances and weights for which Rumbridge was later made responsible, are listed separately from the better known list of navigational instruments.[57] Those lists, when considered alongside the works of Cortés, Medina and Agricola, form yet another instance of England's new technological prowess. Those same accounts for 1576 show that Lok turned to a London instrument maker in Humfrey Cole to make several of the most complex of navigational instruments, including an armillary sphere. He had been trained locally in metallurgy and instrument making by another emigré, Thomas Gemini. Humfrey Cole would contribute as a mineralogist too, locating supplies of sulphurous sea coal from Newcastle-on-Tyne among the furnace additives sought for the new Dartford smelter in 1578-79.[58]

From 1562 to 1572 war and attempts at the persecution of Protestants across the European continent persuaded many Protestants to seek a new life in England. Those bringing their prospecting and metallurgical skills to several parts of England and Wales in this context included many German and Netherlandish metallurgists who made important contributions to the commercial successes enjoyed by a number of English landowners. Although there was a vast increase in the number of such denizenships granted under Elizabeth I, they were mostly given to Dutchmen, with a relatively constant and talented flow from Germany and other parts of Europe. There were strictly limited bounds to this tolerance which were given effect under pressure from the House of Commons. Parliament intervened legislatively to constrain grants to successive generations, forcing some to work as aliens and to tighten the administration of the law concerning aliens.[59] On 12 April 1577 Lok refers to Dutch workmen who had made proof of Frobisher's ores in Lambeth (perhaps in facilities belonging to John Dee, or Richard Dee at the Lambeth Pottery kilns, or at John Wolffe's home). Although not known to Lok, they were all well known as part-time assayers to Sir William Wynter and Sir William Morgan.[60]

John Dee showed a similar realisation of the potential of these technology transfers based on emigrés' advice and on his well used library of European texts and legal knowledge which he analysed and prepared for publication in the midst of Frobisher's voyages in 1577.[61] Dee's account of his involvement in Frobisher's voyages suggests he became involved early in 1576 along with William Borough and Christopher Hall. Dee's tuition is described in a letter sent from Shetland by Frobisher and Hall in 1576 acknowledging his "friendly instructions" and adding, "we doo remember you and hold ourselves bound to you as youre poor disciples." [62]

Concurrently it must be remembered news was filtering back to Europe of gold mines discovered in the new Spanish Pacific colony of the Philippines. As early as 1569 Martin de Rada had written to Philip II about the rich gold mines of Baguinado, Masbate and Luzon. The gold and iron mines of the Bicol region were mapped and recorded by Juan de Slacedo and Pedro de Chaves between 1571 and 1574, but Salcedo found the land of "Igorrottes" too impenetrable in 1573 to find its gold reserves. Nonetheless, between 1569 and 1582 several other gold mines along a great fault line through the region were becoming working gold mines, especially on the island of Masbate and in southern Mindanao following Guido de Levezares's report to Philip II of 16 July 1567.[63] So it was not unreasonable to surmise that if the Northwest Passage could be passed as Frobisher claimed in 1576, the route to southern Cathay's ports would take ships past those gold bearing islands on the fringe of the Pacific. So it was but a small leap of imagination for Frobisher, thinking he had found such a passage, to expect similar gold bearing rocks in islands at the western end of such a passage if it led south westward. It was all the smaller if Frobisher used his officially supplied copy of Ortelius's map of 1564, where the "Philippinas" show up at the far north east.[64]

Had he looked instead at one of Girolamo Verrazano's maps of a passage trending south west (a not unreasonable assumption since Lok actually possessed one) he would have seen much the same point.[65] Lok is likely to have thought that the company's gold or silver bearing ores, duly smelted, could be used to sustain trade that way with China where the demand for bullion was well known. It was Baptista Agnello who led Lok to the idea of keeping secret Meta Incognita's location while according priority to its metallurgical potential. This speculative metallurgical vision informed investment in the unincorporated Cathay Company up to 1578 and accreted further support because of Schutz's industrial successes on behalf of many of the major ennobled investors. The strategic perspective provided by Eden and Dee had by 1576 led naval strategists, such as William Wynter and Francis Drake, to realise that metallurgical wealth combined with improved methods of celestial observation and navigation was buying Spain such marine dominance and great military might that steps must be taken to counter it. By the mid-1570s gold and silver from European mines near the Spanish road from Italy to the Netherlands looked to be sufficient to sustain a Habsburg army large enough both to crush the Netherlandish rebels and threaten England. Yet not until the mid-1570s was there scope in the money markets of Antwerp for the English Crown to borrow abroad and so back Frobisher and Drake in their separate quests for gold.[66] Having mastered the new navigational skills, Drake's plundering circumnavigation of 1577-80 eclipsed Frobisher's failures of 1576-78 which had once seemed the lesser risk because it spread the risks over two new technologies, namely celestial navigation and metallurgy, and made lesser demands of good nutrition and health than Drake's plan.[67]

Frobisher's Miners And Metallurgists

By 1576 Hechstetter and Schutz, as well as Dee, Burghley, Wynter and some other interested Englishmen knew of the metallurgical work recently published by Ercker in Prague.[68] Financial accounts which survive for Elizabethan operations in Cumbria,[69] Staffordshire and Sussex, recorded ores and additives and the increasing use of blast or reverberatory furnaces in smelting. The identities of some the staff so engaged were known to interested Privy Councillors.[70] Works like Daniel Hechstetter's notebook attest to the range of experience, English and foreign, built up regionally by such master workmen and mining proprietors.[71]

Amongst England's mining communities only the gentleman prospectors travelled encumbered with small picks, wedges, and hammers slung on a belt, and divining rods, a miner's compass, slates, glass vessels and acid bottles to hand in the manner of the miner shown in the Greyndour chapel brass.[72] By contrast it was the miners and their life of hard physical work which the textbooks represented. Miners had only a few labour saving devices such as barrows, trackways, hunds, sheerlegs, whipping rigs and simple cranes and winches.[73] Without time to build trackways and hunds Frobisher's miners in 1577 and 1578 had to rely largely on baskets and simply raised lifting devices familiar to seamen. Best confirms that the work done in the Canadian Arctic in 1577 "was not wonne out of rocks without great labour."[74] Best says of the miners' work over just twenty days in 1577 that: "The men ere well wearied, [al]so their shoes were and clothes were well worne, their baskets bottoms torne out, their tooles broken, and the ships reasonably well filled. Some with overstraining themselves received hurts not a litle dangerous, some having their bellies broken, and others their legs lame."[75]

Sellman and Best thought that Frobisher had mercilessly driven the miners beyond what was reasonable, by making them work long daylight hours in the near Arctic summer. Recent biographical research has offered fresh insights into the regional experience which Schutz, and a Keswick associate, one Gregory Bona[r], had brought to prospecting in the vicinity of Baffin Island in 1577 and 1578. For going to Meta Incognita in 1577 Bona was paid on a much lesser scale than Schutz, being awarded just £14 5s., all paid in advance.[76] Bona returned again in 1578 being the only man who knew where the red and yellow ores so commended by Schutz were, although he does not appear in the pay lists for the third voyage, probably because he was to be paid according to such precious metals as were found on smelting. Although probably skilled in recognising the rocks of Cumberland and Saxony, Bona, like Schutz, probably relied heavily on the practice of skills with a divining rod or rods, used in the manner shown in Munster's engraving, although Biringuccio wrote against the practice, denying that "metals they are found more by chaunce than by arte."[77] George Best wrote in 1578 that in deciding what ore to lade "they had no assurance but by gesse of the eie."[78] Gregory Bona[r]'s family had already found the Newlands{Goldscope}copper veins in Cumberland in 1565. Gregory probably conferred a similar name upon part of the Arctic island that also contained Winter's Furnace.[79] For lack of better documentation, Bona's part in the choice of ores loaded remains obscure. An alternative association of the name may have been with a

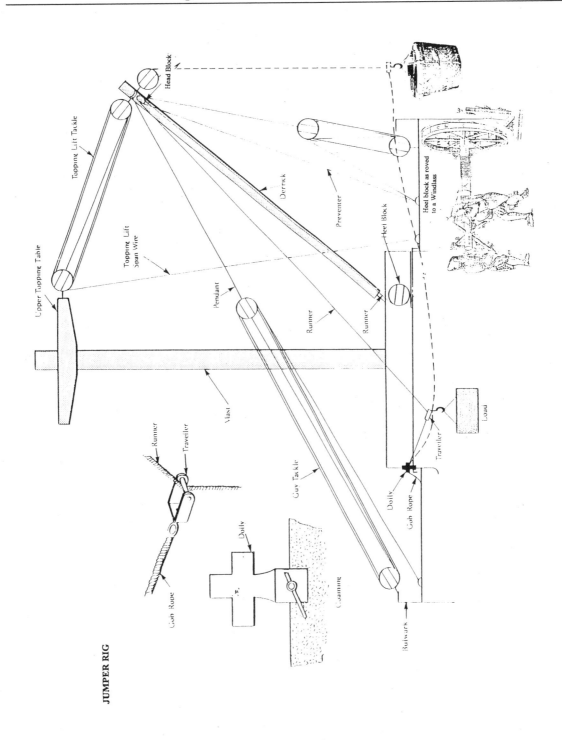

Figure 4: A jumper rig was utilised from the fifteenth century onwards by sailors aboard ship to perform some of the heavier lifting and weighing operations. The rig shown here assumes a wicker cargo basket used for taking inboard a load of hundredweight or so. Given Frobisher and Sellman's recorded concern to have the ores weighed prior to departure from the Meta Incognita mines they were probably loaded in this manner after weighing in cargo baskets on a seaside beam scale, or lifted in cargo baskets onto deck scales and thence into the hold. The same rig was probably used to discharge building supplies, and for lifting out of the hold and moving overside the heavier loads such as the heavy rectangular German stove from which tiles have been found on Kodlunarn.

major investor in Frobisher's voyages who also owned a complex of mines and smelters acquired from the Crown, with other Greyndour chantry lands, at Newland and Lydney by Sir William Wynter in 1559. As a Lydney resident, Wynter must have known the Greyndour memorial, made of Netherlandish brass, showing a Free Miner of the Forest of Dean, and also the carved font at Abenhall.[80]

The interests of Sir William Wynter in respect of his own pre-existing investments in mining and metallurgy in the Forest of Dean are revealing.[81] The Decree of Weisewood issued by the Lord Chancellor Bromley in 1580 mentions the huge environmental damage to ancient woodland which Christopher Schutz had done by operating the nearby Tintern smelter.[82] As a leading Privy Councillor, Wynter expressed his keenness on the potential of Frobisher's ores in March 1577 and on the ores Jonas Schutz had selected on 25 November 1577.[83] In making his London garden available for operating a small furnace Wynter was among the first to appreciate that the Meta Incognita venture might be significant. He certainly wanted to evade the localised traditional legal constraints and litigation over Forest rights. Sharing that perspective, caused by the wood consumed in the local smelters, and hoping to find new gold-rich ores on virgin territory, seven Forest of Dean miners would sail with Frobisher and Schutz in 1577.[84] Forest of Dean Miners who sailed on the second voyage were John Heywood, John Roke, Richard Taylor, William Taylor, Robert Wilcox (or Wilcockes) and William Whitson, plus perhaps, John Jugen (Jugeyn) who certainly sailed as a miner with Frobisher. They all survived the experience. Some characteristic features among the descriptions of the 150 men who joined the third voyage as miners (plus the assayers) allow certain limited deductions to be made about the society, competence and relatively sturdy health of this group. Lok's accounts show that the twenty miners, probably all Forest of Dean miners, were "pressed" for the third voyage by Captain Fenton at Bristol. They enjoyed the benefit of £16 set aside for their victuals prior to sailing, and much of the further sum of £22 advanced to Fenton to recruit them and pay some unspecified advance. The experience did not deter two Forest of Dean miners, Richard Taylor and Robert Wilcox, from taking ship with Frobisher in 1578. By then they had established their credentials with two veteran assayers of the second voyage, Gregory Bona and Robert Denham. Furthermore, James or John Heywood, described as a "miner and cook" on the *Thomas of Ipswich* in 1578 may similarly be a veteran of the second voyage. To them the opinions of Wynter as the local lord and Privy Councillor, and those of Jonas Schutz, so well respected in that locality, must have been significant in encouraging them to go.

Their working practice, clothes and equipment must have looked very like that which Heinrich Groff had first illustrated in Alsace mines about 1526. We know it changed little, for Sebastian Munster was invited to the same mine in 1545 after which he had engraved a fresh image which was ready for his 1550 Latin edition of *Cosmographia Universalis*.[85] This shows very nearly the same content as Groff, but adds a prospector or diviner operating with a rod above the mine much as we must presume Schutz, Bona and Denham did in 1577. The poses in Munster's image, and those on the following pages showing sorting, settling ponds, roasting grounds and smelting, also formed the

Figure 5: Stone carving of miners' tools and smiths' tools drawn from a fifteenth-century octagonal church font at Abenhall, Gloucestershire. This Forest of Dean church bears similar mining tools and some more obvious spades on the Church's tower, but these are replacements dating from 1982.

Figure 6: Illustrations of Forest of Dean miners in their traditional garb.

Figure 7: A brass rubbing of a Forest of Dean miner in full working dress, like that worn by the miners who embarked with Frobisher in 1577, with a basket of similar size to that found at Kodlunarn. The miner's belt shows a leather holder for medicinal ointments or tools similar in size to the leather box for surgical instruments which survives with the Tudor instrument case presented to the Company of Barber Surgeons about 1525. Note too the hammer and simple respiratory aid for use in dusty contexts. The brass is from the Newland Parish Church in the Greyndour Chantry Chapel.

intermediate sources for the Rappolsteiner Pokal, a silver wedding cup made by Georg Kobenhaupt for a Rappolstein family wedding to Hubinsack's design in 1543.

Published studies by Nef and Blanchard[86] have shown in some detail how the miner's work fitted into the largely agricultural communities of late medieval England, and into the productivity of mining regions like the Forest of Dean between 1400 and 1600. That experience clearly has a bearing on the expectations of Frobisher's miners, albeit their diet and working conditions in the Arctic were very different from those to be expected around the mines of the West Country or Cumbria, and much more exacting while they were active around Baffin Island and Kodlunarn through the very long summer days of those latitudes. Because of the content of Sir James Watt's reports on the health of Frobisher's voyagers and the medicine then in use, this study utilises other supplementary medical and operational material which is clearly relevant to expounding the closely interrelated operational and socio-political contexts that established, or broke, the reputations of particular individuals, or which illustrate the self-serving and exploitative attitudes of the major figures involved.

That miners were the skilled pawns in a bigger mineralogical game becomes evident. But this study will also show how in the context of Frobisher's voyages of 1576-78, many of the active members of Elizabeth I's Privy Council used their official responsibilities as a means of informing and attempting to secure their personal fortunes, while treating and advising the Queen as just another speculative investor with much the same landed and strategic interests. All of Frobisher's so-called metallurgists, assayers and prospectors must have known that their contemporaries regarded their alchemical pretensions and their hopes of finding gold with some suspicion. Sometimes they succeeded and gained adherents — sometimes they failed and lost their backers substantial sums. Sometimes their reputations at court and their financial standing were badly dented, as happened to John Dee following his flight to Cracow, Prague and Bohemia's mining towns in 1583-1589.[87]

It is fairly widely known that many who studied those matters had been initiated into the "contradictory and often puzzling secrets of the Green Lion," or alchemy. Amongst that community it was a sort of Holy Grail that they should seek to discover gold in the course of their endeavours, and it was equally thought likely that they would fail. Archival records of the alchemical interest and experimentation carried out by John Dee, Edward and Andrew Dyer survive to illustrate the theories to which they worked. Despite their unscientific basis, John Dee's opinions were among the truly pivotal considerations, as he would have major inputs to both the metallurgical and the navigational evaluations that attracted the investors and Privy Council support. Dee himself tutored Frobisher, Hall, and Griffin in navigation in May 1576, and was one of the Commissioners appointed by the Privy Council to observe and advise on the smelting of Frobisher's ores. His historical and metallurgical studies led him to buy from Sir Lionell Duckett a lease on the potentially lucrative Coombe Martin mine on 13 March 1583. However, his study of European mining, land law and claims to legal possession of mines was, until August 1583, mainly focused on Meta Incognita where, as he wrote on the back of his map made in mid-1578:

> *the lawfull title for the due clayme and just recovery of the same is disclosed. Which in effect is a Title Royall to all the coasts and islands begining at or about Cape Florida, alongst or neare unto Atlantis, going northerly, and then to the most northern islands ... which last Bownds are from our Albion more than half the sea voyage to Cathayen westerly ... particularly discovered and possessed A[nn]o 1576 and the last yere by Martin Frobisher Esquier: and is presently by our people to be inhabited. The totall Content of which Ilands and parcell of land thereabowt by our Sovereign Queen Elizabeth is lately named Meta Incognita.*[88]

Typical of one who was heavily involved as an investor in Frobisher's voyages, as a Privy Councillor, and as the Castellan of Bristol Castle responsible for the secure tenure of some of the Meta Incognita ores from 1577, was William Herbert, the Earl of Pembroke. The extent and sophistication of the Earl's coal mining and metallurgical interests in South Wales, from the Black Mountains to the Gower, and in Gloucestershire just outside Bristol meant that he could afford to gamble on financing new mining ventures. The Herbert family papers from Badminton House reveal much about the economic geography leading eventually to the growth of Swansea's industries, related as they were to the ferrous and non-ferrous metals and the proximity of coal mines. References to title deeds involving coal mining are to be found in 1526, 1595, and 1603-4. The Badminton papers prove the speculative preparedness of those in Court circles, like the Earl of Pembroke and his family, to invest in a range of mining ventures in the 1570s and 1580s."[89]

Through the metallurgical library of his advisor since 1553 (John Dee), if not through his own library, William Herbert must have known of the detailed book on mining techniques written by Georg Bauer, popularly known as Georg Agricola (1494-1555).[90] Agricola studied first at Leipzig University before being formally trained as a physician in Italy in 1524-1526.[91] He resumed medical work in his native Saxony at Joachimstal on the Bohemian side of the Erzgebirge before moving in 1533 to work in Schemnitz with miners active on the Saxon side of the mineral rich mountains. His understanding was such that he laid the foundations of more modern mineralogy. Agricola's influence grew after four of his essays on mines and metallurgy were published in 1546 just as he became Burgomaster of Schemnitz.[92] These works included the latest innovations in pumping out mines and operating powered stamping houses and furnaces. In *De Veteribus et Novis Metalis*, finished in 1546, he noted that ancient mines in Schemnitz and Cremnitz and at Goslar in the Hartz Mountains were still operational, while expounding a socio-political case which appealed to speculators and landowners alike; he noted that:

> *If mining is a shameful and discreditable employment for a gentleman because slaves once worked mines, then agriculture will not also be a very creditable*

Figure 8: Miners at work in Lower Austria, from a tract on mining law entitled *Der Ursprung gemeynner Berckrecht wie die lange Zeit von dem Alten erhalten worde*, **printed by Johann Haselberger between 1515 and 1538. It shows very traditional activity except for the innovation of a flanged rail in use with a truck as the latest sixteenth century improvement to a miner's productivity. Such illustration shows how well informed John Dee could have been through collecting such works.**

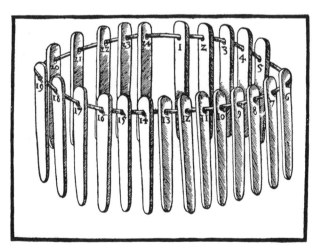

Figure 9: Agricola's illustration in Book VII of a miner's set of twenty four touchstones in 1556. He explains that by the first eleven needles tried against the refined touchstone, the proportion of gold in ingot of silver can be ascertained, while the remaining thirteen are used to test what proportion of gold and copper might also be present in the same bar. In the mine an attempt was sometimes made to rub these fingers against a productive looking vein, a procedure subject to much bigger errors, such as may explain the errors made in 1577 and 1578.

Figure 10: Agricola in Book XI uses a drawing of the simple type of furnace most probably leaving behind the evidence of a similar forehearth in the ground today at Kodlunarn (excavated in 1990). Simple air assisted furnaces created by use of pantiled roof atop the small furnaces marked (A) and (B) with tap holes at (C), discharged into ground holes or forehearths, with dipping pots (F) arranged nearby. Note too the use of wicker baskets (G), in use near a heap of coal (I), and a simple barrow bearing a wicker work top. The tools comprise a simple hooked bar and a spade.

employment, because slaves once cultivated the fields, and even today do so among the Turks: nor will architecture be considered honest because some slaves have been found skilful in that profession; nor medicine, because not a few doctors have been slaves; nor will any other worthy craft, because men captured by force of arms have practised it. Yet agriculture, architecture and medicine are nonetheless counted among the number of honourable professions; therefore mining ought not for this reason be excluded from them.[93]

Agricola's most comprehensive work, *De Re Metallica in libri XII,* was published in Basle in 1556, a year after his death.[94] Within it, books two and three discuss the form of metal desposits, and how to search for them. Book four describes the system of concessions and how to survey them, while book five describes underground mines and what is needed to construct and survey them. Book seven is devoted to assaying techniques, and books nine and ten to the roasting and smelting of ores, and to several techniques for parting gold and silver in the course of such firing or following it. Book eleven dealt with the separation of copper and of silver from copper alloys. This was the essence of the technological know-how which Schutz and the other metallurgists contacted by Lok were attempting to market. As we know from the archaeological record from Kodlunarn, Andrew Dyer must have used small, not very portable, German upright kiln-stoves and ovens, and some much more portable assay techniques: in particular, divining rods, a touchstone and needles, and the technique of nitric acid separation which could be practised with small portable vials slung about his belt when not in use. This suggests a deep study of Agricola's and Ercker's texts and of Biringuccio's more practical recommendations.[95]

A further feature of the 1578 ore collection process so well recorded by Sellman and Fenton is that it left in its trail archaeological records which today provide silent testimony to the heeding of Agricola's advice in Book Two of *De Re Metallica,* suggestions which possibly account for the attempt to diversify the sources and veins exploited in the vicinity of Baffin Island in 1578 to between ten and twelve mine sites.[96] It may well also reflect the influence of Lok and Dee's reading, for Agricola advises:

When a man owns mines but is ignorant of the art of mining, than it is advisable that he should share in common with others the ownership, not of one only but of several mines. When one man alone meets the expense for the long time of a whole mine, if good fortune bestows on him vein abundant in metals, or in other products, he becomes very wealthy; if on the contrary, the mine is poor and barren, in time he will lose everything he has expended upon it. But the man who, in common with others, has laid out his money on several mines in a region renowned for its wealth of metals, rarely spends it in vain, for fortune usually responds to his hopes in part. For when out of twelve veins in which he has a joint interest, one yields an abundance of metals it not only gives back to the owner the money he has spent but yields a profit besides.

Certainly there will be for him rich and profitable mining if two or three or more veins should yield metal.[97]

Whether the idea of opening ten to twelve sites came from Agricola directly, or was mediated via Bona, Schutz or Dyer, this is exactly how Frobisher's men performed in 1578. Furthermore, many of Schutz's clients among England's landed investors were either the sole investors in mines on their own estates, or had succeeded in making returns by investing in shares in one or other of the English mining and metal manufacturing companies who had engaged him. Such buyers of shares in mining enterprises were warned by no less an authority than Agricola not to buy too many high priced shares in mines producing profits, and not to buy too many shares in ventures where metals have not yet been found. Agricola advised cutting the risks,

in the buying of shares as in other matters, there should be a certain limit of expenditure which miners should set themselves, lest blinded by the desire for excessive wealth, they throw all their money away. Moreover, a prudent owner, before he buys shares, ought to go to the mine and carefully examine the nature of the vein, for it is very important that he should be on his guard lest fraudulent sellers of shares should deceive him. Investors in shares may perhaps become less wealthy, but are more certain of some gain than those who mine at their own expense, as they are more cautious in trusting to fortune.[98]

With a peculiarly landlocked experience Agricola wisely contrasted the considerations of the investor and the miner saying "now a miner before he begins to mine the veins, must consider seven things namely: — the situation, the conditions, the water, the roads, the climate, the right of ownership, and the neighbours." [99] In following this way of thinking to its logical conclusions it is tempting to see Denham and Schutz as professional advocates of an industrial order proposed at the time of Frobisher's voyages, comprising newly developed mines near the seashore, and smelters readily accessible from the sea as at Dartford Creek, and so of the unique value of the ship with its much larger carrying capacity and a crew familiar with cargo handling tackle for heavy break bulk loads. It was Baptista Agnello who first confidently pointed to implicit industrial logic in all this in February 1577. All this gives a new coherence and importance to the vision of what might have been achieved through a new company. Lok was clearly helped to take the crucial step of securing further investment by a doubtfully competent assayer, Baptista Agnello. Lok records that:

The xxi [31st] day of January 1577, John Baptista sent for me agayne, as shall appeare by his second wrytinge here inclosed, at wych time he devised that a ship might go seacretly out of sum place, and bring the thynge {the gold bearing ores] to another place farre from London. But I answered him that that was not possible, for none knowe the place but C. Furbisher and the ship master [Christopher Hall], *who would not be corrupted. Then he thought to reveale it* [Agnello's assay results] *to the Captayne. I said I thought he would reveal it to your Ma[jest]ie but I devysed with him that I would send a ship to the place in company of the Captayne [Frobisher] under culler of fyshynge, and when the Captayne were gone through to Kathai, the ship should lade this thing [the gold bearing ores] for ballast, and retorne hither. He allowed well of this devyse, and so I departed for that tyme.*[100]

Lok's account of 12 April 1577 gives statements of the gold yields he expected from Frobisher's ores based on Agnello's advice, and of the higher yields expected from the set of assays which Sir William Wynter had known about, conducted by carefully selected Dutch workmen. Lok also stated then that he was greatly surprised to encounter Sir John Barkley who had readily subscribed to a contact on Agnello's behalf on 19 March 1577. By then the metallurgical, navigational and strategic themes had became inextricably linked in their peculiarly unique form. This was confirmed on 29 March 1577 when Sir William Wynter revealed the similarity of his strategic and personal interests to Lok. This crucial development happened the day after Wynter and Lok had discussed, at the behest of the Privy Council, the details involved in furnishing shipping for Cathay under Frobisher's command. Lok wrote of this equally unexpected circumstance that:

Sir John Barkley had opened the same to Sir William Morgan, and Sir William Morgan unto hym [Wynter], and thereupon he and they and others had made proffes thereof in a house at Lambethe, and also in his own howsse with his own man, the proffes whereof in gold he showed me presently in his chamber window, saying that it was mooche richer than I was informed of, and that it was a matter too great for hym and me to deal withall, and belonged onely to the prince.... And it is very likely that where the ewre lay on the face of the earthe, there is far morre more riche ewre undar the earthe. But of this matter I think your Majestye has been fully certifyed by Sir William Wynter and C. Furboisher, but only I put in mynd of your Ma[jes]tie parte of my first writinge delivered, that your Ma[jes]tie gyve order in this matter in secreto quanto si puo et con fortessa, et con expeditione, least forayne princes sett foote therin. Whereupon, that your Ma[jes]tie maye the better consider, I beseche your Ma[jes]tie to beholde the situation of the world in this small carta [sea chart] herewithall presented trewly thoughe grossly made according to my skill.[101]

Although some assayers were rightly sceptical of the ore samples brought from Meta Incognita in 1576, subsequent disappointment afflicted the City of London. There Michael Lok — led on by Baptista Agnello, John Dee and William Wynter, to follow up Eden's ideas — had overstated the commercial synergy and gains expected from two major and distinctive new technologies, oceanic navigation and non-ferrous metallurgy.[102] Lok persuaded Dee into taking two Adventurers' shares he could not afford, believing that gold bearing ores had been discovered midway along the Northwest Passage.[103] Dee's support seemed to give a high level of intellectual credibility to the metallurgy which in turn provided the commercial underpin to those speculators who supported the establishment of a colony. So in 1578 an expedition with fifteen ships was sent to establish a permanent mining colony where Fenton intended to winter with a party of miners. But this investment was thinly justified by doubtful assays and sustained by unproven theories about the circulation of water underground and the formation of metals. Dee's review of the same subjects, was published in the *Monas Hieroglyphica* in 1564. It re-appears in his influential preface to Henry Billingsley's influential mathematical work, the *Elements of Geometrie,* published in 1570 by Henry Bynnyman (later to be George Best's publisher too).

By contrast with Dee's theoretical and mathematical approach, Schutz set considerable store by practical Germanic methods such as small scale assaying with nitric acid to determine suitable ores to process, as suggested by Zimmerman in 1573.[104] Andrew Dyer and Jonas Schutz were clearly familiar with the technique by 1577.[105] Lazarus Ercker, had also published in 1574 about the newest metallurgical practices in the mining area in southern Saxony and Bohemia, illustrating the preparations necessary for acid assays.[106] Ercker's title blandly translates as "A Treatise describing the foremost kinds of metallic ores and minerals." But while Ercker was thorough on mining and smelting matters, he concentrated on an area left less well covered by Agricola, assaying for precious metals. A good measure of the respect in which his work was held is shown by Lord Burghley's concern to have a translation made of it by another émigré smelter, Joachim Gansz.[107]

Lok and Burghley's correspondence shows why they were determined to secure Schutz's services in 1577.[108] But he was too busy with supervision of building work at the Dartford furnace to sail again or prospect for ores in 1578. The red ore he had found in 1577 was not laded in quantity in 1578 but 1,136 tons of amphibole and black hornblende ores from about a dozen Meta Incognita sites were brought home.[109] It was Robert Denham, assisted by Dyer, Bona, and Stafford who chose the ores to load.[110] Nonetheless, the assayers working as Bona's junior colleagues on the third voyage were well paid, with William Humfrey Junior getting 50s per month for seven months, John Lambell 26s 8d per month, and Robert Peacock just 20s per month.[111]

Spreading the Risks of Mining Investment Amidst Tales of Deception, 1576-1583

The justification for the second, and to some extent for the third, of Frobisher's northern voyages was the unexpected assay results derived from a single rock sample, retained as a souvenir from Meta Incognita by Robert Garrard, which was accidentally melted and produced a small quantity of gold.[112] The rock sample was thought then to have been the first to be collected from Meta Incognita in 1576. It could just as easily have come from Shetland, where a minor source of silver had long been exploited, or from Orkney where silver bearing rocks were known and where such a mine site was visited by Hall, Frobisher, Denham, Schutz and Dyer during their fortnight's enforced stay in Kirkwall during the second voyage. In one sense this met the terms of Dee's promise to find a mine within these islands, cited when a short account of it was written up by George Best in 1578. Best notes their visit to a mine in Orkney, and that they anchored off Saint

Figure 11: Small scale equipment for the making and firing of crucible and cupels as illustrated by Ercker in 1574. (A) shows a brick furnace with a crucible ready for firing; (B) the brick furnace closed; (C) the crucible; (D) a sager; (E) the internal hearth of the sager; (F) a sieve for preparing ashes for a cupel; (G) a pot for bone and beech ashes to be fired dry prior to making a cupel, while (K), (L) illustrate how the pottery sager was made up with a hearth tray inside and iron handles outside to hold the material to be taken to a large furnace and fired into crucibles; (H) represents an inspection hole which could have the bellows attached behind to increase the heat.

Figure 12: Ercker's view of the crucible assay of copper ores in a blast assisted furnace (A) using crushed ores (C), roasted ores in sagers (D) whose temperature could be raised by means of a lever operated bellows (E), or in a draught assisted aeopile (F). *Beschreibung aller furnemsten Mineralischen Erzt und Berckwerkscarten*, Prague, 1574, fol. 98v.

Magnus (that is, the Cathedral at Kirkwall), putting in the margin "A myne an silver found in Orkney," and in the main text explaining: "And heere our Goldfyners found a myne of sylver."[113] Frobisher is favourably reported by Best as intent upon the main chance of wealth, ignoring Orkney's potential. But by early 1578 as the Meta Incognita ores began to prove of doubtful worth, vehement criticisms of Lok were made. Lok determined that what Frobisher had alleged of him during 1578 was much more serious:

> "He hath made false accounts to the company and hath cossened them out of iii m li of money [£3,000].
> "He hathe cossened my Lord of Oxford of m li [£1,000].
> "He hathe not one grote of venture in these voyages.
> "He is a Bankerot knave."[114]

Lok's first counter allegation suggests that until late in 1576 the potential of almost all the rocks collected on the first voyage was scorned until Lok confronted Agnello about just one of the rock samples reputed to have had a high gold content. The story is dramatic in that the earlier negative opinions of George Needham, William Williams, and Whelar are actually vindicated in full by the subsequent turn of events. On 28 January 1577 Edward Dyer too had been given samples to test. He also thought that they bore no gold. Dyer's part is also very revealing of the whole, misleading impression given to subsequent backers of the voyages of 1577 and 1578, a circle that included Dyer, Dee, Lok and many of the leading courtiers. Were they following fashion, were they following where the dictates of their competence led, or were they opportunistically trying to latch onto knowledge they all knew to be held in greater measure among Italian and German metallurgists?

Part of the answer emerges again in January 1577 when Lok gave a sample of the rock to Baptista Agnello and exposed his own gullibility, writing three days later that:

> He shewed me a very little powder of gold: saying it came thereowt, and willed me to give him another pece to make a better proof. I did so and within three dayes agayne, he shewed me more powder of golde. I told him I would not believe it without better proof. He asked another pece to make better proof: Saying, that he wold make anatomy thereof, I gave it to him: Saying that I marveyled much of his doings, sith I had given peces to other iii to make proof who could find no such thinge therin.[115]

Lok then says that Agnello answered knowingly in Italian saying "Bisogna sapere adulare la natura." This translates as "It is necessary to know how to coax nature."[116] Lok was duly misled, seeing at once in these findings the prospect of a trade route made viable just because of precious ores in its path. Hogarth feels this marks the beginning of the scam, failing to see that it also provided a possible key to the economic viability of a Northwest Passage that might operate in competition with the main Iberian routes over the Atlantic further south. Because members of the Privy Council themselves were enticed into risking further investment on this basis, including the Queen, they took some steps to give themselves some security and access to the best skills available. Among them, William Wynter, who had the highest of hopes of what was to be landed at Bristol,[117] Francis Walsingham[118] and Lord Burghley[119] shared information on what the ores were expected to be worth. Their solution to the problem of assessing the ores' value was to appoint Commissioners, and to look closely at what the venturers were proposing to do. The most successful of their number in metallurgical ventures, namely Lord Burghley, the Earl of Pembroke and the Earl of Shrewsbury, had had contact with Jonas Schutz and William Humfrey. Knowing these men's ambitions, Jonas Schutz outlined five explicit steps on 25 November 1577 costing them as written promises about how he would smelt, and what the ores would be worth.[120]

The Privy Council quickly realised they would have to accommodate Frobisher's vanity about the alleged importance of his discoveries, so he too was made a Commissioner in 1577. Lok illustrates how Frobisher thereafter pushed his own opinions and then vented his violent frustrations on Jonas Schutz, implying that this might cause serious damage to the venture. In fact the causes of failure were neither so simple, nor the leadership of Frobisher so good, as to allow for an explanation involving only those men. Lok certainly felt that Frobisher should have shown him more respect and gratitude. In drafting "The Abuses of Captain Furbisher against the Company An[n]o 1578" Lok claimed that:

> *[in margin]No 1. The ewre promised was not brought.*
> *In the first voyage he brought home by chaunce a stoane of riche ewre, and being examyned by Sir William Wynter, Mr Randall and Mr Hogan, and the rest of the Commissioners, what quantitie was to be had, he said that in that countrie was inoughe to lade all the Quenes ships and promised to lade the ships of the second voiage therw[i]th all, whereupon the second voyage was prepared, and the commyssion given him to bring home the same: but he performed nothing at all and brought not so much as one stone thereof, for there was none to lade, as Jonas and the rest do witnes, but laded the ships with other mynes founde by chaunsse.*

> *[in margin] No 2. the ewre promised was not brought.*
> *In the second voyag he retorned the shippes laden with stoanes of strange ewr found by chaunce ther, saying they were of gold myne worth iii xx poundes a tonne, which is not yet so found; and also he brought home stoanes of red ewre and yellow ewer of Jonas Mount, verye riche of gold, as D. Burcot witnessed, and the stoanes are yett to be seen. And promised to the comissioneres that ther was mountaynes therof, and he would lade all the shippes with therw[i]thall in the third voiage, whereuppon the thirde voiage was prepared w[i]th so great chardg; but he brought home not one stoane therof afterwards that is yet found.*

[in margin] **No 3. Superfluous shippes and chargs. He carried 4 ships, and c men wthout comission.**

In the third voiage he promised to lade all the shippes w[i]th the ewr of Jonas Mount, and other so riche ewre as the best of the second voiage was, and carried owt a nomber of ships for that purpose, and a c.[100] men to inhabit there under coller of the Frenche mens preparacon to that countrie, and besydes the nomber appoynted to him by the comissioners, he carried mor 4 shippes and c.[100] men more for his owne purpose, w[i]thout the knowledge of the comissioners, wh[i]ch now rest uppon the chardge of the Companye, and he brought home those ships laden w[i]th none of the ewre that he promised but w[i]th other strainge ewr, wher he could fynd yt, wch he said was better then the best that was brought the yeare befor, w[hi]ch is not so found.

[In margin] **No 5. He made no discourie of passage.**[121]

If this and the rest of the eighteen allegations were Lok's considered opinion it was only a marginally less hostile opinion than that held of Frobisher by Christopher Hall, Jonas Schutz and Edward Fenton. To examine whether its bias is justified it is possible to look beyond Lok's evidence to see why the Privy Council came to trust Fenton ahead of Frobisher. The events of 1577 to 1579 show that Fenton had a more careful and scientific manner than Frobisher, even if both were capable of considerable arrogance. In particular, SP12/129/2, 6 and 7 illustrate how Fenton first located and then gained credibility with Mr. Edgcumbe in his search for the sources of additives Kranich wanted for smelting in late 1577 and early 1578. This led him to the site on Mr Nance's land two miles from the north Cornish coast at Newquay, and to the recently abandoned silver/lead mine at St Colomb Minor. Significantly, Fenton noted the potential if the Company of Mines Royal re-opened the mine because it was "hard by the see side, the loade scant a foate broad."[122] This was one instance of that appearance of scientific and strategic learning which Fenton had shown in translating and publishing Boasistuau's ancient work *"Certaine Secreate Wonders of Nature"* in 1569, and which was again demonstrated in January 1578 in his care over the cataloguing and identifying of the various Cornish ores that had been located in earlier years by Messrs Godolphin, Arundel and Dr. Kranich. Later, in planning the hundred man colony it was Fenton who would be chosen to lead the party to stay on over the winter of 1578-79 in Kodlunarn, to defend it and hopefully locate more ore.

While the events of the summer of 1578 ensured he was not to do that, Fenton's reputation was sufficiently assured by his work in the West Country in January 1578. His systematic approach was evident in the manner in which he had labelled his carefully boxed and assayed samples. It is sad that after careful lading they were to be scattered and destroyed in an Atlantic storm, along with one of his two journals of record.[123] Subsequently, Denham also learned much from Frobisher's bad example, and by the labour relations and disciplinary problems of the 1578 voyage, showing particular attention to the miners' health and safety in the 1580s when managing the extraction of St. Colomb Minor's silver/lead mine. By taking a very different stance from Frobisher in managing the day by day operations of other local Cornish mines from the early 1580s Denham became pre-occupied, as Donald has shown, with the support of some of the most eminent investors who evidently sought to recoup their losses in Frobisher's voyages by means of other more profitable investments in the domestic metallurgical industry. In the 1580s over a dozen of Cornwall's silver lead and tin mines proved profitable when under day to day management by Denham, Frosse and Loner. This explains a major shift in the pattern of English investment.

Others with contacts and allegiances sealed in the unhappy voyage of 1578 looked to different remedies, having had clear insights into the personalities involved. One Devonian born at Northam into a mariner's family who was the subject of much discussion by contemporaries was William Borough whose navigational talent was much respected, and whose involvement was well known in the shipboard community. He had begun his career as a seagoing pilot sailing with his distinguished brother Steven for the Muscovy Company. His part in the investments of 1578 brought into play strong feelings in that community, just as Frobisher's behaviour did. But Lok, knowing him as a Limehouse resident, and as Pilot Major of the Muscovy Company, listed him as a City Adventurer for just £25 in the Cathay Company's last voyage, although he must have known that expedition also needed good and well equipped ships like William Borough's *Judith.*

Proving to be a tight and cunning investor, William Borough would subsequently seek a different way of recouping his fortunes at Lok's expense, while perhaps also hoping to extract out of Lok's distress significant metallurgical concessions in the North West ores. While sailing under Fenton's command in November 1582, the Rev. Richard Madox, enciphered another relevant and prejudiced group of opinions about Borough uttered by the former Master's Mate of the *Judith* in 1578, namely Luke Ward. Deciphered, that text states that:

> *William Burrows is one who could fill his honeycombs with someone else's*
> *honey and so far as he is accustomed to feed French dogs while they bring in*
> *hares....For thus he made use of a certain learned and noble Scot.* [possibly
> Jean Rotz alias John Ross] *He also conjectured that he had thrown Lok into*
> *prison as the master [Hall] reported. Lok, however, is a man of great wit and*
> *admirable honesty, as the master reported to me, but unhappy.*[124]

Madox, writing during Fenton's Atlantic voyage of 1582-83 and relaying Christopher Hall's views under the alias of Pallinurus or Master, condemns Frobisher too, writing in his diary on 13 September 1583 that "Pallinurus told me Furbisher received £1600 for buying victuals and some other necessaries considered useful for the ship, but that he spent only £500 on provisions, reserving the rest for himself. He affirmed that others similarly engaged in such business were able to take care of themselves and to do this destroyed at that instant the whole purpose of the enterprise."[125]

Lok certainly realised Frobisher's preference for acting as a greedy privateer, and his unscrupulous keenness to acquire wealth in gold by whatever means offered. This too can be separately attested[126] for Sir Martin Frobisher and Sir John Borough clashed again over their intentions to make as much money as possible in 1592.[127] Thus we can see that Lok's hostile judgements on Frobisher's character and business ethics, their mutual hostility to Borough, and the opinions of Lok's allies among the seamen on William Borough, were all to be borne out by later experience. But the full economic context of the northwest voyages made by Frobisher was a much more complex matter. The alluring prospects of finding lucrative metals permeated almost every major decision made in 1577-78 and twisted ambitions in directions which reflected pre-existing interests and ideas, the roots of which do not lie exclusively within the concerns of the unincorporated Cathay Company.

That Frobisher's metallurgists' opinions continued to be accepted with respect by most of their investing contemporaries, cannot be because of their scientific correctitude over the Meta Incognita ores. That respect must therefore rest much more on their reputations among the circle of investors they served. In seeing whether there were, possibly, parallel agendas in the minds of the metallurgists involved, and whether or not their reputations stood up to those tests, we have to look beyond the mere catalogue of failure of the fourteen bulk assays traced between 1577 and 1583 to the legal context of those assays and at the other interests of the assayers themselves. Then it becomes clear that there was a social agenda almost as powerful as the investigation of possible fraud. The possibility of financial fraud was also subjected to a detailed investigation between 1579 and 1582 as McDermott has shown. That it came to no decisions that were readily enforced suggests that it is the socio-economic context which explains why no gentleman investor tried prosecution of Schutz and Denham. Those investors needed men with such skills to sustain similar ventures in England, Wales and Ireland.

By contrast with those landowners, the seaman, William Borough was a cunning man keen to try litigation in furtherance of his interests, particularly as he had an eye on official promotion. Using that status as cover for personal ambition Borough directed his charges at Lok as the administrative co-ordinator of the whole enterprise. Lok enjoyed no professional protection from litigation, being the more exposed to it by virtue of his having none of the metallurgical skills so wanted in that circle of major landowning gamblers.

The Consequences of Trusting Judgement by the Assayers

The Assayers and their Furnaces

The assayers' opinions were crucially important because in the event it was not Frobisher's bad behaviour, or even Agnello's ingeniously suggestive opinions of January 1577, which led to the bulk of the debts for which Lok was held responsible. Lok paid casually to Schutz and Denham a sum of £5 for making small assays in London early in 1578[128] and it was upon their opinions that the speculators seized, creating a bubble of expectation in 1577-78 fuelled by Dee's concurrent publication devised for a limited and erudite circle of Privy Councillors and eminent Londoners. The speculators might as readily have lighted upon John Wolfe's assay which cast real doubt on the value of the ores early in 1578.[129] Hogarth, Boreham and Mitchell omit reference to Wolfe's assay, although they rightly stress that it was Agnello, in performing a bigger assay of a full hundredweight of Meta Incognita ore in his own London furnace beginning on 23 January 1578, who failed to find any silver or gold but lamely reported "yt succeded not well."[130] That document contains too the significant findings of Jonas Schutz's prospecting; namely, that equal charges of one hundredweight of black Meta Incognita ore, and of red ore from Meta Incognita, produced seemingly commercial quantities of gold (13.3 oz. to the ton).

Unjustified confidence in the belief that the rocks from particular rocky and watery contexts held precious metals that could be extracted by smelting in a blast furnace had stemmed from that spurious theory about the generation of metals published posthumously by Biringuccio in 1540 and translated into English by Richard Eden in 1555, and from his description of the operations of a gold mine.[131] Confidence that Frobisher's discoveries matched that type of context derived from the unjustified assumption that the assayers were right and that the business would be as successful as that of the Armazén da Guiné, Miná et Indiá in Lisbon.

This study will show that the judgements of Lok, the Commissioners and the Privy Councillors rested more on the perceived reputations and local successes achieved by foreign born metallurgists pedalling a chimera of imperial aspiration and industrial synergy in the new technologies, rather than on any objective ways of testing their chosen metallurgists' opinions and prospecting skills. In addition to an unknown number of very small-scale assays undertaken in small portable German stoves on Kodlunarn in 1578, there were innumerable small-scale chemical tests made of small rock samples in 1577 and 1578 on-site in Meta Incognita by Jonas Schutz, Robert Denham, Andrew Dyer, Edmund Stafford and Gregory Bona, assisted by Rumbridge in his care for the tiny beam scales and balances and associated delicate equipment.[132] In London there were at least half a dozen assays undertaken before the second Frobisher voyage, as well as twelve large-scale assays, and a few in Paris and Madrid undertaken because some ores were the subject of espionage. The latter confirmed that the ores contained no metals of commercial value.

Moved by anxiety late in 1579 Schutz suggested that Wynter's small London furnace might be better designed to extract metals than the much bigger Dartford smelter despite its four pairs of bellows arranged to Schutz's specification. In the course of the last of five assays conducted with the Dartford smelter, Schutz recorded that 35 oz of silver to the ton had been extracted. He opined then that the same amount again remained in the slags.[133] His reasoning was consistent, given that he was working much as Biringuccio envisaged, and so expected more than he had recovered at Tower Hill by 6 March 1578 in his third assay, using two hundredweight of the second voyage's ore which yielded 64 ozs of silver and 2.6 ozs of gold to the ton.[134]

In the event his last assay, as conducted in Wynter's garden furnace at Tower Hill, recovered only 49 ozs of silver to the ton, and 1.7 oz of gold, in both cases much less than he had obtained a year earlier with the same furnace. Outside circumstances forced Schutz to contend that 28oz of silver to the ton remained in the slags.[135] This was an implicit criticism of his design of the Dartford smelter, compared with the small one in Wynter's London garden which he had modified with Denham, reversing changes made at Kranich's instance.

In 1578 Lok would produce two short accounts and one long account covering all but one of Schutz's assays. Before compiling a draft submission to the Commissioners and the Privy Council as "The causes and fiundacyon of the iii voyages,"[136] Lok made a transcript of Schutz's assay records and accounts.[137] With Schutz's help he compiled data for the Inquiry about "small proofes and sayes made at London of the mynerall Ewer brought home by Mr. furbisher in this second voyage."[138] From that record Lok compiled a much more colourful account, Lansdowne 100/1, presenting Kranich in a particularly bad light.[139] Although Kranich claimed to have found gold and quite a considerable silver charge which he separated with "antimony," i.e. stibnite, he did so in circumstances which brought disrepute on his methods of charging and assaying.[140]

Meanwhile Schutz found that Kranich's counter-charge, by raising the issue of the Dartford furnace's design and management, provided a source of controversy that raged on until 1580 when an outside opinion was invited on the Dartford smelter from Daniel Hechstetter and George Needham. They were trusted men with whom the prime investors in the Company of Mines Royal and the Company of Mines and Battery Works, William Humfrey and Lord Burghley, were still in regular and close contact.[141] This time Hechstetter, assisted by George Needham, could not point to easily rectified practice, as he had done at Tintern in 1569, or even suggest different feedstocks. Wisely, Hechstetter and Needham evaluated the blast furnace and the layout of its expensive bellows, where "in smelting yeures we found such want in the building of the furnace and in the disorderly placing of the bellowes that we could not by any meanes possible p[er]fectly smelte downe the said [Cumberland] ywers. If the bellows and blast had been good we might hjave gotten iii qtrs [¾] or at least Di th [1/10] of the copper w[h]ich we doe nowe loose."[142]

They also evaluated the processing of the Arctic ores, and the use made of Cornish and Cumbrian additives. In consequence their report amounted to criticism of the work of their erstwhile advisor at Keswick. Their report dated 21 March 1580 indicated that they had tested the Dartford smelter with 2.3 tons of copper ore and 0.3 tons of lead-rich ores from Caldbeck and Newlands such as they had used at Keswick and had sold through Robert Denham to the Cathay Company in 1578. Hechstetter and Needham recommended but one operational change: having the twenty-three day pre-smelting roasting of the ores done "in Mr Pope's soulpher potts" at Queensborough first.[143] Impractically they envisaged that the roasted ores could be cooled and safely taken by ship from the Isle of Sheppey to Dartford Creek for the smelter.

Having seen the work of Schutz and others at first hand both at Dartford and in London, and having discussed its theoretical basis with them, John Dee too must have realised that during the winter of 1578-79 Schutz had failed the investors. We also know through the work of modern geological scientists that William Williams was correct to report nothing but the most minute quantity of gold in his two assays undertaken at the Tower of London starting on 28 July 1583.[144] By early August in 1583, if not before, Dee and his contemporaries must have realised that it was Schutz's six assaying failures in 1578-79 which had finally pricked the speculative bubble (despite talk of defects in the design of the furnace), writing off the ores as being "marcasite."[145] That was probably enough to cause him to flee to Bohemia from fear of blame.

Lok's accounts show that Schutz had ordered materials to try acid parting, antimony or sulphide parting, and cementation using salt, and that he had specifically done this in the course of the Dartford assays. Some loads of antimony-rich ore were shipped from Fowey after Fenton had located it with Edgcumbe's help.[146] But Lok's accounts also recorded "paid for strong water ii lib [2lb] and a glasse and a plate for parting of gold and silver,"[147] and in a last desperate hope to extract a result on 8 October 1578, he had ordered in eight bushels of salt.[148] Lok's records give a partial explanation of the cold processing attempted unsuccessfully by Burchard Kranich, and provide the basis of "strong waters" or nitric acid assay tests carried out by Andrew Dyer at various Arctic mines in 1578.

This was just five years after another German, Samuel Zimmerman, in an unusual "*Problierbuch*" published in Augsburg, had advocated small-scale "wet assay" (or acid assay) to test ores for gold or silver content after utilising a short roast of an ore with coal and lime. Performed in German stoves on Kodlunarn and Little Hall's Island, or the ship's furnaces, that process would oxidise the green mica therein to a misleading golden finish.[149] Then after that rather simple processing, the final stage of the field assay process was to add nitric acid (strong waters or aqua fortis).[150] Golden looking samples were then weighed. The difficulty was to add just the right amount of nitric acid to reveal silver at the outset so as to avoid obfuscating any visual evidence with light sensitive silver nitrate. If insufficient silver was added the acid consumed most other metals, creating salts with them. If small quantities of gold were present they might survive the process.

The nitric acid method, properly used, was a relatively quick and convenient way to assay rock samples, and for that reason it is likely that Schutz had taught Robert Denham and Andrew Dyer a variant of this technique in 1577, if they had not already learned it from Sir Edward Dyer or John Dee. Schutz certainly saw it used at Keswick in 1576.[151] Kept in tiny vials the acid could be carried in an assayer's belt between mine sites as was the case on Frobisher's last two voyages to Meta Incognita.

Because of the obscurity and doubtful purposes of the alchemical work done by Dee and the Dyers, and the prominence given to Andrew Dyer's field assays by the naming of its vicinity, Dyer's Sound, most historians have overlooked the small-scale assays done in

Figure 13: Agricola's drawing from Book IX of *De Re Metallica*, showing how a water wheel could be mechanically linked to a set of three bellows feeding a furnace or foundry, whose fires can be seen burning above the tiled roof. Note the corresponding care taken to properly ventilate and cool the foundry worker in long loose clothes. The dog wisely remains on the cool side of the plant near the reservoir feeding the water wheel.

Kodlunarn in facilities uncovered by archaeologists since 1990, and turned instead to the State Papers, and in particular to their results of the large-scale assays and the remarkable 16 page summary statement of Michael Lok completed on 26 January 1579.[152] The third part of that document makes clear the spirit of that inquiry conducted by the Commissioners, who themselves had lost money in speculative investment. Lok's view was that the Commissioners, and Messrs Neale and Baynham who signed a report as the Auditors of the three voyages, presented it so that "it may appeare that you have a thorne in your owne foot w[hi]ch dothe somewhat prick you w[hi]ch now you would pull owt and put into myne who am not able to cure it so well as yourselves."[153]

The sources traditionally favoured by historians are State Paper 12/131/20 which had appended to it the famous thin sections of ore from Kodlunarn, and the descriptions, accusations, and counter accusations in SP12/129/62 and 63, especially the "The doings of Jonas Schutz in the new mines of gold." The same series was until 1920 wrapped by a large drawing, now MPF 304, showing three furnaces associated with the project, namely a small one belonging to Sir William Wynter in London; a vast one, powered by water wheel which must be Dartford; and one marked as Burchard Kranich's. It was itself described in the "Dooings of Mr Burcott in the Newe Mines of Golde," where Burcot Kranich criticised Jonas Schutz's location of bellows, writing "afterwards, Mr Furbisher did shewe to[o] Mr Locke a paper platt, made by Mr Burcott, of the furnace that he would have with a pott by yt. And nowe, at the 20 February, he shewed an other platt thereof made cleane contrary too the first, but even just the coppie of the plate of the furnaces, whereof Jonas dooeth woorke."[154]

The initial circumstances described in Lansdowne 100/1 are worthy of close comparison with the drawings of the furnace at Wynter's house and two others. The group of drawings was removed in 1920 from SP12/122/63, and is now known as MPF 304. That drawing had identified the small complex by the topmost furnace with the label "Winter." The men working it must be Jonas Schutz and Robert Denham for we know they initially worked together in Winter's garden. Dr. Burcot Kranich is also identified in MPF 304 and shown again beside a rival and much larger furnace with a similarly dressed assistant, who can only be Robert Denham wearing the same colour of red tunic.[155] It seems likely that the attached text of "The dooings of Mr Burcott in the newe Mynes of Gold" was first drafted by Jonas Schutz, although it bears evidence of later additions by Lok. Damning Frobisher's support for Kranich's incompetence it notes that:

> *he shewed a peace of antimonye ewer vouching that therein was noe manner of mettal, but a prooffe thereof was made on xxii daye, and they founde therein bothe silver, xxx ouncs in a tonn, and some copper, and very muche leade. And Mr Burcott sayd that without that antimonnye ewer he would not stand to his former promys of the golde and silver to be deliveryed. And Denham saye that Burcott did not knowe of the metalls that are in the antymonie ewer untill Thursday, being the xx February, when as he told yt to Burcott, and was the mann that did first fynde it to be so by his owne tryalls. And Mr Burcott was ignorant of the weight of gold amd silver accompted after at xxiiii to a*

pennyweight, and xxiiii pennye weight to the ounce untill that Denham did shewe him his errore.[156]

The next paragraph with its more measured judgement, must be the collaborative conclusions arrived at by Schutz and Lok working together on a draft early in 1579 shortly after Burcot Kranich's death. It reads thus:

And yet it is manyfest that Burcott was more ignorant then Jonas, in the knowledge of the nature and workinge of this ewer: for him selfe Burcott doeth confesse that he hathe made more than forty sundrye ways of tryall thereof, and yet is not well satisfyed therein; but Jonas hath made onely syxe proofs thereof, and those after the order of the great works" [at Dartford].[157]

Lok's account of Frobisher's behaviour throughout these assays and the voyages is very damning of his character in terms of obstinacy, insolence, prodigality, greed and denial of accountability. Detailed textual study of Lansdowne 100/1 suggests the main substance of its allegations may be justified. It seems very likely that this lengthy but important document was an early personal collation of conversations and recollections into a draft from which Lok hoped either to damn Frobisher or to derive evidential proofs which might help him to fight off his creditors. It was not envisaged as legal evidence, for a reason that will become clear. In commenting on its content Hogarth, Mitchell and Boreham suggest the red ores of which so much was hoped were probably rich arsenides or "gossans" which are not now much in evidence in Meta Incognita, Dartford or the Smerwick Bay fort. Unable to deny in the face of several sources that such red ores were loaded on the second voyage to Schutz's satisfaction, they suggest that Lansdowne 100/1 was probably never produced as legal evidence, and that the "Doynges of Captayne Furbisher amongst the Companye's business" were fabricated allegations. But Lansdowne 100/1 offers vivid first-hand insights from Denham into the events of January to March 1578 when the disreputable practices of Baptista Agnello and Burchard Kranich were exposed by Robert Denham as barely a serious attempt to smelt the ores assigned to them for assay. It shows that Dee and Dyer and Lok were among the first to know of this defective methodology. But Lok could have not wanted that cheat put before a Court.

Based on expectations that he had established between November 1577 and March 1578 with Wynter's furnace, Schutz had expected quite positive results from use of the red ores of Meta Incognita, but not so much from the black ones. Through February and March 1579 Schutz expressed a rather similar quantitative series of opinions that the slags created by smelting at Dartford contained proportionately almost as much silver as had been extracted from Wynter's London furnace in March 1578. But he found they contained very much less gold than expected. Subsequently the Hechstetter/Needham report of 21 March 1580 would confirm Schutz's opinions as to the defects of the Dartford Furnace.[158] Yet Schutz was not allowed to return to it, Sellman being the only official of the Company to have much to do at the site in the years up to 1585. In 1585-86 the Dartford site was taken over by John Spilman and expensively converted for operation as a paper mill. That decision was probably motivated by a desire of both the

Crown and the adventurers to escape any further exposure to cost there, and to realise a capital sum for it. Much of the ore was also disposed of in the years up to 1589 when both Dee, and for parts of the time Sir Edward Dyer too, were living and experimenting in Central Europe.

By 1583 the Cathay Adventurers had news of the last and unsuccessful assay of the Meta Incognita ores which were completed in a small furnace within the Tower of London by William Williams. As a Commissioner Dee would have seen its completion on 28 July 1583, knowing the ores to be worthless. During August 1583 he became anxious that he might be held responsible for the failures and expenditure at Dartford now that Lok had changed the target of his criticisms.[159] As Lok's criticisms of the Commissioners had hardened, the Commissioners' confidence that the Dartford smelter would smelt hornblende and amphibole ores and so isolate precious metals looked misplaced.

Dee was not alone in believing that the Dartford smelter had had great potential, and that there were only operational faults to remedy, perhaps with its bellows as Kranich thought, or perhaps in the way its charges were conceived and how its smelted metals were separated, as Dee's small experiments designed to test Biringuccio's advice about the nature of marcasite suggest.[160] On 28 March 1579 Sir Thomas Gresham intervened, concerned that some still had not paid up their shares and that the investors needed to make better use of the new Dartford smelter. He had contacted "John Barton, gentleman, who semethe to have experiens of myneral works, who hathe offered to make a profit of ewr at Dartford, at his own charge in the great works at Dartford, and thereupon will procede in all the ore there ... And for the procedinge of the great works at Dartford by Jonas, we thynk ytt very requysytt to procede in the same ... by a new cessment on all the venturers."[161]

Lok's texts are used as the main first-hand source for the criticisms laid by Hogarth Boreham and Mitchell against Schutz, but they fail to spot the movement in the force of Lok's criticism away from Schutz and towards increasing reliance on Schutz's records and guidance as to the significance of the findings of the assays. Schutz takes an increasing part in Lok's affairs from 1578, and as he does so, Lok gradually shifts the target of his accusing finger. For Lansdowne 100/1 to take its dramatic and vivid form, Denham, as Schutz's trusted assistant, must have told Lok first-hand about Kranich's practice.

But Schutz had evolved a shrewder idea about how to recover his reputation as early as November 1578 when Lok begun to take Schutz into his confidence. As Lansdowne 100/1 shows, rather than have him as another well advised and litigious enemy, Lok would take Schutz's advice. Lok thereby found both a clever interpreter of the morass of litigation he faced, and one who would lead many prominent investors towards other mining ventures that enabled them to recover lost fortunes during the 1580s. Thus Schutz did derive a sustaining advantage and virtual immunity from attack through litigation by Cathay Adventurers due to the strategy he had devised during 1579, albeit one that eluded Hogarth, Boreham and Mitchell as they concentrated their criticism on his assaying and prospecting as fraudulent, failing to see that his practices both followed theories established by Biringuccio and relied on techniques that had brought success to investors in other English and Irish contexts. This becomes the clearer when the way he avoided litigation is examined.

Offers and Counter Offers Made Under the Spectre of Litigation

On 16 November 1581 Lok pleaded that his main problem was that Frobisher had failed to discover Cathay on the first voyage. There is some equivocation about his target in that text, for Lok was admitting financial responsibility for promoting that initial voyage. Lok now put the failures of the second and third voyage down to the consequences of trusting judgement by professional assayers, saying that the cause of the second voyage was the opinions of Baptista Agnello, Jonas Schutz and Robert Denham. They had all worked on the ores brought back on the first voyage, and their opinions were credited with veracity by Sir William Wynter and the Commissioners. By November 1581 Lok was also suggesting that the ores from the subsequent voyages had not come from the same place as those assayed from the first voyage, a fault he attributed to Frobisher.

Lok also felt that considerable fault was of Frobisher's making to the extent that he did not return from his third voyage, as expected, with 500 tons of the rich sandy red ore of which Jonas Schutz as its discoverer was so confident. The effect of this was partially to exculpate Jonas Schutz. The inclusion of remarks to that effect was probably the direct result of data that Schutz had shared with Lok in the manner we have already seen. That red ore Hogarth and others now consider might have been a rich gossan, that is an iron-rich capping over various sulphides, which, in parts of northern Canada today, is known to contain the high concentrations of gold and silver that might have justified Kranich's opinions.[162] Unfortunately they found none of the red ore to test their conjecture. Yet it was the red ore which had formed the basis of the case for the third voyage. Lok added on 16 November 1581 that the cause of the third voyage's costs of £15,000 was the reinforcement of the opinions of Jonas Schutz and Robert Denham, chiefly by Dr. Burchard Kranich who gave a personal bond on his property for the value of the ores from the second voyage.[163]

For all his equivocation about the responsibility of others, the account Lok gave on 16 November 1581 is quite clear as to why the investors in Frobisher's three voyages had lost over £20,000, and himself over £5,000. Lok pleads "yet was not I the cause."[164] Lok's more thoughtful remarks of November 1581 differ greatly from his vehement criticisms of 1578, similarly made of Jonas [Schutz], of Denham, and most significantly, of Frobisher. In drafting "The Abuses of Captayn Furbisher against the Companye, An[n]o 1578," Lok hoped in conclusion that they "as causars of the costs of fetching and working the same," were "punished sharplie."[165] By November 1581, he wished no more punishment upon them. Indeed he had by then become Schutz's ally, and simply wanted to get out of prison and ensure the resumption of assaying and commercial smelting at the new Dartford Furnace. His chief target of criticism had shifted to William Wynter and the Commissioners for promoting the second voyage and all that followed.[166]

Lok's problem in 1581 was that he had no office in the venture. There were insufficient funds to meet all the creditors' claims made on him and to secure the Adventurer's creditors despite all the influence that the Privy Council could deploy. Wynter, and indeed most of the Privy Council, needed to shelter behind the Commissioners' status and the Auditor's opinions. For a while Borough's litigation served them almost as well, obscuring their mistakes and ensuring Lok was seen as the scapegoat arguing from prison from May 1581.

If William Borough's litigation over unpaid liabilities had forced Lok to write from London's debtor's prison in June 1581,[167] the circumstances of his release in 1582 expose a much bigger factor — the help of influential legal friends plus the advice of Jonas Schutz. Although Lok thereafter led a sad life, much of it under the threat of debtor's prison while facing a barrage of new legal claims that arose largely because of the failure of the bulk assays, he managed to earn a sufficient amount to meet most of the creditor's claims through Schutz's guidance to Lok on the international alum trade, its main market in Venice, and fresh sources in Ireland and the Isle of Wight. The other dynamic for change in Lok's position by 1582 came as some Privy Councillors revealed their preparedness to gamble on yet another voyage under Fenton's command — a gamble which only led again to costly failure by 1583. Others, like Dee, Duckett, Walsingham, and Burghley, sought new metallurgical leases in England.

After Lok secured his release in 1582 he began to deal more effectually with litigants over his earlier commitments, including William Borough whose motives were noted with disgust by Luke Ward (as the former master's mate under Fenton's command on Borough's ship, the *Judith,* for the summer of 1578).[168] It was not just a matter wherein some litigants had undoubtedly exaggerated their legal claims against Lok, apparently believing that his ability to afford legal resistance was much reduced. In fact Lok kept intact his propertied inheritance from his father in London and Essex through all those legal battles when he learned how few would befriend him.[169] How did Lok manage to achieve that, and why did he regularly re-visit Dublin and the nearby Wicklow Coast, and Venice, the centre of so much metallurgical activity and trading finance?

The clear implication is that he and Schutz had devised a trading position or positions which it was beyond the will or capacity of his pursuers and English accountants to investigate. In 1580 the House of Commons took a close and hostile interest in the role of accountants, addressing Bills which, although they never secured third readings, served to put on pressure for regulation of accountants like Lok, and those who would offer opinions on such accounts like Baynham and Neale. The interest of those debates is that they show the vendetta pursued by men whose families lost money in the Meta Incognita venture and who chose to speak on the Bill. The speakers included Sir Herbert Croft, son of Sir James Croft and subscriber for £50 in the second voyage and Sir William Bowyer, a relative of Simon Bo[w]yer, who subscribed to £25 with an added cessment of £15 for the second voyage, only paid up as to £28 15s. by 29 April 1579.[170]

The Commons' Journal shows the House of Commons must have done this twice more, and to some considerable effect as debates on a later Act of 1604 show.[171]   One effect was to boost business taken to the Court of Exchequer where Michael Lok was faced with a succession of suits.   Although his fortunes improved he was faced with the prospect of other terms in prison, for not only was he also cited in Bonham's suit for compensation over the *Thomas of Ipswich's* use in 1578, he was party to a similar Frobisher related suit on which in 1608 he had to brief Thomas Ellis, as Counsellor at law.[172]   As contested Exchequer Decree and Orders show as late as 1615, Lok was still contending with a claim for unpaid stores provided for Frobisher's ships.   Yet for all that pressure Lok was able to defy his creditors quite effectually.   This must in part be explained by his many competent children and legally qualified relations, it is also appropriate to determine whether that litigation, and the subsequent shift in Lok's own criticisms, throws more light on the quality of the metallurgists' opinions and schemes, than on weaknesses in his less than thorough, though extensive, accounts.

In this context it becomes clear that it was the possibility of litigation which moved Lok and Schutz to put the blame on other peoples' dishonesty, and in particular on Agnello, Kranich and Frobisher.   In "The Abuses of Captayn Furbisher against the Companye, An[n]o 1578," dated 1578, Lok alleges Frobisher "did practyse to advaunce D. Burcot into the place of Jonas, and mayntayn Burcot's false proffes made of the ewr, to th[e] end he might be sett on agayn in this third Voyage as the Commissioners and Denham can witnes[s]."[173]

Yet today's historians, geologists and metallurgists can agree that it was only Burcot Kranich's methods and reputation amongst his contemporaries which was destroyed when exposed by Robert Denham, in the circumstances explained most convincingly in Lansdowne 100/1.   Depression at the unravelling of these consequences soon brought Kranich to his death on 22 October 1578.   Kranich had rashly promised to secure the investment of the second voyage against his opinions on the ore, and the voyage's costs against his own assets.   This guarantee was recorded by Lok as crucial in persuading him to invest.   Kranich's death now undid Lok's certitude and made him more dependant than ever on Schutz's technical opinions and general competence.

Missing this in 1994, Hogarth, Boreham and Mitchell identified Jonas Schutz as the person principally responsible for poor performance as a mineral prospector, and for the major costs associated with the poorly designed furnace at Dartford, and for most misleading bulk assays conducted there and in London.   Their modern scientific analysis used sixty-six ore samples taken from identified mine-sites in Meta Incognita, and twelve more from Dartford and Smerwick Bay, as representing largely the hornblende rocks collected from Meta Incognita.   They did not sample the red sandy rocks by which Lok and Schutz put considerable store.   They conceded obliquely that had Kranich used the red ores (which Schutz had first located), he might have achieved a figure of 1,200 parts per million or 40 oz to the ton of gold.   There are even today some very red stones also built into the walls at Dartford, some taking a sandy form, some looking much more like local ironstone and ragstone.   Some of those redder sandy items may be worthy of examination in future along with one black stone in the gatehouse wall itself, crossed by a sandy red vein of much the same consistency as the redder powdery ones used at other points. Yet Hogarth and Mitchell use all the sophistication of the late twentieth century's scientific and technical analysis to adjudge Schutz either an incompetent, or to suggest the more questionable deduction that "that Jonas Shutz, Robert Denham, and perhaps others, added gold bearing material to the charge deliberately. However what sustaining advantage the assayers hoped to gain in fraud is difficult to imagine."[174]

As regards the black ores, the modern molten assays showed that one contained some gold, another appreciable silver, and, significantly, that both came from Dartford. But their analysis showed that gold was only present in quantities between one hundred and eighty times and over three hundred times less than Schutz had claimed to be present in those ores when asserting that he had not extracted half as much as he thought the samples contained. The twin problems with this analysis are that while the red ores were available to Schutz's contemporaries from November 1577, they were missing from analyses conducted by both Tilley and Roy in Cambridge in 1937, and by Hogarth and Mitchell in 1993 in the Universities of Ottawa, Carleton and at the Canadian Museum of Nature, and at commercial assay laboratories in Toronto. These analyses involved technology that was self-evidently not available to Schutz's contemporaries, or to the Courts of his day in judging him and his contemporaries. Quite reasonably, we have to conclude that in the absence of such modern technology, the investment decisions and gambles of 1576 to 1579 depended on the opinions and reputations of men like Schutz and that they were only established over a wide range of contemporary experience and not on some project as narrowly focused as Frobisher's voyages.

What Elizabethan men did respect were the opinions of a group of Elizabethan Ordnance and Mint officials like Wynter, Paynter, Bowlande, Humfrey and Burde who all worked in and around the Tower of London in the Mint and the Armouries and who backed the venture with their own money as Adventurers. Those officials probably did so largely because they professionally respected Schutz's capabilities. This suggests that Needham, Whelar [Wheeler] and Williams should have been the ones to whom the influential investors around Elizabeth's Court turned when they realised the scale of their misjudgements, or the falsification possible within the disciplines of small-scale assays done by Agnello and others in January 1577. They were confronted by that reality on learning of the full-scale furnace assays done by Schutz, Kranich, Broad and Agnello, to so many of which Denham was party between 1 November 1577 and the end of March 1579. William Williams made the final negative assessment of their commercial value in a small double assay which he began on 28 July 1583 within the Mint at the Tower of London. He found no measurable gold and only the tiniest quantities of silver — results in line with modern analyses.

Yet William Williams was responsible for day by day decisions concerning the soundness of the Royal Mint's practice where accuracy in testing of the pyx was important. Williams had had experience dealing with German miners who settled in the Wicklow Hills before coming to the Tower workshops of the Royal Mint in London as

Deputy Assay Master in 1567. He produced one of the negative assays in 1577. His assays of 28 July 1583 were presumably used only to justify disposing of Meta Incognita ores stored under the Mint's care and within the secure confines of the Tower of London, and to show the ores offered no residual value to those who now had to face the failure of Fenton's voyage too. Those assays by Williams may well have been the formal means used to avoid further litigation based on the concept that the ores had a material value and to clear the Mint of the need to store the ores. Recently B.J. Cook and C. Challis have shown Richard Martin imposed a new broom on the Mint's operations and staff after 1578.[175] As they did not have any significant metallurgical value it was easier after 1583 to approve the disposal of the ores for building stone, embanking and reclamation works.

The remarkable feature of all this is that William Williams, although correct in his analysis in July 1583, enjoyed a much lower commercial profile than many of his predecessors as Master of the Mint, such as Sir John York (1551-1553), Dr. Robert Recorde (1553-1558), an investor in Welsh mines whose navigational manual was taken to sea by Frobisher in 1576, and most famously, William Humfrey the Elder (1561-1582). If Williams was the model of the incorruptible official needed by the Mint to succeed William Humfrey, it is necessary to ask why even higher reputations and rewards were accorded by his contemporaries to Schutz, Humfrey and Denham.

It is notable that as one involved in even more of the disastrous assays than Schutz himself, Denham's reputation rose steadily through and after the events of 1577 to 1579, for he was engaged in a sequence of important and successful mining operations in the West Country for the Company of Mines Royal through the 1580s. He was evidently trusted as a prospector, as a mining engineer, as a metallurgist and as a manager of a significant workforce. So he continued in his chosen profession with a secure income looking after an important national asset, and one that proved lucrative to the Crown. For all his London family connections in the Goldsmith's Company, Denham remained uncluttered with an expensive lifestyle or with the problems of litigation that affected Schutz, Lok, and Humfrey and which so worried John Dee and Edward Dyer as their creditors pursued them.

Certainly that litigious sequence of claims which so damaged Lok's reputation as a City merchant led to his having to shoulder most of the blame for misplaced trust in the formal assays conducted in England. It was a tale of blunders, inappropriate technology, the uncontrolled addition of additives to the feedstocks, unsound understanding of the role of catalysts, and in particular of an unsound confidence in the new technology of a blast furnace operated with water-powered bellows. As those were matters of technology much of that blame perhaps ought to have been attached to the metallurgists.

By contrast with Lok who was hurt and duped by Agnello, Sir William Wynter, who was equally confident in the misleading assay results early in 1577 and the whole trans-Atlantic strategy, evaded criticism from all but Lok, and remained free to use incomes from his Crown offices to supplement his Lydney estate incomes with further metallurgical developments. The explanation for this lies in the fact that Wynter, unlike

Lok, was an accomplished political operator in Court and naval circles, and a landowner who became wealthy through sound metallurgical investments. Wynter both managed to avoid responsibility for his judgements and to keep favour with the Privy Council. Lok lacked Wynter's political adeptness and influence, and later suffered grievously from the fact that he had himself invited the subscriptions and carried responsibility as Treasurer of the Cathay Company until 1579. Yet by 1579 Lok was carrying his own prejudices to work and so into the surviving historical evidence.

During the year 1579, and intermittently for many years afterwards, Michael Lok tried in the face of many law suits to clear his name and explain his offers in respect of the ore. His view in 1579 was that the Privy Council should investigate the Commissioners who are listed as "Sir William Wyntar, Sir William Pelham, Mr Thomas Randolphe, Mr Dyer, Mr Dee, Mr Yonge, Mr Hogan, Mr Lok, and Mr Palmer," and the workmen that they were to oversee whom he listed as "John Baptista Agnello, Jonas Schutz, Robert Denham, William Humfrey, Humfrey Cole." He added curtly "Dr. Burcott is deade."[176] That shift of criticism from the assayers themselves towards the Commissioners would accrete little sympathy from the Privy Council.

This suggestion of Lok's, throwing some doubt on the good offices of the Commissioners, repeated in 1581, first appears in the context of the very acrimonious accusations by Frobisher against Lok, and vice versa, which appear again in the State Papers. The idea may have originated from discussions with Schutz, for those allegations are overshadowed by the incident where Frobisher drew his dagger on Jonas Schutz when about his work in William Wynter's garden at Tower Hill. This was reported in Lok's eighteen "Abuses of Captayn Frobisher agaynste the Companye. An[n]o 1578." where allegation no. 14 reads thus:

> *He drew his dagger and ranne upon Jonas, being in his worke at Tower Hill, and threatened to kill him yf he did not fynish his work owt of hand, that he might sett owt again on the third voiage, whereupon Jonas did conseave so eavell a nature in him, that he made a sollemne vowe he would never go to see any more with him, which hath been no small damage to the Company in the ore brought home on the thirde voyage.*[177]

As if to show such behaviour by Frobisher was not unprecedented he also picked upon another incident when Fenton, who knew rather more than Frobisher about assaying, was similarly attacked. Lok put this directly into his allegation No. 16, saying Frobisher "drew his dager on captayne Fenton at Darteford, upon a quarrelous humour, and wold have mischesed him upon the sodayne, yf Mr Pelham and others had not bine present."[178]

In contrast with his attitude to Frobisher, it is very unlikely that Michael Lok set out to damn Jonas Schutz's reputation irretrievably. Indeed as late as November 1581 he skates over the matter very quickly without reference to punishment because Lok and Schutz had clearly met regularly and respectfully, and had shared their opinions on the voyages, and on Frobisher in particular. Traces of those conversations have shaped Loks' account in the form of Lansdowne 100/1. In assessing the quality of the decisions that were made in 1577, Lansdowne 100/1 shows what Lok thought Schutz had achieved in identifying appropriate ores, but in so doing reveals information that could only have come directly from Schutz. It says of Frobisher:

> *"He brought a stone of vitre redd found in second voyage and promisseth to lade ships therewith all on the Third Voyage but did nothing at all."*
> *" In this same voyage weare discovered certayne (alyn ?) mines of Redd Ewre and Yellow nowe at a place named Jonas Mont, whereof divers forms were brought home and much was digged as they said, but was not laden into the shippes, because the shipps were already laden with the black ewre, and as he sayed the time was round for them to depart out of the countrye, and the red Ewre was discovered but even at their departure thence."*
> *"So they took not, nor tarried to change their ladinge. And of this ewer were made divers small sayes by Jonas and Denham, and found verrie ag. like gold."*[179]

Instead, Lok exploits that insight only to offer further criticism of Frobisher's probity adding data that could only have come from Schutz himself :

> *There was found by Jonas amongst the Rocks a great Ambre stone of more than an inch square, a present meet for a Prince. This jewell did Jonas value to Mr Furbisher for at his departure from Milford Haven towards the court he promised him to put the same to her Majestie in Jonas's name. Which Mr Jonas doeth not therewith nor cannot learn what is become of it.*[180]

A marginal note adds: "This jewell is mete for a present to her Majestie unto whom Capt Frobisher did present it, in his owne name and not in the company's name to whome it did belonge." The potential value of this commentary is rather devalued by Lok's desperate attempt to justify his investments, which immediately follows, namely that: "There was founde and brought home on this second voyage many small jewell stones, diamants, rubies, saphires and others by divers persons which were put upon privately, and so nowe accompt be taken of them though they be of valewe."[181]

In judging Schutz's other skills as a mineral prospector Lok's allegations on jewel stones might be ignored as rhetoric although the latest evidence suggests that Schutz was perhaps correct.[182] There was probably nobody else in England whose breadth of experience could match that accumulated by Schutz and Bona by 1577 as prospectors, and by Schutz and Denham as proponents of blast furnace technology. Given that Schutz's reputation as a respected smelter was still considerable, if dented, by mid 1579, why did Borough not try to take legal action directly against the Master Workman for his handling of Meta Incognita's ores at Tower Hill or at the Dartford furnace?

The answer has to be that he chose to act against Lok instead, using the metallurgists' opinions as incidental evidence. The Commissioners' formal concern, which made the later assays difficult to challenge, contrast with the records of the Schutz's assays on 1 November 1577 and on 6 December 1577 which appear very differently in the account of them compiled rather later by Thomas Alleyn, Lok's successor as Treasurer of the unincorporated Cathay Company.[183] Significantly, it is only from the summaries of them provided to the Commissioners and kept among the State Papers that we learn two of the three earliest assays concerned the red ores found by Schutz.[184]

By 1579 Borough, who acted as Alleyn's successor in the Tresorial job, clearly had possession of tangible evidence in the form of two small ingots of gold and two of silver — but that was the only security in the form of precious metals extracted which the whole venture enjoyed. Alleyn's document, later misfiled by a Chancery Court official, originally appeared in the context of William Borough's law suit against Lok over his own ship, the new *Judith*. It was a suit based in part on data available to Borough only because he briefly became Treasurer.[185] It suited Borough's purpose well for he knew that Schutz had completed his last assay by late March 1579 in Wynter's London garden at Tower Hill probably using the second voyage's red ores, and that Lok still depended on Schutz for he had not given up hope that the ores and the smelter still had considerable worth.

Borough finally secured judgement against Lok for not meeting his liabilities in chartering the ship in mid-1581, sending him to London's debtors prison. Perhaps more significantly, Lok was freed in 1582 just as Schutz himself became free of other legal entanglements and could quietly help Lok. In guiding Lok back to viability, Schutz probably knew Agricola's work backwards and was also quite prepared to litigate to defend worthwhile metallurgical interests with his erstwhile patron and patentee, William Humfrey. In this context it should be noted that Schutz's will provided generously for his legal advisors.

Lok undoubtedly knew that Christopher Schutz and William Humfrey had taken successful legal action for breach of their joint patent on the construction of a lead smelter at Beauchief in Derbyshire. Their action had started while Schutz was in Meta Incognita prospecting in August 1577 with Humfrey's letter written to Mr. Wendesley on 13 August 1577 alleging unauthorised use of their patented technique, followed by another solicitor's letter written on 14 August to Lord Burghley about the same matter.[186] This was a dispute which rumbled on to 1582, with more complaints from Wendesley to Burghley about the patentee's injunction.[187]

Schutz was not a significant owner of London property like Lok, but travelled widely and lived modestly in rented property in Aldersgate Ward between commissions. Consequently he was quite difficult to litigate against especially as he lived on rather uncertain metallurgical incomes. To have brought him to account for a fraud, the prosecution would have to rely on both financial and assaying records. But was the Cathay Company's record of the practitioners work a full and objective enough source?

The answer is that in 1579 the appropriate records were not fully available except to the Privy Council. Furthermore, considerable parts of the record were in the sovereign's privileged correspondence in the form of State Papers and so not available to a Court except with the Privy Council's approval. As C47/34/6 shows, Borough had available for use only a limited part of the official documentation of the metallurgist's performance to use in evidence against Lok. Borough's hand can be seen behind the choice of data now to be found in the Chancery records associated with the prosecution of Michael Lok nominally over the *Judith*. The evidence was the "Declaration of the accompte of Thomas Allen," [188] recording the gold and silver extracted from the four hundredweight of ores, "Brought from Meta Incognita in the second voiage by the workemanship of Jonas Shuts in a furnace buylded at the Tower hill....the same being the furst great proofe and triall made by the said Jonas Shuts of the valewe of the said ewre of Meta Incognita."

This furnace used for that assay was one built in William Wynter's London home on Tower Hill, a site that was convenient for his work at the Tower of London as Master of Ordnance and subsequently illustrated by a contemporary observer.[189] In those accounts by far the greatest outlays were those for work by "Henricke Williams brickelear, & £7 9s.6d. and Robert Den[h]am goldsmithe for the stuffe and workmanshippe for the building of two furnaces to saye one melting furnace, and one refining furnace at the storehouse at Towere Hill," a total cost of £11.0s.6d.[190] This first furnace in Sir William Wynter's premises was of modest size and was to be used four times, and was thrice relined. Schutz's assistants were Humfrey Cole, the instrument maker, Robert Denham, the erstwhile goldfyner, and John Borde of the Royal Armouries. Its formal supervision by the Commissioners thus mimicked the ceremonial "testing of the pyx.," and should have been beyond dispute. Its costs were obviously much larger than the £2.5s Lok paid to William Humfrey to build a small proofing furnace at Frobisher's London house. Agnello was paid just £4 for his first, later notorious, assay, while "Richard Goodyeare, alcamist" had received £2. 3s. 4d for undertaking a small proof to Sir Lionel Duckett's orders.[191]

By contrast, the bills to survey, design, build, and operate the Dartford furnace were much larger, as were the bills for additaments, and payments to the Company's workmen. Thus within the Dartford buildings whose costs of conversion and rebuilding alone amounted to over £400, Lok paid "Thomas Hichcockes, carpenter, ...for two great houses for the mills for the works at Dartford, £145"; "Thomas Kennion for felling, squaring and carriage of 130 trees, £39. 5s."; and "Sebastian Copland german for making ten pair of bellows of 12 foates long for the furnaces at Dartford £17."[192] In fact the assembly costs associated with the bellows were much bigger than this suggests for each supplier of parts and time is also identified. Each time Jonas Schutz used the plant he had designed, he must have thought about the effectiveness of that array of bellows, for he was the assayer in chief, relying on their performance, as Commissioners appointed by the Privy Council watched everything.[193]

The best insight into how their supervision worked comes through Lansdowne 100/1 wherein Lok used data which he had copied and discussed privately with Schutz. That text was probably retained by Lok to serve a polemical rather than an evidential purpose. By contrast, Schutz ensured most of his papers were made available to the Privy Council, whence they became State Papers. A few others can be found in the Exchequer records because they were thought worthy of further examination by the Auditors and the Treasurers who succeeded Lok. By contrast, those records in the State Papers sequence applying to the same sequence of assays were placed there on the Privy Council's instructions, from motives concerned with the protection of the Queen's and Privy Councillors' interests. Thus they were unlikely ever to be presented to the Court of Exchequer as the Queen's evidence. This ensured that the major assay findings were not of commercially significant quantities, and they gave rise to little readily accessible documentation. Schutz duly provided a summary of his proofs for the Auditors, but otherwise only some very small ingots that were to be used in legal evidence as Thomas Alleyn's legal submission shows. What Schutz had assayed in February 1579 was the ore from the *Judith's* hold, plus 13 cwt of Caldbeck galena. That choice of ores and furnace was cleverly devised to divert Borough's litigation, for he would not want to prove that his ship had refused a lading of potentially more valuable red ore.

So despite Schutz's collaboration with Lok, we see the practical reasons why Borough's case had to be made against Lok alone, and could use only the earliest of the metallurgical opinions and assays as incidental evidence. Borough's own account as Treasurer shows he ran down its cash to just £16. 10s. 4d, having met many of the outstanding liabilities of Schutz and Denham which in consequence he understood, having required that Schutz and Denham each hand over the proceeds of smelting 17 tons of ore at Dartford. This included fine silver, gold, lead and seven hundredweight of copper to Richard Young for which he was to give separate account. Borough's account does not break down the income received from all this very far, but he does suggest that much of the £30. 12s. 8d which he realised came from lead rather than from the parting of gold and silver pieces. He received a further £20 from Lok for the *Judith's* tackle, sails, and munitions worth £40. However, he still had to pay Denham and Schutz for their labour at Dartford, a debt for which he used up most of the £240 in cessments which he had managed to raise.[194]

We might conclude it was Schutz's position as Borough's creditor which he was able to exploit initially to avoid litigation. Thereafter it was the decisions taken about the Commissioners' formal involvement which made the later assays and resultant finds of useful metals so difficult to challenge. In consequence it was only the records of Schutz's earliest bulk assays on 1 November 1577 and on 6 December 1577 that were presented in evidence by Thomas Alleyn.[195] Significantly it is only in the summaries provided in State Papers by the Commissioners that it is recorded that two of the three earliest assays were on the rarer red ores.[196] Such an outcome suited a decision of Borough in pursuing a suit to be determined between 1579 and 1581. He did not want a Court to consider whether Schutz had completed his last assay by April 1579 in Wynter's London garden at Tower Hill, or the implications of Schutz's having used the second voyage's red ores for it. The red ores could thus remain a formal reason why Lok still had not given up hope that the ores and assets of the venture still had considerable worth, and a reason why Lok should be made to pay Borough in due order.

But such evidence was insufficient to prosecute an assayer, neither does it advance very far any understanding of the thoughts circulating among the leading assayers. However, Lok writing in Lansdowne 100/1 fol. 12v and 13r and v does gives details which showed that Jonas [Schutz] was keen to take over much of the risk of smelting those seemingly unproductive ores. Schutz's offer was but part of a much cleverer strategic position taken up by Schutz. Lok records that as early as 18 November 1578 Jonas Schutz had made a formal offer before some of the Commissioners, namely Mr Field, Mr Lock and Andrew Palmer, to recover gold and silver to the value of £23. 15s. from a ton form the Meta Incognita ores. For the Meta Incognita ores he would pay £8 a ton, and to smelt it with equal quantities of copper ores from Keswick costing £1, pure lead costing 10 shillings, and lead ores costing 24s., plus wood coal for roasting, bringing with his fees and extraordinary charges, his offer on costs to a value of £13. 15s. a ton.[197] The key to his plan lay would lie in the fact he said nothing of his sourcing of lead ore because he could probably envisage using prolific silver/lead ores alongside the Lake District's copper ores, knowing that the latter also contained both gold and silver. He simply concluded "Hereof Jonas will deliver gold and silver to the value of xxiij li xvs" [£23. 15 s].

On 24 March 1579 after a sequence of disappointments with the Dartford smelter, and again significantly near a financial year end, Schutz began his last firing in Wynter's furnace at Tower Hill finding some silver and asserting that slightly more than half as much again remained in the slag. After, Schutz agreed with John Baptista Agnello, Robert Den[h]am, William Humfrey and Humfrey Cole to buy all but 150 tons already selected by Lok, valuing the ore no longer at £8 to the ton but at 20 marks a ton [£6 . 16s]. — not £10 a ton as suggested by Hogarth et al. in 1994. This offer was much more cunning in its details than its predecessor. It worked both as part of an increasingly complex attempt to deter litigants, and as an attempt to regain access to the Dartford [Bignors] smelter which had seemingly failed. On his last assay at Dartford, finished on 17 February 1579, Schutz had reckoned arbitrarily that it showed the precious metal content could be worth as much as £10 to the ton. By April 1579 those metallurgists were clearly intent on circumventing William Borough's litigation, for their offers based on a lower, and possibly negligible value for the Meta Incognita ore went straight to Lord Burghley on 18 April 1579. Burghley relayed them to the Privy Council table where so many of the leading investors sat. Thereupon the Council took the advice of Frobisher, presumably as the representative of the Commissioners appointed by the Privy Council. Massively in error, Frobisher believed that the Meta Incognita ore was still to be worth as much as £40 a ton, for he still wanted to envisage a big profit and reputation to match.

So the Privy Council had refused Schutz's initial offer, as well as a revised version that implicitly accepted Lok's interest in the remainder of the ores. That refusal and the reasons for it formed some encouragement to Borough in looking for material of possible financial value or which might implicate Lok, who as late as 1578 was anxious to indict Frobisher, Schutz, Denham Agnello and Kranich in formulating his defence. But

Figure 14: Coombe Martin, 1998. A view showing the dangerous harbourside rocks and the seaside cliffs where earlier silver and silver lead mines had operated since the Middle Ages, and thus the shore from which outward shipments of ore were made. Photo by Robert Baldwin.

Figure 15: Traditional mining tools from the Coombe Martin mines as displayed at the Coombe Martin Museum in 1998. Photo by Robert Baldwin.

Borough as Treasurer to the Company could only note the declining valuation Schutz's offer put on the extracted ore from £24 to ore worth just £6 16 s per ton.

It is likely that Schutz or one of his close German associates had collaborated to formulate that offer, just as Hans Sta[d]dler, his assistant at Dartford, had helped to frame the 1579 scheme. They had earlier worked together at Keswick, Staddler being promoted from a sorter to a smelter in 1573 before accompanying Schutz from London to Keswick in 1576. Staddler was a regular traveller to London throughout the 1570s, and often went on the Continent, as he did in July 1578 to recruit four more Dutchmen to work for Schutz at Dartford.[198] Schutz, Staddler and their erstwhile boss, Daniel Hechstetter, had an entree to a wide range of English and Continental financial advisors, notably Haug and Co. of Augsburg, but as that German finance house was embarrassed for funds by 1579 they might more readily have persuaded Burghley that Crown finance, or a lease on Crown assets, would ensure the opening of a new, very profitable adit at Coombe Martin in Devon by 1587.

There was good reason for the Crown to agree in mid-1579 because the most prominent of the consequential losers from the Meta Incognita venture was the Crown. In rejecting Schutz's offer, formally made in association with Denham and some unknown but virtually identifiable German workmen, the Privy Council ensured that the losers included the Queen herself, who had invested and lost £1,350. She was forced at the time to dishonour her promise of a loan to the Dutch rebels against Philip II, an event with considerable long-term damage to English credit in Antwerp's money market. The Queen had in earlier years turned to Sir Thomas Gresham for help in such matters, but during 1579 he died, having taken Cathay Adventurers shares to the value of at least £470. That liability, plus the extra assessments he had to pay, amounted to £800. This was duly recognised in the Cathay Company's finalised accounts of 1581.[199] But Gresham's large incomes arising from clever currency speculation and the wool trade's needs meant his large trading debts extended far beyond the Cathay venture and caused the House of Commons to take a close interest in the matter of his estate. That led to Parliament passing a special statute, which began as "A Bill for the relief of Sir Thomas Gresham's creditors" that secured its first and second readings on 15 and 20 February 1580. It passed quickly through Committee stage between 28 February and 4 March 1580.

It further constrained the Queen's finances, although it ensured that Gresham's widow and his estate itself (and so the finance for Sir Thomas' plan to teach a new quadrivium of trading, mathematical and scientific subjects) were not exposed to further litigation for unpaid debts before she died in 1596. But its effect was to interfere with the terms of Sir Thomas' will that determined how his widow's inheritance would be regulated. Its legislative purpose was to ensure that all his exposed trading positions, especially those involving City and Royal interests, were fully unwound so as to satisfy all claimants on his large estate. This in its own turn served to put the Privy Council into the embarrassing position of potentially facing similar actions over their exposure to Cathay Company debts.

Another to lose through the venture was the Queen's favourite Sir Edward Dyer, to whom she would then unaccountably grant the much bigger sum of £5,000 on loan. In 1579, a year or so before Drake's huge booty from his circumnavigation transformed her accounts late in 1580, the Queen had had prepared a statement of her loan exposure. It showed she had lent £32,000 within her realm, and within that £21,000 to Robert Dudley, Earl of Leicester for operations in Holland, and £1,900 to the Company of Mines Royal, which they were anxious to pay off.[200]

Yet by 1583 fourteen bulk assays of the Meta Incognita ores had convinced most investors that there was no significant gold or silver extractable from them.[201] By 1583 virtually all the justification for the venture was unravelled by discord, huge financial losses and disillusion over the metallurgists' skills, although Dee was busy planning a further return between 23 January to 6 March 1583. These led to a formal proposal submitted as "A brief collection of the substance of the grant desired by the discoverers of the North West partes."[202]

Under this a fifth part of all discoveries of gold, silver and pearls would be due to the Queen, but power to make laws there would be surrendered to the "Fellowship of New Navigations Atlantical and Septentrional" in which Adrian Gilbert, John Dee and John Davis were to be exempted for ever from payment of customs "having been the chiefest travellers to find out this northerly voyage, and being of that company." Dee's advocacy of the spatial realities conveyed by the circumpolar chart not only seemed to qualify him as one of the chief armchair travellers, it also led a desperate Michael Lok to produce a similar one in 1582 engraved on copper for Richard Hakluyt showing the form and location of Frobisher's discoveries.[203] It is significant that, as armchair geographers and metallurgists, both Lok and Dee produced their charts amidst work on vastly detailed assemblages of supporting data and metallurgical advice exactly as if they had something to prove. They had. Both mens' reputations had been badly damaged by the catastrophic failure of the Cathay Company's speculative attempt to colonise and extract the ores of Kodlunarn Island and other sites in Meta Incognita in 1578.[204]

In many ways Dee was correct in his assessments of his economic prospects when he took flight for Rudolph's Court in 1583. English investors were not in a position to make an immediate success from exploration and metallurgical discoveries in America. Deacon's hypothesis misinterprets this context as pressure exercised by Walsingham in a determined attempt to recruit Dee as another secret agent or technological spy.[205] In fact it was nearly four months after Dee left that the next step was taken to organise further English colonial enterprise. On 6 February 1584, Adrian Gilbert, John Davis and Sir Walter Raleigh (a name entered in Dee's stead) gained the letters patent they had sought with Dee in 1583. But in 1584 they only just managed to fund another exploratory voyage to North America's shores, with Simão Fernades acting as pilot. Further settlement was not attempted until May 1585. Under Governor Lane, the first Virginian settlement contained a comparable mathematical intellect in Thomas Harriot, and in Joachim Gans, a brilliant metallurgist who would successfully operate a furnace at Roanoke.[206] Dee did not return to England until after Thomas Harriot's *Briefe and True*

Report of the Newfoundland of Virginia had been published in 1588, with just a few hints about the presence of copper resources inland. John White's belated attempt at re-supply in 1590 marked the failed end of that venture, and it was becoming clear that Dee had little new to offer. The embarrassed circumstances of Dee's return in 1589 serve only to suggest that in 1583 he had faced a personal and financial crisis in choosing whether to exploit his knowledge of navigation or metallurgy. Dee was evidently fearful of the consequences of the resentment in court circles about the failure of the Commissioners like himself appointed to oversee its smelting operations. But Dee did make a lucrative investment in a lease on Coombe Martin's mines in the 1580s.[207]

Despite Dee's tuition, and even William Borough's help with ruling up blank charts for them to add their landfalls, we can now see with the invaluable benefit of hindsight that Frobisher's crews deceived themselves in 1576 when they took as evidence that they had nearly reached Asia by describing the one native they brought back as a "strange man of Cataye." Nonetheless, his kayak and his hunting skill made a brief popular impression in Bristol, while the black rock was subject to preliminary but unfavourable assays by Williams, Wheler and Needham. Doubts must have assailed others even as fresh ethnographic records were being compiled by Cornelius Ketel and John White. Settle described their place of origin as one where:

> *There is no manner of creeping beast hurtful, except some spiders (which as many affirme, are signes of great store of Gold) and also certaine stinging Gnattes; which bite so fiercely, that the place where they bite, shortly afterward swelleth, and icheth very sore. They make signes of certaine people, that wear bright plates of Gold in their foreheads, and other places of their bodies. ... There is much to be said of the commodities of these countries, which are couched within the bowels of the earth, which I let pass till more perfect triall be made thereof. The Countries, on both sides of the streightes, lye very highe with roughe stonie mountaynes, and great quantitie of snowe thereon. There is very little plaine ground, and no grasse but a litl [lichen], which is much like unto mosse that groweth on soft ground such as we get turfes in. There is no wood at all. To be briefe, there is nothing fitte, or profitable for the use of man, which that country with roote yeildeth or bringeth forth.*[208]

Through Dee's tuition in 1576 Nicholo and Antonio Zeno's accounts of north Atlantic exploration by a Venetian family up to 1390 had became known to Hall, Frobisher, Jackman and later John Davis. Indeed, Frobisher is known to have taken a copy of the Italian interpretation of Zeno's findings to the Arctic, because in his account of Frobisher's brief landing in Frisland [Greenland] George Best remarked on his General, confirmining that "Nicholaus and Antonius Genoa" were "The first knowen Christians that discovered this land."[209] But Dee's teaching and interest in gold found from the River Ob,[210] from the African shore near Sofala, and from the mountains of the Philippines must have been redolent of themes from Frobisher's childhood. From an early age Frobisher had been placed under the tutelage of his widowed mother's brother, Sir John York, Master of the Mint in London. Sir John was evidently aware of

Portuguese practice in respect of their gold supply, and even helped finance Wyndham's expedition to the river of Mina in Guinea in 1553, sending along his young, spirited nephew, Martin Frobisher to learn from the wise, experienced Portuguese pilot, Pinteado. Eden recorded that Pinteado was thrust among the boys of the ship to die, having taken them to trade for gold on the river of Mina and then to the unhealthy shore of Benin. Forming thereby a respect for the professional skills taught in Lisbon, Frobisher must have gleaned many of the ideas he advanced after 1569 from other exiled Portuguese pilots, including Pedro Bayou, Diogo Homem and Simao Fernandes.

All would have known the type of technical gossip typical of the Armazéns da Guiné, Mina e India where they had been trained. Sir John York and John Dee long remained interested in much the same matters. Dee maintained a significant correspondence with Pedro Nunez, the most senior navigational and mathematical tutor in Lisbon. Those Jewish religious exiles from Portugal, often called "marranos," were also all distinctly irascible and impatient men making them unfortunate role models for Frobisher, who himself lacked patience for technical advance and yet was all too capable of sustained anger and frustration. In fact, as Hall's narrative shows, Fenton, Frobisher, Hall and others had some very angry exchanges over their location as they neared Baffin Island in 1578. There is good evidence that they all knew and respected John Dee and, as if to confirm the circle involved, one of Fernandes's North Atlantic charts that survives today bears an inscription showing that it was copied in Dee's home in Mortlake in 1580.[211] After the last of Frobisher's voyages Hall's manuscript account also came into Dee's library, specifically against the instructions of the Cathay Company but not so obviously in conflict with the Privy Council's instructions that they be handed over in their entirety to their Commissioners. This indicates the peculiarly trusting relationship between Dee and Hall before the latter became an alcoholic, and a very depressed secretive one, on Fenton's unsuccessful South Atlantic voyage.

It was with the Rev. Richard Madox, on Fenton's Atlantic voyage in 1582-83, that Hall shared many of his most revealing insights on this circle and an absent Frobisher, exposing their characters and some innovative new ideas, for he still needed the type of searching quasi-scientific relationship he had enjoyed with his old tutor. George Best would reveal that Dee had already put the pilots of Frobisher's Arctic voyages onto Portuguese ideas about measuring terrestrial deposits of iron by means of a variation compass. Dee's reasons for making that suggestion have their roots both in observations made with compasses in his library and in the hope of navigational gain. The grant of arms to the copper producing Company of Mines Royal made on 26 August 1568 also illustrate this duality of concern, for at its crest is a demi-miner with a boxed, gimballed compass.[212]

Hall realised the value of his tutor's ideas in both contexts. He followed his tutor's instruction carefully, perhaps using Dee's variation compass or one identical to it in 1578, and presented the results on the Hatfield House chart prepared by William Borough for Frobisher, but actually updated with Hall's observations.[213] While that chart came into Lord Burghley's hands, Hall was free to share more thoughts on the measurement of variation, showing he understood more than most pilots and mining prospectors about what the compass could reveal to its users.[214] Yet it was clear by 1582 that Hall, for all his scientific bent of mind, had taken the disappointments of 1578 badly, turning to drink and becoming the sad alcoholic Madox tried hard to protect from Fenton's vengeance, hiding his identity behind the pseudonym of Palinurus. Meanwhile Dee chose the lesser of two speculative risks by concentrating on his metallurgical and alchemical opportunities, rather than the seaborne risks associated with more sub-Arctic exploration — risks which were more appropriate to younger, but seasoned mariners.

Modern science confirms the relative correctness of some of those Elizabethan assays. Hogarth suggests that those largely negative results were contaminated by precious metals in the additives brought from Cumbria and Cornwall.[215] Whereas today such practices would lead to a condemnation for attempted fraud, there was no basis in chemical understanding which existed to challenge the assertions of the metallurgists that their methods and knowledge of additives were the only way to release precious metals from the ores loaded into furnaces. Indeed, as if to illustrate, by contrast, the primacy of the successful Elizabethan practitioner in choosing the furnace charges, no matter how ill-informed they were, Schutz, Denham and Kranich are surrounded by different black and brown ores in the only surviving illustration of their work on Frobisher's ores. They put reputations at stake largely in the belief that the furnace was a tool inherently capable of separating such precious metal as there was in any rocks. Choice of the right feedstocks was in their eyes the key to success. Two images of three furnaces, one taken by u/v light, illustrate that contemporary ideas in turn concentrated on the control of furnace feedstocks and smelting.[216] But it was exactly this control of fired charges which Schutz's older rival, Burchard Kranich (who died late in 1578), had so obviously lacked. Thus Kranich's practice so appalled Denham as he tried to avoid smelting significant quantities.[217]

If Kranich's practice smacked of large-scale alchemy, William Humfrey's younger associate at the Mint, Humfrey Cole, who procured Northumbrian coal for the Dartford smelter, is known to have been a member of the old fashioned alchemical "Society for the New Art" from 1571.[218] Reasonably successful as an instrument maker, and as a user of copper plates on which to engrave maps,[219] he too tried unsuccessfully to master several other metallurgical skills. Early in the 1580s he tried unavailingly to persuade Burghley of his prospecting skill too, using ore samples from North Yorkshire. Unlike Dee and Dyer, Cole did not flee to Bohemia but chose to reposition his business in 1582 as a maker of brass land survey instruments.[220] He had by 1578 also lost his main income and career at the Mint as a die sinker, which he owed to Burghley's earlier intervention in 1563 to secure his succession to John Lawrence. For all his engraving talent and his supposed skill as a metallurgist his reputation sank along with the old style alchemists like John Dee and Sir Edward Dyer, as reputations fell in official circles after witnessing and implicitly approving the Schutz's failures of 1578-9.

Those with Establishable Motives for Commercial Espionage

The speculative investment made by some with relatively little means proved both costly and illusory. Persistent rumours that some of the associates in the enterprise eventually looked for income from espionage against their homeland are well enough explained by the failure of Frobisher's enterprise. But the case against any individual has never been proved. The most conclusive evidence seems to be that laid against William Bodenham, who took sea charts to Seville in November 1578.[221] He was not amongst Frobisher's crews. He was active in resuscitating the fortunes of the Spanish Company, which until the mid 1580s briefly flourished in promoting trade with Corunna and Seville.[222] As Dr. Pauline Croft has shown, this was done with the full encouragement of the Privy Council, with Bodenham virtually expected to play the role of a double agent for the sake of the trade. But there are others implicated who had far more pressing financial reasons to engage in espionage. Frobisher and others like Sir William Morgan, Sir Edward Dyer and Edward Stafford were amongst those whom the Spanish targeted from 1575, as first de Guarras and then Bernardino de Mendoza would pay for such information from their official resources as successive Spanish Ambassadors to the Court of St James.

Sir Edward Dyer, who had known John Dee since 1566 and became godfather to his son, Arthur Dee, in 1579, coveted a personal reputation as an alchemist, although his brother Andrew was seen as more competent in that respect. One of the Dyers, probably Edward, had conducted one of the small-scale early assays for Lok in 1577. This family's penury made them targets for Spanish interest after Edward witnessed the initial London assays and most of the rest of the Dartford assays as a Commissioner. He would also have had opportunity to confer with John about such matters. Indeed, Edward Dyer is thought to have been the author of an alchemical text, *The epitome of the Treasure of all Welth*.[223] In 1583 Edward Dyer felt able to visit Dee's library with Sir Francis Walsingham and Adrian Gilbert to discuss Meta Incognita, its ores, and possible further action. Concurrently, Andrew Dyer chose a seagoing career, and even recruited mercenaries, until his death in Tunis in 1584.[224] His brother, Edward, seeking a career at Court and living close to Walsingham in London, accumulated vast debts despite holding minor offices and enjoying special Royal grants of the income from concealed lands.[225] Edward Dyer kept closely in touch with Dee and Kelley during their exile in Prague. He was eventually sent there in 1589 to secure the release of Kelley and to bring him and his tinctures home to help Elizabeth I with the expensive metals and other costs associated with opposing the Spanish forces, and with gunfounding. Edward Dyer's continued closeness to Dee elicited a letter from him dated 7 September 1597 entitled "Thalattokratia Brettaniki" which was a coherent piece of legal thinking on "The sea jurisdiction of a British Empire" which harked back to Dee's *General and Rare Memorials* and a Royal claim over Meta Incognita which was only adopted after it had been actively pressed by Dee between 1576 and 1578.[226]

Rumbling criticism of Sir Edward Dyer's practices continued until 1604 when he was once more the specific subject of vehement criticism for making diplomatic contributions of dubious value, and accused of being "an informer."[227] This stemmed from suspicion that he had a part in espionage over the Frobisher voyages but also from his dubious legal work done in conjunction with the almost equally impecunious Sir Edward Stafford and Edward Tipper over land holdings and titles. It was certainly true that he could ill afford the gamble of his lost investments in Frobisher's voyages, and his close association with the failure of the bulk assays. He had subscribed for £50 in the second voyage which after cesssment became a demand for £80. By 3 May 1578 he still owed £67 of that debt, with £28. 15s resulting from unpaid freight and a very reluctant £15 subscription to the third voyage.[228] As tougher moves were made to collect the subscriptions in 1579 by William Borough, the Queen lent him £5,000 from the Exchequer which he never managed to repay. Was it payment for acting as a double agent in 1578-79? Yet late in 1578 he may well have found Spanish money tempting. Who else might have been subject to such financial temptation?

The pretentious gentleman assayers on Frobisher's third voyage, Andrew Dyer and the mysterious Edmund Stafford, chose to draw a certain income of just £25 each by sailing on the voyage.[229] By 1584 William Humfrey junior, Bona's assistant, would inherit a much bigger annual income from the metallurgical patents and shares that had once been shared between his father and Christopher Schutz. William Humfrey senior, as one the Commissioners appointed by the Privy Council in 1577 to oversee the processing of Arctic ores, had gone so far as to secure a second patent for rights to search for calamine ore and to mix it with other minerals. It was granted on 2 July 1584 just before he died, providing his wife with a major source of income about which Burghley was curious. Thereafter Schutz must have enjoyed an even more secure existence.[230]

Denham has been suspected by Allaire and Hogarth of engaging in espionage for Spain.[231] His circumstances, however, are less open to suspicion than those of Frobisher himself. Frobisher had negotiated for pay and a pardon from Spain in September 1575, saw the navigational charts for Meta Incognita and the mining and lading of ores there, and witnessed both the assays and the collection of ores recorded in documents reaching Madrid in 1579.[232] There is the possibility that William Bodenham who is known to have taken documents to Madrid might have been confused with a Bob Denham; but the documents always say Robert Denham. George Best probably hid Edmund Stafford's identity in a similar way. Best's integrity is impugned by his publishing of data and maps about the voyages in defiance of Privy Council instructions in collusion with his publisher, Henry Bynnyman. That Best's text was ready so quickly suggests his reliance on a London scrivener, Henry Best.[233]

Commercial espionage occurred in spite of precautions taken to prevent it. On 2 November 1578 at the instance of the Privy Council a long letter was sent to

> *the Commissioners imployed about the voiage to Meta Incognita, now returned*
> *with all safety with Mr Furbisher, forasmuch that their Lordships are informed*
> *that in their last voiage divers newe places and mynes have been discovered,*
> *their Lordships do require them to have a care, and to call before them the*
> *Generall, the Captayns, masters and pilots of the ships, and to demand their*

accounts in writing severally of their proceedings in the voiage, with discourse of things happening in the same, and take of them such plattes of description of the places as they had made, and to forbid them and others to publish any description of those countreys.

Furthermore, they were required "Thoroughly to consider the state of the works at Dartford that with all expedition some tryall may be had of true value of the oare brought here in this voiage as in the others before ... knowing Mr Furbisher has brought home double the quantitie of oare that was expected." [234]

This shows that Best was even further on the wrong side of his instructions than his book published by Henry Bynnyman late that year suggests. Bynnyman was no stranger to controversy through his work with Dee, and would be brought before Parliament for contempt in 1580. A printer's letter, a preface to Christopher Hatton and a further internal reference to the constraint on chart publication, are used to try to exculpate himself for including so much as two crude maps and his account of the events on Frobisher's voyages.

Mendoza knew that his spy was in England in mid November 1578, and that he had a chart and account of the voyage despite formal efforts to deny the Ambassador any such chart. This man could not be Bodenham who was already sailing to Seville with maps that were probably proofs of the ones Best would soon publish. We have to ask who in the circle had direct knowledge of the enciphered descriptive and cartographic data on Meta Incognita and its mines which were sent on 15 November 1578. Mendoza's further letter on the subject, sent on 7 February 1579, says:

As I have no safe opportunity until now I have not previously sent the chart about which I wrote on 15 November, when speaking of Frobisher's voyage. I now forward them with specimens of all the kinds of ore brought. They are of but little value as the Englishmen and assayers confess, and no matter what heat is employed they cannot smelt them satisfactorily, owing to their great crudity which is a certain sign that they are not rich. To remedy this it occurred to the Germans who were managing it that it would be advantageous to mix the ore with powdered pyrites, of which they ordered a cargo from Plymouth. This proves conclusively that the assays last year were exaggerated to increase the fame of the business. It is not thought of much now for the sailors have not been paid and the merchants who took shares in it have failed, so that people are undeceived. [235]

The next letter written the same day, but this time to Philip II's Private Secretary, Gabriel de Zayas, explains the enclosure as a present from Mendoza to Zayas of a novel design of drinking vessel made by a German silversmith, who had not taken Mass for fifteen years or so. It took the nominal form of an owl.[236] That is to say its smooth cup-like interior was covered by an embossed sheet detailing features of an owl, perhaps with a closing top in the shape of an owl's head. Daniel Hechstetter had been working on marketing

Cumbrian copper made up into household items, employing German coppersmiths to widen his market between 1574 and 1579. Such an item, or even the finishing touches to more novel forms, could easily be overlaid with silver by a London silversmith. As a goldsmith, Robert Denham might have had the skills to make the owl, but he never seems to have practised in delicate artistic contexts, but rather as a workman before a large furnace. But Mendoza was neither well nor promptly paid himself, so he could not readily afford to simply give solid gold or silver presents to colleagues. In fact he was widely thought to be rather mean personally. So the owl cup probably constituted his "safe opportunity" to dispatch the chart and ore samples to Philip II. The surmise is made all the more likely by other correspondence. On 1 April Philip II, not Zayas, replied that: "The marine chart was *recovered* and was so good your diligence in obtaining it is approved of. With it came pieces of ore of which an assay has been made, and they have been found of little value."[237]

Writing later about Mendoza's courier, John Ley could give only approximate information on the timing of Henry Carew's progress to Spain.[238] But there must be other possibilities for the identity of the carrier of the long and slow journey made by the owl cup. The gentleman assayer Edmund Stafford must remain another. He had disguised his real identity behind an eminent family name, a ruse which could hardly have passed muster with Burghley, Walsingham, or Wynter who had all suffered at the hands of the Staffords over the Thornebury Gilowen estate when Sir Edward Dyer co-operated with Edward Stafford in exposing poor conveyancing and concealed lands. As a Remembrancer of the Pipe Office, Edward Stafford claimed to have improved administration of the Pipe Office of the Exchequer but actually he only shared the cost of a deputy, Tipping, with Sir Edward Dyer, so as not to expose their mutual penury.[239] But Edmund Stafford's real identity and ancestry were probably known to George Best, for Best's aunt, Anne Best of London, had earlier married Thomas Stafford of Bradfield in Berkshire. The main Best estates were at Wath, near Doncaster, and so close to Frobisher's.[240] This explains why George Best feels able to bracket himself socially with Stafford in the *Ayde's* hierarchy,[241] and perhaps explains the interpolation that Mendoza added to his enciphered espionage sent to Madrid on 15 November 1578, saying: "This makes me wonder why someone who took part in this venture, a gentleman and a scholar, should sell that which they returned with and then suggest that they could extract gold profitably."[242]

Conclusions

Despite the background of legal and socio-political intrigue, it is tempting to see Denham, Schutz and Best,[243] each coming from a different background, as pioneering professional advocates of a coherent English industrial and colonial order extending across the oceans which was first tested out on Frobisher's voyages. That new order and synergism appealed equally to Burghley, Dee, Eden and Wynter. It envisaged both newly developed mines near the seashore and smelters accessible without long transits from the sea, as at Dartford. It also provided the long-term strategic thinking to justify a trading purpose in exploring the Northwest Passage. Contact with Agnello led Lok to see the potential of this conjuncture in February 1577.[244] The core of the idea was certainly acted upon in the next decade as developments at Neath in Glamorgan[245] and at Amlwch in Anglesea illustrate.[246] Concurrently, William Wynter, having discussed suitable locations with Lok, Schutz and Denham, chose the site for the new furnace at Dartford because of its riverine access in December 1577.[247] He also developed his Lydney mines and smelters in coastal locations, shipping pig iron and unprocessed ores up and down the River Severn, some for further processing in the Midlands, some for naval ordnance cast in London. Wynter also bought the ferry and the stages used in shipping Mendip ores to Tintern via Lydney.[248]

Taking a wider European perspective, competence in the design of water powered blast furnaces and assaying advanced with the migration of German practitioners.[249] Smith and Forbes in their sweeping study of early modern metallurgy and assaying have shown that it was those practitioners employed by speculating landowners, not scientifically trained men, who were often in the van of the important technical advances.[250] Whether their movements were induced by religious fears, opportunism, commerce, diplomacy or espionage, their migration entailed strategic risks and competition based on the internationally transferable and real skills of the metallurgist and the prospector. It is important to see this as the speculative industrial and socio-political context in which Frobisher's metallurgists acquired their industrial reputations — reputations which shaped the form of speculation in the Cathay Company up to 1578 but which are as important as archaeological science to understanding what Frobisher's metallurgists thought, what was expected of them, and where they failed. Some influential figures were concurrently engaged in futile alchemical experiment, such as that which Dee undertook in Mortlake on marcasite — an inquiry provoked by the inherent conflict between Biringuccio's advice about that rock and Schutz's several unexpected failures at Dartford. More important were the speculative investors who sustained them afterwards for the basic economic geography, metallurgical synergism and maritime confidence which emerged at the time of Frobisher's voyages proved of surprisingly sound and of long term strategic value.

Notes

[1] W.R Scott, *The Constituton and Finance of English , Scottish and Irish Joint Stock Companies to 1720,* Cambridge University Press, 1911, and Thoemmes Press, 1993, vol. 1, pp.39-44.

[2] PRO S.P.12/ 119/46.

[3] PRO S.P.12/144/17. Parts 1 and 2 details Drake's profits and the treasure to be removed to the Tower of London, estimated at over £250,000. It notes that over £10,000 was retained by Drake. See Scott, *op. cit.,* pp.53-85. R Hakluyt, *Principall Navigations,* G. Bishop, R, Newberie, C. Barker, London, 1589, includes "The famous voyage of Sir Francis Drake into the South Sea, and there hence about the whole Globe of the Earth, Begun in the yeere of our Lord, 1577," before p.644 but it is not paginated for it was printed and added after the rest of the book.

[4] AGS. Ingalterra, leg. 818/ 72. Sebastian Cabot to Charles V, a transcript clearly mis-dated 15 November 1554. Presumably the original dated from 1553 or earlier. As taken forward later to Philip II it also contained a map now lost. It may well have formed part of Cabot's reply to a letter written by Emperor

Charles V to the young Queen Mary on 9 September 1553, following the failure of the Duke of Northumberland's plot to put Lady Jane Grey on the throne. The Duke was executed for it in August 1553.

[5]B.L. Cotton Vespasian CVIII, fol. 12.

[6]By the summer of 1574 Grenville had bought the *Castle of Comfort,* as a Spanish agent reported in May 1574. Court of Admiralty proceedings in HCA/9 show that in 1574 she was later involved in the questionable seizure of the *Saveur* off St Malo. Thereupon in an apparently unresolved case Grenville and Hawkins claimed to have sold her to a French Protestant, having fully victualled and crewed her for a long voyage. See R. Pearse Chope, "New Light on Sir Richard Grenville," *Devonshire Association Transactions, 49,* 1917, pp. 210-246 and 247-282.

[7]PRO S.P.12/ 95 nos. 63 and 64, and further copy S.P.12/229 fols. 1-5 and a draft patent at S.P. 12/235/1. The former was a petition and letter to the Queen for "A discovery of lands beyond the Equinoctial ... and to establish the authors and fellowship of this voyage in the nature of a corporation." Lok probably took it as a model, but Lord Burghley who saw the plan and the accompanying letter, and no doubt tested them against his maps, was not so impressed before endorsing it with the date 1573. More is to be found in B.L. Lansdowne 100 /4 fols. 142-146, A. Grant, *Grenville,* North Devon Museum Trust, Appledore, 1991, pp. 14-18. A derivative of the scheme but expressed in considerable detail was later penned by Richard Hakluyt as "A discourse of the Commodity of taking the Straight of Magellanus." It was probably prepared for Sir Francis Walsingham in 1580. See S.P. 12/229/ 97.

[8] V. Stefansson and E. McCaskill (eds) *The Three Voyages of Martin Frobisher,* vol. 1, Argonaut Press, London, 1938, p. xcvii.

[9]PRO . S.P. 12/27/63. Dee to Sir William Cecil from Antwerp, 16 Feb 1563. From this letter it is clear that both Burghley and Dee were concerned to evolve better ciphers based on Trithemius's *Steganographia* and Dee's *Monas Hierogluphica,* and to use alchemical, astronomical and metallurgical annotations knowingly thereafter in their correspondence.

[10]Stefansson, *op. cit.,* p. 46. See too B.L. Cotton Otho E. VIII, fols. 41-43. This volume contains all Best's *True Discourse*, pp.1-129. See below for a fuller discussion of George Best's contibutions.

[11]B.L. Cotton Otho EVIII, fols. 9-16, 42-54 and 68-80.

[12]Pierrepont Morgan Library Ms. MA 2637 (R-V Autogrs. Misc, English). Dee's letter of 16th January 1577, written from Mortlake, covered cartographic and navigational issues and the politics of the Netherlands. See: J.H. Hessels, *Abrahami Ortelii Epistolae,* Cambridge University Press, Cambridge, 1887, pp.157-160. This extract is cited from p.158; and H.Wallis, "Across the Narrow Seas," in *Studies in the History and Bibliography of Britain and the Low Countries presented to Anna E Simoni,* British Library, London, 1991, pp.31-54.

[13]British Library Ms., Cotton Vitellus C.VII, f.264-269. *Of Great and Rich Discoveries,* incorporates Mercator's letter and Dee's translation of 1577. See also: E.G.R. Taylor, "A letter dated 1577 from Mercator to John Dee," *Imago Mundi, XIII,* 1956, pp.56-68.

[14]British Library Ms., Cotton Vitellus C. VII, f.79. While this "periplus" may refer to various Dutch rutters published from the 1540s onwards, there is far more detail about Norway's coast in an English text that seems more closely related to both William Borough and Dee, namely British Library, Harley Ms. 167, fols. 39-72 which contains "Borough's Rules" relating to a passage along Norway's coast and past the North Cape.

[15] For the Exchequer case see: PRO E 159/109/ Michaelmas Commentaries and E 159/231 rot. 28d. For a summary of the case and the issues involved see: J. Donald, *Elizabethan Copper, The History of the Company of Mines Royal, 1565-1605,* M. Moon, Whitehaven, 1989, pp.124-145.

[16] J.S.Brewer , ed., *Calendar of Letters and Papers Henry VIII,* vol. IV, pt II, pp.1596 and 2089, and 4834 nos 4018, and pt III, No.5029. N. Kratzer and P. Filius's survey of all the English mines in 1524-1529, is particularly interesting in respect of mines at Coombe Martin, West Challacoombe and Knap Down in Devon. Kratzer came to England in 1517 having lived in Munich, Wittenburg, and Maurbach monastry near Vienna. Famous for his astronomical and horological instruments he became a close friend of Hans Holbein by 1527. He was joined in the surveying of English mines by Joachim Hochstetter as "Principal Surveyor and Master of All mines in England and Wales" in 1528-9 when they surveyed Cornwall's mines too. They expected a profit of £30,258 for a new smelt mill to be built at Coombe Martin and operated by Master Piere {Filius} and another German for ores brought by sea

from Cornwall and overland from the Mendip Hills. See P. Claughton, *Out of the World and into Coombe Martin,* Coombe Martin Local History Group, Coombe Martin, 1987, p32. Note his short articles on Coombe Martin and Fullabrok mines in *Plymouth Mineral and Mining Club Journal,* volumes 5-8, 1974-1977.

[17]Hans Holbein's view is of a working mine in the Swiss Jura or the Vosges in 1519. It is in the British Museum Print Room.

[18]H.Groff, Ms. des Mines de la Croix, Bibliothèque L' Ecole Nationale Superiéure des Beaux Arts, Paris. Reproduced in: E. Brugerolles, ed., *La mine mode de L'emploi. La rouge mynr de Sainct Nicholas de la Croix dessinée par Heinrich Groff, 1526,* Editions Gallimard, Evreu, 1992.

[19] V. Biringuccio, *De la Pirotechnia libri X,* Roffnelo, Venice, 1540. It was translated by Richard Eden in 1555. A later translation and introduction was prepared by C.S Smith and M.T. Gnudi and was published by the American Institute of Mining and Metallurgical Engineers, New York, 1943.

[20] G. Agricola, *De ortu et causis subterraneorum ; De Natura ortum quae effluunt e terra:; De natura fossilium; De veteriis et novis metallis;* [with a glossary of mineralogical terms] *Rerum metallicarum interpretatione,* Froben, Basle, 1546. G. Agricola, *De re Metalica libri XII,* Froben, Basle, 1556. Bristol Record Office's copy is ref. BRO 04569. Translated under the same title with an introduction by H.C and L. H Hoover, *Mining Magazine,* London, 1912. Reprinted by Dover Publications, New York, 1950. Agricola was a physician and politician better known in the Erzgebirge as Georg Bauer. His first essay *Bermannus* was published by Froben at Basle in 1530. He later acquired shares in a mine at Albertham.

[21]W.B. Turnbull , ed., *Calendar of State Papers (Foreign, 1547-1553)* Longmans, London, 1861, No. 245. J. Kundelfinger to the Privy Council, 18 October 1550. His confidence in an assay of ore delivered by Garet Harman, goldsmith from Sir William Cecil (later Lord Burghley), to Kundelfinger and the Burgomaster of Antwerp, caused him to take ship via Zealand to Ireland, as PRO SP.61/4/47 confirms. This journey has close echoes in the much altered start of Sellman's account of Frobisher's third voyage, which in the printed version erroneousl;y suggests a start via Zealand and Ireland. Kundelfinger's concessions in Wexford probably acoount for Humfrey and Schutz only receivng a concession for the Pale, that is for the immediate environs of Dublin.

[22]PRO SP61/4/17-19, 47-59 and 76-78, and "Books of check and charges of the Almain" which are in SP61/4/55 and 56. D. Cowman, "The German Mining Operation at Bannow Bay, 1551-52," *Journal of the Wexford Historical Society,* 11, 1986, pp.67-82

[23]M.B. Donald, "Burchard Kranich (c1515-1578) Miner, Queen's Physician, Cornish mining stamps, antimony and Frobisher's gold," *Annals of Science,* 6, pp. 308-322. And "A further note on Burchard Kranich," *Annals of Science,*7, pp. 107-8.

[24]J.Gairdner, J.S.Brewer, R.H. Brodie, eds., *Letters and Papers Foreign and Domestic, Henry VIII, 1509-1547,* HMSO, London , (1862-1932) vol. II, No. 1370, and vol. V, 296 and 306. H.L. Blackmore, *The Armouries of the Tower of London,,* HMSO, 1976-87, particularly vol. 1, 1973, pp.1-21 and 1259. Particularly important as Master of Mines in 1522 were the Venetians Francesco Arcanis and Rafaelo Archangelo who entered Henry VIII's service in 1522. They cast guns in London and Calais with a Frenchman, Peter Baude (d.1546). They mostly worked on the making of bronze ordnance, but developed cast iron guns too, such as 36 made in conjunction with Robert and John Owen of Buxted, Sussex in 1531.

[25]D.Crossley and H.Cleere, *The iron industry of the Weald,* Leicester University Press, Leicester,1985. E. Straker, *Wealden Iron,* David and Charles, Newton Abbott, 1969.

[26] Donald, Elizabethan Copper, *The History of the Company of Mines Royal, 1568-1605,* Pergamon Press, London, 1955 and M. Moon, Whitehaven, 1989. W.G. Collingwood, *Elizabethan Keswick [comprising] Extracts from the Original Account Books 1564-1577 of the German Miners, in the Archives of Augsberg,* M. Moon, Whitehaven, 1987

[27] C.E. Hart, *The Industrial History of Dean,* David and Charles, Newton Abbot, 1971. C.E.Hart, *The Free Miners of the Forest Of Dean and Hundred of St Briavels,* British Publishing Co., Gloucester, 1953. C.E .Hart, *The Metes and Bounds of the Forest of Dean. The origin and Extent of the Hundred of Grevil,* British Publishing Co., Gloucester, 1947. G.F. Hammersley, *The history of the Iron Industry in the Forest of Dean, 1562-1660,* University of London PhD, 1972.

[28]PRO C66/1016 membrane 28.

[29]For Schutz's early work for the Company of Mines and Battery Works see:M.B. Donald, *Elizabethan Monopolies, The History of the Company of Mineral and Battery Works,* Oliver and Boyd, Edinburgh, 196; Scott, *op.cit.*, vol. II, pp.430-435.

[30]PRO C66/1047 mem. 28. Lok did not know this in 1577, so presumed he needed the Duke of Saxony's approval which he recommended was sought, writing accordingly on 19th January 1577 to Sir FrancisWalsingham. See PRO SP12/122/9.

[31]PRO SP12/37/40-44; SP12/41/12 and SP 12/41/42.

[32]PRO SP12/37/73 and C 661049/ membrane 16-17. Also B.L. Sloane, 2843, fols.18-26. Bristol Records Office, AC/B 62/210, 216, 266, 284, 297, and litigation over it by Schutz , PRO, E 315/472/13and 14. William Camden, *Britannia,* W.Hole, London, 1610 p.83 said those calamine ores were found at the western end of the Mendip Hills. What is important about this knowledge is that the metallurgists associated with Frobisher's venture in England were sixty years ahead of the French in understanding the value of "calamine stone." It has been claimed that the first description of the making of brass by alloying zinc, lead and copper was Savot's in *Discours sur les medalles antiques,* Paris, 1627. But Schutz used the Somerset calamine stone at the Tintern smelter from 1568. The same prospectors of the Company of Mines and Battery Works also found "osmond stone," and chose to call their main works, built later in Bristol, the Osmond Works after the extra hard finish it gave to metals. C.S. Smith & R.J. Forbes , "Metallurgy and Assaying", in C. Singer, *A History of Technology (vol. 3),* Oxford University Press, 1957 pp.27-71; also: J. W. Gough, *The Mines of Mendip,* David and Charles, Newton Abbot, 1967, pp.64-89.

[33]PRO SP12/41/17 and 18 shows that Daniel Hechstetter suggested the idea of sieving the ores to Schutz and Humfrey.

[34]Donald, *op. cit.*, 1989, pp.216-239, 289-292. Scott, *op. cit.*, pp.391-394.

[35]Collingwood, *op.cit.* Originally these Haug and Co accounts for 1564 to 1577 when Haug and Co went bankrupt, were published as the *Cumberland and Westmoreland Archaeological Society, Tract Series No. VIII,* 1912. For Schutz's appears therein as both Jonas and Christopher. See pp. 3, 183,186,189.

[36]PRO C66/ 1173 membrane 32-33. a grant for life "to Jonas Schutz, born at Annenbergh in Saxony, of the office of master worker and principal workman of minerals lately discovered in the North Parts by Martin Frobisher or to be brought to England from the said North parts." He or a deputy would draw £100 yearly from the profits of the said minerals from Michaelmas 1577. At his own suit Orothea, his wife, would enjoy £20 for life "in consideration that he hath greatly travelled the sea and land." Orothea is however not mentioned in his will made in 1574. The long delay in proving his will before the Prerogative Court of Canterbury suggests some controversy surrrounded it and his wife.

[37]PRO SP12/ 118/41 and 42. fols.100-101. It needs to be compared with the outurns, and much revised promises he gave on 24th March 1578 in SP12.130/15 after the first three proofs. Later still Agnello Cole and Denham offered with Lok to buy and process the remaining ores at their risk on 18 April 1579. See B.L. Lansdowne Ms. 31/65.

[38]L. Stone, *Crisis of the Aristocracy,* Oxford University Press, Oxford, (abridged version) 1967, p.166.

[39]A few Elizabethan cupels, crucible fragments and furnace slag, now in the Museum of London, were found dumped outside the wall in London Wall and so within the parish of St Giles, Cripplegate. Other metallurgical finds in London, closely related to material found on Kodlunarn, are discussed in D. Gaimster, R. Goffin and L. Blackmore, "The continental stove tile fragments from St Mary Grace's London and their British and European contexts," *Post Medieval Archaeology,* 24, 1990, pp.1-49. M. Cowell & D. Gaimster, *The Provenancing of English and Continental Stove Tiles using Neutron Activation Analysis,* British Museum Occasional Paper, London, 1988.

[40]PRO PCC PROB.11 [Harington] 5. Will of Christopher Shutes made the 8th November 1574 who died in the Parish of St. Giles, Cripplegate, 1592

[41]B.L. Sloane Ms. 2483B. fols.18-26.

[42]The justification of rivalling imperial Spain and being assured of sufficient skilled mariners for that is added by Richard Eden in the preface to his translation of Martin Cortes, *Breve compendio de la esphere y de l'arte de navigar.* A. Alvarez, Seville, 1551 appears in the preface of the *Art of*

Navigation, R. Jugge, London, 1561, but it also shows the respect in which Stephen and William Borough held Spanish technology, especially at the time of Stephen Borough's visit to Seville in 1558 as an honoured guest. At the time the third editions of the work appeared William Borough, an experienced Muscovy Company pilot and navigational instructor, would sell his astrolabe (E164/35 fol 17) through Lok in 1576, and charter his ship *Judith* for Frobisher's third voyage, (SP129/11 and C47/34/6) as well as playing a leading role in planning of all those voyages.

[43]Eden wrote in the *Decades of the New World,* William Powell, London, 1555, as follows : "It seemeth to me a thing undecent to read so much of golde and sylver and to knowe lyttle or nothing of the naturall generation thereof... the second cause; that if in trauayling in straung[e] and unknowen countreys he may knowe by the information of th[e] inhabitaynts or otherwyse, that such regions are fruitful of the riche metal[l]s he may make further searche for the same." Cited from Eden's preface to a translation of Biringuccio's *De la Pirotechnia,* Rofnello, Venice, 1540, reprinted E. Arber, *The First Three English Books on America,* Birmingham, 1885, p.355. Vannuccio Biringuccio's text follows at pp.356-368. It was later re-issued in London in 1895. See too R. Baldwin, "The new scientific skills that Cortes and Eden sought to teach," *Navigation and Cartography, 1440-1640,* Headstart History, Oxford, due out 1999.

[44] S.P.12/113/12.

[45] Magdalene College, Cambridge, Pepys Ms. 2133.

[46]R. Baldwin, *Navigation and Cartography 1440-1640,* Headstart History, Oxford, in press for 1999. Also a chapter entitled " Symbolism in Hans Holbein's portrait of the Ambassadors painted in 1533" in *Holbein's Globe,* to be published by Greaves and Thomas, London, 1999.

[47]K.R. Andrews, *Trade Plunder and Settlement,* Cambridge University Press, Cambridge, 1984 (1991) p.173.

[48]Lok's description is in PRO E164/35 fol. 14. The only terrestrial globe large enough, and up to date enough, to be convincing about the Northwest Passage, and readily available in gores that could be engraved through in that way onto brass, were the twenty four gores published in Venice about 1574, and which when assembled made up a globe very nearly 30 inches in diameter. Lok had close family friends in Venice and would easily have been able to use them to obtain those gores, probably engraved by Guilio and Livio Sanuto after Ortelius's world maps. Those globes as produced in 1574 were among the largest produced to that date. They needed a copper plate bigger than the limits of the engraved gores, that is bigger than 1090 by 2220 mm — a size that pushed the contemporary limits of practicality for a good quality impression from a single pull through a flat bed printing press.

[49] Jonas Schutz concurrently introduced English founders to sieved and wet calamine ore as a treatment for furnace burns.

[50] V. Biringuccio, *Pirotechnia,* Venice,1540. It remained popular until 1678 when the last edition of eight editions appeared in Bologna. This citation is taken from a translation provided by M. Hallett, for G. Hadley, *Citizens and Founders, A History of the Worshipful Company of Founders,* London, 1365-1975. Phillimore, London, 1976, pp.169-170. There were also French editions.

[51] PRO C66/ 1016/ membrane 28.

[52]L. Ercker, *Beschribung allerfurnemensten mineralishen Ertsz-vnnd Berkwercks arten,* Georg Schwart, Prague, 1574.

[53] J.G. Hawthorne, and C.S. Smith, *On divers Arts - A Translation of Theophilus's Schedula Diversarium Artium,* University of Chicago Press, Chicago and London, 1963. And J. Day, "Brass and Zinc in Europe from the Middle Ages until the 19th century," in P.T. Craddock, *2000 years of Brass and Zinc,* British Museum, Occasional Paper No.50, 1990, see only pp. 126-134 of the longer article. Joan Day's footnote on p.146 acknowledges that the potential of calamine ores was perhaps understood in limited circles in Oxford in 1380s if one is to accept the evidence from a brasier dispute of those years as to the meaning of "graycobber." J. Day, "The Continental origins of Bristol Brass," *Industrial Archaeology Review,* 1984, No. 1, pp.32-55.

[54]M.B. Donald, *Elizabethan Monopolies, The History of the Company of Mineral and Battery Works,* Oliver and Boyd, Edinburgh, 1961.

[55]J.W. Gough, *Mines of Mendip*, David and Charles, Newton Abbott, 1967 for all its insights into the role of Jacob Momma and other Swedish practitioners with links to Ecton Hill in Staffordshire and alternative sources of cheap copper from Sweden, now needs revision because the construction of a water reservoir on the flank of Worle Hill in the 1980s revealed local calamine stone with a much higher lead content than in calamine ore from other parts of the Mendip Hills. This may have meant Worle Hill was more suitable for Bevis Bulmer's purposes at Coombe Martin than for Christopher Schutz's at Tintern. This would not have gone unnoticed by Schutz in the 1580s, and may go some way to explaining how Schutz readily restored his fortune at Coombe Martin from his own experience. Schutz's discovery of how useful zinc rich calamine ores were in treating burns was also passed on thereabouts.

[56]PRO E164/35/ fol. 256.

[57]E164/35 fol. 27 in the original ms. numbers, and at 28 in PRO's stamped numeration.

[58]E164/35/ fol. 181-183

[59]*House of Commons Journal, 1547-1581 1604-1607, volume 1.* Printed by Order of the House of Commons, London, 1742. A flavour of the concerns of February 1575 is given by the Bill before the Common entitled "A Bill concerning children born in England their parents being strangers." .
BL. Harley Ms.167 /.9. "The chardges which will appertayne unto the due and well executyng of the Office of Register of the Names and Strangers Ale[i]n Borne." [folios 181-182.] R.E.G. & E.F. Kirk, *Return of Aliens dwelling in the City of London, 1523-1571.* Huguenot Society Series. London. 1894. See the editors' introduction.

[60]PRO, SP 12/112/25. .

[61] J. Dee, *General and Rare Memorials Pertayning to the Perfect Arte of Navigation,* John Daye, London, 1577. See too: Bodleian Library, Ashmole Ms. 242, No 83; British Library, Add Ms. 59681 *Britannici Imperii Limites,* between 1576 and 1578 when final corrections were added. It anticipates in some ways Dee's *Thalattokratia Bretanniki* completed in 1597, which is British Library, Harley 249. Another manuscript copy in his hand is bound in with his master printed copy of *General and Rare Memorials*, now British Library C.21.e12. A further nearly contemporary copy forms British Library, Royal Ms. 7, C. XVI, fols. 158-165. Dee's tuition may be surmised from references to it in :British Library Ms., Cotton Otho E VII, fol. 44 verso.British Library Ms. Lansdowne 100, Art. 1, fol. 4. See a paper given in April 1995, R. Baldwin, "John Dee's interest in the practical application of nautical science and mathematics within the context of English naval and commercial affiairs, 1553-1583," to appear in S Clucas, (ed) *John Dee: Interdisciplinary Studies in English Renaissance Thought*, Kluwer Press, Leiden, in press and due out in 1999 and W. Sherman, *John Dee, The Politics of Reading and Writing in the English Renaissance*, Massachusetts University Press, Amherst, 1995, pp 171-189.

[62] J. Dee, *General and Rare Memorials Pertayning to the Perfect Arte of Navigation,* John Daye, London, 1577, (sig. A2 recto).

[63] Salvador P. Lopez, *Isles of Gold, A History of Mining in the Philippines,* Oxford University Press, Oxford, 1992, pp.18-26.

[64] PRO E164/35 fol 17.

[65]The most likely candidate for that Verrazano map described by Hakluyt as Lok's copy is not the one in Henry VIII's library, but that now at Greenwich NMM Hydrographic Collection G.201/1/15 Ms. and in Chenies House during the seventeenth century. It bears manuscript additions, corrected in the light of discoveries to 1540. Its provenance is further discussed in M. Destombes, Nautical Charts attributed to Verrazano (1525-1528), *Imago Mundi, XI* 1954, pp.57-66. See too L.C. Wroth, *The voyages of Giovanni da Verazzano 1524-1528,* Yale University Press, New Haven and London, 1970, p.172 and footnote 3 above.

[66]Scott, op. cit. vol. 1, pp.39-43.

[67]PRO SP12/144/17 parts 1 and 2 details Drake's profits and the treasure to be removed to the Tower of London, estimated at over £250,000. It notes that over £10,000 was retained by Drake. See Scott, *op. cit.,* pp.53-85.

[68]L. Ercker, *Beschribung allerfurnemensten mineralishen Ertsz-vnnd Berkwercks arten*, Georg Schwarz, Prague, 1574. An English translation of a revised German edition of 1580 was published by A.G. Sisco and C.S. Smith, Chicago University Press, Chicago, 1951. It has good illustration of furnaces in operation.

[69]Collingwood, *op. cit.,* uses Haug's accounts of the business done in Cumberland and reveals much on Hechstetter's home. .

[70] The Rydal Mss. and Leconfield Mss in Cumbria Record Office, Kendal and Carlisle; the Middleton Mss in Nottingham University and the National Library of Wales reveal much about mining in Staffordshire and Shropshire, while the excellent records of the De L' Isle and Sidney Papers at Kent Records Office, Maidstone, show much about the steel making operations at Robertsbridge conducted in conjunction with a Welsh smelter in the years, 1541-1575. They end with a survey of the local woods available to support smelting (E20/2). Some are available in print edited by D.W. Crossley, *Sidney Ironworks Accounts, 1541-1573*, Royal Historical Society, 1975. Dr Burcot Kranich attended sick men there in 1566, see p.216.

[71]A seventeenth century transcript of most of Daniel Hechstetter's notebook is Cumbria Record Office, Kendal, once Rydal Ms. R. now WD, Rydal Ms. 28 fols. 146-169. The original is in the Percy Archives at Alnwick Castle, Northumberland, and reveals more about his deals with Haug & Co and the viability of the operations giving recipes for smelting ores dating from the 1560s.

[72]Compare the Greyndour miner, probably in fact a gentleman assayer, with the grant of arms to the Company of Mines Royal made on 26 August 1568. Those who had a mining task or a smelting task dressed lighter, a feature confirmed by the drawings of Henrich Groff, drawn c.1526, and Sebastian Munster, drawn c.1544-1550. Active miners needed baskets, wedges and various picks, and sledge hammers. They each carried a rock iron, crack irons, sump iron to fix to their picks, and wedges known as keil, plotz and feders. At many European sites, and in Cumbria and Wales, they also used wooden tracks and barrows or hunds.

[73]The most revealing insights into these devices, especially hunds and truhen, balanced lifting devices and simple cranage are given in M.T. Lewis, *Early Wooden Railways*, Routledge & Kegan Paul, London, 1970, pp. 8-22, and 43-75 where they are illustrated. Truhen [trucks] were employed in Europe and in Cumbria at Newlands, Caldbeck, and Grasmere, and even at Talybont in Wales between 1570 and 1608.

[74]G. Best, A *True Discourse of the late voyages of discoverie for finding of a passage to Cathaya by the North Weast under the conduct of Martin Frobisher,* Henry Bynneman, London, 1578. Cited as in Stefanson, *op.cit.,* vol. 1, p.61.

[75]Stefansson, *op. cit.,* vol.1, p.75.

[76]PRO E164/ 35/ 185.

[77]S. Munster, *Cosmographia Universalis,* H.Petri, Basle, 1544, p385 et seq. The 1550 edition of Munster's Cosmographia Universalis was bigger, incorporating further engravings by Hubinsack. A bigger edition issued in Basle in 1628 has mining illustrations and maps of the Leberthal at pp. 809-816. See too V. Biriguccio, as cited in Arber, *op. cit.,* pp.357 and 361.

[78] Stefansson, op.cit., vol. I, p.113 cites this alongside Frobisher's concern to " make triall of the goodnesse of the Ore."

[79] W.G. Collingwood, *op. cit,* pp.69,89, 109, concern John Bonner of Newlands. Christopher Bonner's find of St Reichart's mine in 1577 is at p.194. Stefansson, *op.cit.,* vol. II, p.222 describes Gregory Bona as a goldfiner, citing Huntington Library Ms. 715, fol. 19 . The same entry shows that Denham was paid £3 and Lambell £1.6.8d, John Pecock £1, and William Humfrey [jnr], goldfyner, £2.10s.

[80]N.M. Herbert, [ed.]*Victoria County History of Gloucestershire, Forest of Dean,* vol. 5, Institute of Historical Research, London, 1986, p.327 illustrates the Abenhall font complete with carvings of miner's tools. The tomb of Robert and Jane Greyndour bears a brass in Newland Chantry Chapel showing a Forest of Dean miner and is illustrated as Plate 26. See too: M. Grey, *Coal. British Mining in Art, 1680-1980*, Arts Council/National Coal Board, London, 1982, p.9.

[81]Herbert, *op. cit.,* pp.46-51, 79, 224 and 326-356.

[82]Decree of Weisewood issued by the Court of Chancery at Westminster on 20th December 1582. National Library of Wales, Badminton Estate Records, Nos. 8924 and 8925. It found against Henry, Earl of Pembroke, the defendant, and in favour of the the tenants, residents and inhabitants of Usk, Caerleon, and Treleck. The judgement was that "*too many of the oak and beech trees that represented the growth of two and three hundred years, and that these trees had helped them both feed to swine and in the provision of bacon which..... her majesties noble progenitors and also her Highness herself used*

to have and take for the provision of her Navy: and further that the Right Honble. Henry Earl of Pembroke under Colour and Pretence of a licence granted the Queen's majesty unto one Christopher Schutes & William Humfrey for the making of iron wire, battery and such like, hath of late caused to be errected and maintained near to the said Woods divers Furnaces and Forges..."

[83] SP12/12/25; SP12/118/39,41,42,43and 54; SP12/119/8 and 9; finally PRO SP12/122/9 dated "Januarie 19th 1577[8] from Mr Michael Loke, what charges Sr William Wynter and the rest upon their meetynge have though presently to be requisite..[after privy council direction to] Wm Wynter, Mr Randolph, Mr Dyar, Mr Younge, Mr Furbisher, and myself (except Mr Randolph) have sit together these ii daye past, and have considered thereupon.. and have had before us all the chief workmasters for the erecting the house and furnaces at the mills of Dartford with costs estimated at £900 including charges for a man to go to Germany for two Chief Workmen...[and]that Her Ma[jes]tie be moved for her favourable letter to the Duke of Saxonia declaring the staying here of Jonas for her Majesty's service which shall be sent by the parson that goeth for the workmen." This is wrongly dated by Stafansson as written in 1577 at pp.119-120.

[84]PRO E164/35 fol. 290.

[85] The 1550 edition of Munster's *Cosmographia Universalis* was bigger, incorporating further engravings by Hubinsack himself. The bigger still version issued in Basle in 1628 has the full set of mining illustrations at pp. 809-816.

[86]J.U. Nef, "Mining and Metallurgy in Medieval Civilisation," [in] *Cambridge Economic History of Europe*, Cambridge 1952, vol. ii, p.429 et seq. I.S.W. Blanchard, "The Miner and the Agricultural Community in Late Medieval England," *Agricultural History Review,* Second series, vol. 20, No 2, 1972, pp.93-106. I.S.W. Blanchard, "Labour Productivity and Work Psychology in the English Mining Industry, 1400-1600," *Economic History Review,* vol. XXXI, No1, February 1978, pp. 1-24.

[87]R.C.D. Baldwin, John Dee's interest in the practical application of nautical science and mathematics within the context of English naval and commercial affairs, 1553-1583, in S Clucas, (ed*) John Dee: Interdisciplinary Studies in English Renaissance Thought,* Kluwer Press, due out in 1999.

[88]British Library, Cotton Augustus I. i. 1. Inscriptions on the verso of Dee's North Atlantic map of 1578, revised in 1580.

[89] NLW Badminton Records, 2013 and 2014 show that Sir William Herbert through his father's executors and administrators shall be discharged rent arrears for speculations in coal extraction on the Gower before 1586. Others mention Christopher Schutz.

[90] J. Roberts and A.G Watson, *John Dee's Library Catalogue,* Bibliographical Society, London, 1990, p.35, and Dee's catalogue Nos.177,178, 215, 1051, 1919. For the Elector of Saxony's mining ordnances in *Bergordnung* 1574 were Dee's cat. no. 227.

[91]Georg Bauer's [Agricola's] medical works included: *De Medicatis Fontibus; De putridine solidas partes; Castigationes in Hippocratem.*

[92] G. Agricola, *De ortu et causis subterraneorum ; De Natura ortum quae effluunt e terra:; De natura fossilium; De veteriis et novis metallis;* [with a glossary of mineralogical terms] *Rerum metallicarum interpretatione,* Froben, Basle, 1546. *De Animantis Subterranis* appeared in 1549. He also published works on mining law and mining machinery which are not now known to survive. He also published religious tracts between 1522 and 1554, and prepared a medical student's edition of Galen in 1525. In 1529 he was recommended to Cardinal Wolsey as an expert in mineral affairs.

[93]G. Agricola, *De re Metalica libri XII,* Froben, Basle, 1556. Translated and fully annotated under the same title with an introduction by H.C and L. H Hoover, *Mining Magazine,* London, 1912. The Hoover's translation was reprinted by Dover Publications, New York, 1950. See Book I p.23 and the key to it, p.5.

[94]Ibid . Note the Italian translation also published under Froben's mark at Basle in 1563, *Opera di Georgio Agricola de L'arte de Metali Partita in XII libri,...tradotti in lingua Toscana da Michaelangelo Florio Fiorentino,* bore a dedication to Queen Elizabeth I of England just as she was making news in Protestant Europe by creating new corporate mining concessions.

[95]Much is known of John Dee's large library of mining, alchemical, legal, navigational and astronomical and astrological subjects kept at Mortlake because catalogues he made of it survive as British Library, Cotton Vitellus CVII , f.1-13. Dee had two copies of Biringuccio's text and multiple copies of Agricola's

study, *De Re Metallica,* Freiburg 1556 and Basle 1558, and copies of major works by Ercker, Munster, Oviedo and de Barros. All were heavily annotated, especially the last two works in those sections dealing with mines in the Iberian empires. Dee took most of these metallurgical works to Prague in 1583. See: R.J. Roberts and A. Watson, *John Dee's Library,* Bibliographical Society, London, 1990: and R. Baldwin, "John Dee's interest in the practical application of nautical science and mathematics within the context of English naval and commercial affiairs, 1553-1583," to appear in S. Clucas, (ed) *John Dee: Interdisciplinary Studies in English Renaissance Thought,* in press and due out in 1999.

[96]Hogarth, Boreham and Mitchell, *op. cit,* p.107 list ten minesites with their finders in 1576-78 while further evidence from the vicinity of Tikoon Rock and Napoleon Bay suggests at least two more minesites were operated.

[97]H.C and L.H. Hoover, *op. cit,* pp.27-28.

[98]Ibid., p.29.

[99]Ibid., p.30.

[100]PRO S.P.12/ 112/25

[101]PRO S.P.12/ 112/25. Stefansson, *op. cit.,* vol. 2, p.89-90.

[102]PRO SP12/112/25, SP12/115/35 ; SP12/122/62 and SP12/ 118/39. But Professor T.A. Rickard gives Schutz, Kranich and Wynter a much harder appraisal in a passage cited by Stefansson , *op. cit.,* vol. II, pp.249-252.

[103] PRO: SP 112/119/No 14, SP 12/126/ No.56, SP 12/130 /Nos.19, 21 and 35, SP 12/130/No.21.

[104]S. Smith and R.J. Forbes, "Metallurgy and Assaying," in *A History of Technology,* vol. 3, Clarendon Press, Oxford, 1957, p.64 cite Samuel Zimmerman, *Probierbuch,* Augsburg, 1573.

[105]BL Harley Ms. 167/40. fol. 174. Dyer discovered Denham's Mount, a mine in Dyer's Passage. Sel[l]man described how on the 16th of August, "The Generall and Denham with him, is gon to a sownd, called Dyers Passage, which is upon the southern land of the Countess Sound, to vew a mayne there, found by Andrew Dyer and to make assayes thereof." Lansdowne Ms. 100/1 offers many insights into the miners themselves, especially into Andrew Dyer, who sailed aboard the *Ayde* on Frobisher's 2nd voyage. Best singled him out for praise with Christopher Jackman "then master's mates, both very expert Mariners." He was not paid all that well for as a Master of the *Ayde* he earned just £4. 14 s for the trip. But he was later deemed, perhaps wrongly, to be a competent prospector and metallurgist, and so was eventually taken on the Third Voyage under Captain Henry Carew.

[106] L. Ercker, *Beschribung allerfurnemensten mineralishen Ertsz-vnnd Berkwercks arten,* Georg Schwart, Prague, 1574. An English translation of a German edition of 1580 was published by A.G. Sisco and C.S. Smith, *Lazarus Ercker's treatise onores and asssaying, translated from the German edition of 1580,* Chicago University Press, Chicago, 1951.

[107]Hatfield House, Cecil Ms. 276.5 ...first written in the high duc[t]h by the experte and chiefe M[aste]r of the Emperors mynes in the kingdom of Bohemia, Lazarus Erkerne, nowe translated into English by Joachim Gaunz of Prage." Lazarus Ercker died in 1593.

[108]PRO volume SP12/122 much of which is Walsingham's correspondence; Burghley's is in SP12/119. Later their notes and opinions are to be found in SP12/129 and SP12/130. Burghley's mining interests are scattered throughout BL Lansdowne Mss.

[109]J.A. Pantheus, *Voarchedemia contra alchemicam,* Venice, 1530. Reprinted by the Newcomen Society, 1954. Schutz's anti-alchemical stance may account for his interest in Pantheus's work

[110]Bills paid to John Fisher, Smith for three iron furnaces, to Jeronias, miner for two more, and Jacob Johnson for earthenware pots suggest, as does the archaeology, that Denham made hot assays in small German stoves.

D. Hogarth, "Mining and Metallurgy of the Frobisher ores," and R Auger, "Sixteenth Century Ceramics from Kodlunarn Island," in W.F Fitzhugh and J. Olin, (eds.) *The Archeology of Frobisher's Voyage*s, Smithsonian Institute Press, 1993, pp.37-146, and 147-149 and 253-254.

[111]PRO E164/36 / 56, 57, and 152.

[112]PRO 12/131/ No.20.

[113]Stefansson, *op.cit.,* vol. 1, p.53.

[114]PRO S.P. 130/17.

[115]PRO S.P.12/122/25 Also reproduced in Stefansson, *op.cit.*, vol. 2, p.83. Compare this with another short account in B.L Cotton Otho E VIII, fol 45 which unlike most of this collection is not in Dee's hand.

[116]PRO S.P.12//122/25.

[117]See Sir W. Wynter to F. Walsingham 25 November 1577. PRO S.P.12/118/ 39. fols. 97-98.

[118]Dr Burcot Kranich to Walsingham, SP12/122/44 and 84 dated February 19th and February 21st 1577. Also: PRO S.P.12/118/40, Edward Fenton to Sir Francis Walsingham, 25th November 1577. An enclosure to this was Dr Dodding's report on death of an Eskimo brought from Meta Incognita. It is the first mention of Walsingham's knighthood.

[119]PRO S.P.12/119/ 32-45.

[120]PRO S.P.12/ 118/41 and 42. fols.100-101. It needs to be compared with the outurns, and much revised promises he gave on 24th March 1578 in SP12.130/15 after the first three proofs.

[121]PRO SP12/ 130/17

[122]PRO SP12/129/2.

[123] Magdalene College Cambridge, Pepys Ms. 2133. This records the existence of the boxed assay material and of another register lost in the storm of 15th September, 1578. Annotations in Burghley's hand on Lok's draft of the third voyages's official instructions (preserved among the Conway papers for the Dutch campaigns PRO SP11/25/81) note that Frobisher too was responsible for keeping a second copy in another ship. Possibly Andrew Dyer held onto it well into 1583 when he began work for Sir John Conway, explaining why Burghley took interest in it, adding several annotations in his hand and all about records of the ore.

[124] BL. Cotton Ms. Titus BVIII, fol. 198v. transcribed by E.Donno, *op. cit*, p.224. The interpolated identities are those of the author, not Donno's. Donno explains that the Greek encipherment refers to Borough for it transliterates as "Borows." Hogarth et al. op. cit assume the master to be Admiral Fenton, not Hall who then held that post and whom Madox calls "Palinurus" and "gubernator" that is helmsman or master and keeper of the ship's log.

[125]BL. Cotton, Titus BVII, fol.47v.

[127] BL. Lansdowne Ms.60/30 and 31; BL Lansdowne Ms. 52/11.

[127]BL Lansdowne Ms.70 fols. 55 and 183-187.

[128]E164/35/110.

[129]E164/ 35/fol. 150. Agnello was paid £4 followed by a further £5 to prepare his furnace at home for firing, but Wolfe just £3 to make a furnce, fire it for the proof, suggesting his was a much smaller assaying furnace. The next entry in Lok's account confirms this for it was for Thomas Taylor, labourer, who was by comparison paid for 30 days work at Tower Hill for the first and second proofs completed by Schutz and Denham for which he earned £1. 10s. — the same sum as food provided at "hostesse house where Jonas lodgeth", presumably Orothea's London house.

[130]PRO SP12/122/62.

[131] See Eden's translation in Arber, *op. cit.,* pp. 356-366.

[132] R.Auger, M. Blackburn, W.W. Fitzhugh, "Martin Frobisher's Base camp on Kodlunarn Island; A Two year Time Capsule in the History of Technology", in S. Alsford , ed., *The Meta Incognita Project: Contributions to Field Studies,* Canadian Museum of Civilization, Ottawa, pp.56-80 especially pp. 65-73. W. Fitzhugh, "Archaeology of Kodlunarn Island", in W. Fitzhugh and J. Olin , *Archaeology of the Frobisher Voyages,* Smithsonian Institute Press, 1993, pp.59-97, especially pp.66-70 and 88-91 and R. Auger, "Sixteenth-century Ceramics from Kodlunarn Island", *op. cit,* pp.147-151.

[133]PRO SP12/129/43. All the other Dartford assays are to be found in SP12/123/5.

[134]PRO SP12/123/5.

[135]PRO SP 12/130/15 and BL. Lansdowne 100/1 fol. 13 r.

[136]PRO SP 12/149/42(iii).

[137]PRO SP12/149/42 (ii).

[138].PRO E164/35, fols. 149-154.

[139]BL. Lansdowne 100/1 fol. 5v.

[140]Lok's allegations rest on Denham's report to Schutz. Denham had also acted as Assistant to both Broad and Schutz. Schutz wrote it up as *The accompt taken at Muskovie house the VIII of March 1577."* It was copied up by Lok as SP12/149/42 (ii).

[141]PRO E 164/36, ff. 307-313.

[142] Ibid.

[143] Ibid.

[144]BL, Lansdowne Ms. 30, Art 4, fol 6. & Lansdowne Ms. 100/1 f4r-5v, 10r, and 12r.   PRO SP12/118/ No.56, SP12/119/ No.46, SP12/122/3, 4, 9, 10, 61 & 62, SP 12/129/ 43, SP 12/130/15. Assays by Agnello, Broad, Kranich and Williams are also known: They are to be found in SP 12/122/Nos.62 and 67: and at SP12/161/41. The last two by Williams took place on 28th July 1583, and those two failures served to corroborate Dee's decision to leave for Prague. See also: Huntington Library, San Marino, California, Ms. 715.

[145] Public Records Office,12/130/15, and British Library Ms. Lansdowne, 100/1, fols. 10r-13r.

[146]PRO SP12/129/2, 6 and 7; E164/35/fol.255 and 261 details charges "for sending down the Additement to Darford that came from M.Fenton from the West Cun..7s"; Also E164/36 fol 185 which records."ten shillings paid to Jonas Schutz 14th December 1578 for additaments from Plymouth."

[147]PRO E164/35/f.153.

[148]PRO E164/36/f182.

[149]D.D. Hogarth, DT. Moore, P.W.Boreham, "Martin Frobisher's Mines and Ores", in *The Meta Incognita Project, Contributions to Field Studies,* Canadian Museum of Civilization, Ottawa, 1993, p.152. Subsequently small and large pieces of the ornamantal tiles from those German stoves were found on Kodlunarn.

[150] S. Smith and R.J. Forbes, "Metallurgy and Assaying", in *A History of Technology,* vol. 3, Clarendon Press, Oxford, 1957, p.64.

[151]Collingwood, *op. cit.,* p.189 where 20oz aquafortis for assays was purchased for 3s 4d in 1576. .

[152]PRO SP 12/129/36-43.

[153]PRO SP12/129/44 (3).

[154]PRO SP.12/122/62.

[155]It was once part of SP 12/112/63 and not as Hogarth, Mitchell and Boreham say SP 12/112/53.

[156]PRO SP12/122/62.

[157]PRO SP 12/112/63.That drawing was taken from SP 12/112/63 for exhibition in the PRO Museum at Chancery Lane.

[158] PRO E 164/36 fols. 307-311.

[159]PRO E 164/ 35/ fol.36 and 36A. " The Accompt of Michael Lok giving chardge to a mill and certain other houses now builded at Dartford necessary for the tre[a]t[ment] of ewre brought from Meta Incognita in divers ships under the conduct of Martin Furbisher."

[160] Bodleian Library Ashmole Ms. 1486, fol 35r.and 47-55r. For a detailed discussion of this text see: U. Szulakowska, *John Dee and European Alchemy,* Durham Thomas Harriot Seminar, Occasional Paper No 21, 1996, pp.15-19. U Szulakowska, The influence of John Dee's alchemical geometry on Michael Mair, in , ed., S. Clucas, *op.cit.*

[161]PRO S.P.12/ 130/21. This letter to the Privy Council is signed by Sir Thomas Gresham, John Dee, Thomas Allen, Xopher Hoddesdon, Michael Lok, Lionell Duckett, Martin Frobisher, Edward Fenton, Gilbert Yorke and Matthew Fyeld.

[162]Hogarth, Boreham and Mitchell, *op. cit.,* p.137

[163]PRO SP12/122/61.

[164]Ibid.

[165]PRO SP12/130/ 17.

[166]BL Cotton Otho VIII, fol.44.

[167]BL. Cotton, Otho VIII, fol 44 written by Michael Lok from the Fleet Prison, London, 16 November 1581.

[168]BL. Cotton Ms. Titus BVIII, fol. 198v.

[169]See J. Mc Dermott, *Michael Lok, Mercer and Merchant Adventurer,* in this volume.

[170]PRO S.P. 12/121/48 (ii).

[171]*House of Commons Journal, 1547-1581&1604-1607, volume 1.* Printed by Order of the House of Commons, London, 1742, p. 240. See too PRO S.P. 12/ 130/ 42 . There were probably yet more speakers with similar experiences speaking to the Bill in its progress in the House of Lords before it

became An Act for the explanation of a Former Act, 13 Elizabeth [1571], to make the lands and goods of Accountants liable to payment of their debts" passed on 15th June 1604

[172]For Bonham's suit see SP12/16/33. B.L. Lansdowne Ms. 147/70. On subsequent suits for debt see Coote's entry on Michael Lok in the *Dictionary of National Biography,* Oxford University Press, Oxford, vol. 34, pp.92-93.

[173]PRO SP12/130/17 No.7.

[174]Hogarth, Boreham, Mitchell, *op. cit.,* p.138.

[175] B.J. Cook, *op. cit.,* p25 and C.E. Challis, *A New History of the Royal Mint*, Cambridge University Press, 1992.

[176] Lansdowne Ms. 30/4.

[177] PRO S.P. 12/130/17 cited in Stefansson, *op. cit.* Pt II p.210.

[178]Ibid.

[179]BL Lansdowne 100/1 fol. 5. [agentia — translates as activity or characteristic process of acid action on metal]. In the context of the rest of the sentence it is unlikely to be intended as the alchemical symbol for silver since gold was the suspected mineral.

[180]B.L. Lansdowne 100/1. fol.6.

[181]Ibid.

[182] P. Berkowitz, "Frobisher's Quest for Gold," *University Affairs, Journal of the Universities of Canada*, November 1997. pp19-21. At p. 21 she reports indirectly on Hogarth's discovery, reported at Trent University in 1997 of unmined "ignis", a very hard rock form then unmineable that might well have held diamonds and tantalised Frobisher's prospectors in much the terms reported by Lok.

[183]PRO C47/34/6 says "Thomas Allen aforesaid recived of Michael Locke ii ingotts of fine golde wayeng ix penywgt and Vii graines and ii Ingottes of fine silver weing Vii ounces xviii penywgt and xii graines which said gold and silver proceded of the melting and working of CCC wgt of ewer, brought from Meta Incognita...."

[184]PRO SP12/119/9. This briefly presented the facts with tiny amounts of gold attached in red wax, beside each of four entries perhaps designed to clear up the matter of additives by comparing that from "Hynnesbury hilles." This may refer to the hills of Tyneside or Cleveland whence Cole bought additives for the furnaces, for "hynney" is a term much used thereabouts but not elsewhere in England. It was almost certainly one region well-known to Schutz in his travels around England. It states only:

"The great proofe of thee black oure of Alom and chayne.

The thurd proofe of the read sand and of Alom and chayne.

The second proofe of the read sand of Alom and chayne.

The aure of Hynnesbury hilles."

[185]PRO C47/ 34/6

[186]BL. Lansdowne Ms. 24/45 and 46.

[187]BL. Lansdowne Ms. 34/58.

[188]PRO C 47/34/6.

[189] PRO MPF 304.

[190] PRO E164/35 fol. 149.

[191]PRO E164/35 fols.

[192]PRO E164/ 36 fol 184. The accounts for the building of the Dartford furnace begin at folio 177

[193]It is illustrated and labelled as such in PRO MPF304.

[194]PRO E164/36/333.

[195]PRO C47/34/6 says "Thomas Allen aforesaid recived of Michael Locke ii ingotts of fine golde wayeng ix penywgt and Vii graines and ii Ingottes of fine silver weing Vii ounces xviii penywgt and xii graines which said gold and silver proceded of the melting and working of CCC wgt of ewer, brought from Meta Incognita...."

[196]PRO SP12/119/9. This briefly presented the facts with tiny amounts of gold attached in red wax. See footnote 184 above.

[197]PRO SP. 12/126/47. "An offer then made at Moskovey House by Jonas Sute before Mr Field, Mr Lok and Andrew Palmer" which is endorsed "Mr Palmer's note touchynge Jonas offer abowt Furbishers ewre 18th November 1578."

[198] To trace Hans Staddler see: W.G. Collingwood, *op.cit.* T.Wilson for Cumberland and Westmoreland Archaeological and Antiquarian Society, 1912, pp.136, 138, 153,171,183, 184. Reprinted by M. Moon, Whitehaven, 1987. Lok's acounts reveal subsequently that the Dutch/German recruits were Christopher Ryer, Jacob Walter and Andrew Bucker.

[199] From E164/35 it is clear that Sir Thomas Gresham's shares were £100 for the first voyage, £100 for the second and a further £270 for the third. His final installment of £230 was paid to Thomas Allen in 1579. State Papers further describing Gresham's investments are SP12/111/48, SP12/119/nos.30, 41, his will and concern about his creditors in SP12/126/nos.2, 8, 32 and 56, SP12/127/nos.8 and 16, SP12/130 nos.16, 21, 35. More detail about Sir Thomas Gresham's College, endowed under his will of 1575 (but not put into full effect until his widow died in December 1596) is to be found in: J. Ward, *The Lives of the Professors of Gresham College*, London, 1740, pp.iv-viii; S. J. Teague, *Sir Thomas Gresham, Courtier and College Founder*, London, Synjon Books, 1974; F.R. Johnson "Gresham College, Precursor of the Royal Society," *Journal of the History of Ideas*, I (1940), pp.413-438.

[200] PRO SP12/1131/49.

[201] British Library, Lansdowne Ms. 30, Art 4, fol 6; Lansdowne Ms. 100/1 f4r-5v, 10r, and 12v and 13r.
 Public Record Office, SP 12/118/ Nos 41, 42, 43, 54 and .56; SP 12/119/46; and much more detailed papers about them in SP 12/122/ Nos. 3, 4, 9, 10, 17, 52, 61 and 62; SP12/123/5: SP 12/129/43; SP 12/130/15. Early assays by Watterhows (SP12/118/36) who was perhaps the Dutch assayer in Lambeth known to Wynter, Whelar, goldfyner, George Ne[e]dham of the Company of Mines Royal, and better documented ones by Agnello, (SP119/15) Broad,[Brode] (SP12/122/62and SP12/123/5) Kranich, (SP12/122/67), Geoffrey le Brumen, (SP12/122/17) and William Williams (SP12/161/41) are known to have taken place, for Lok describes them in SP12/112/25 : More details are to be found in SP 12/122/Nos.62, and 67: and SP12/161/41.Huntington Library, San Marino, California, Ms. 715. The last two assays by Williams took place on 28th July 1583 and served to corroborate Dee's decision to leave for Prague.

[202] D.B. Quinn (ed) *The Voyages and Colonising Enterprises of Sir Humphrey Gilbert,* (2 vols) Hakluyt Society, 2nd Series, 83-84, London, 1940 illustrates Dee's opportunism.

[203] Michael Lok's chart was sought for Richard Hakluyt's *Divers Voyages,* Thomas Woodcocke, London, 1582, where it was published opposite (sig. B4 second count). It is entitled " ILLUSTRI VIRO DOMINO PHILIPPO SIDNAEO MICHAEL LOK CIVIS LONDINENSIS HANC CHARTAM DEDICABAT, 1582."

[204] D. Hogarth, P. Boreham, and J. Mitchell, *op.cit.*, 1994, pp. 73-99.

[205] R. Deacon, *John Dee, Scientist, geographer, Astrologer and Secret Agent to Elizabeth I,* F. Muller, London, 1968. See also the Garland and Simkinson request that Dee attend the Court of the Russian Emperor, see Public Records Office, SP12/196/ 143 recto dated 18 September 1586, later reproduced by R Hakluyt, *The Principal Navigations, voyages, traffiques and discoveries of the English Nation,* G. Bishop, R. Newberie, and R. Barker, London 1598, vol.1, p508

[206] D.B Quinn, *Set Fair for Roanoake, Voyages and Colonies,* University of North Carolina Press, Chapel Hill, 1985, p.92. Hatfield House, Cecil Ms. 276.5 "...first written in the high duch by the experte and chiefe M[aste]r of the Emperors mynes in the kingdom of Bohemia, Lazarus Erkerne, nowe translated into English by Joachim Gaunz of Prage." G.Grassl, *German Mineral Specialists in Elizabethan England and Raleigh's Virginia,* [In press]

[207] R. Baldwin *op. cit.* in S. Clucas (ed), *John Dee: Interdisciplinary Studies in English Renaissance Thought*, for 1999.

[208] Stefansson, vol. 2, pp.23-25

[209] Ibid. p.55.

[210] This Dee charted on a fine manusript circumpolar map (now in Burghley House) in 1580, showing the Ob in gold. .

[211] British Library, Cotton Roll XVIII, 48. The full title on this manuscript map says: " This counterfet of Mr Fernando Simon's, his sea carte which I lent unto my Master at Mortlake A(nn)o 1580 November 20. The same Fernando Simon is a Portugale born in Terçera being one of the Isles called Azores."

[212]Royal College of Heralds, Dethick Grants, fol.25, and Vincent 162, pp.80-82

[213]Hatfield House, Cecil Papers, Chart No 98.

[214]BL. Cotton Ms. Titus BVIII, fol. 199v.

[215]D.D. Hogarth, P.W.Boreham, J.G. Mitchell, *op.cit.*, pp. 73-141. D.D. Hogarth, P.W.Boreham, J.G. Mitchell, *op.cit.,* pp.148-175. Canadian Museum of Civilization, Ottawa, 1993. But in addition to the sources Hogarth, Boreham and Mitchell cited and illustrated about 60 tons were used in harbour repairs at Bristol. See Bristol Record Office 04026 (1) fols. 60 and 99 and 04026 (9) fols. 23, 28-29, 33, 94-95, 99 and 104. Much more was probably used in the 1580s in Plumsted and Erith marshes reclamation scheme. Parliament discussed the scheme on 4th March 1580 whether provision for strengthening the cuts at Erith was required. A Mr Bowyer M.P., a Cathay Company adventurer spoke to it in the House and later saw the scheme undertaken . See entries in the *Commons Journal* through 1580-81.

[216]PRO, MPF 304.

[217]PRO, SP12/122/62 which begins by distinguishing Schutz's first interest in the voyage as an expert in mineralls and metals as opposed to Agnello whose discipline was alchemy. M.B. Donald, Burchard Kranich, 1515-1578, miner and Queen's physician, Cornish mining stamps, antimony and Frobisher's Gold, *Annals of Science,* 6, pp.308-322 and a further note on Burchard Kranich, *Annals of Science,* 7, pp.107-108.
See: B.L.Lansdowne 100/1; Frustration caused Sir Thomas Gresham to suggest John Barton, Gentleman, perform an assay in Schtuz's new Dartford works. See SP12/130/21.

[218]*Dictionary of National Biography*, vol. 11, Oxford University Press, Oxford, p.270.

[219]S. Ackermann, *Humphrey Cole: Mint, Measurement and Maps in Elizabethan England,* British Museum Occasional Paper No. 22, 1998. See here J. McDermott, "Humphrey Cole and the Frobisher Voyages," pp.15-19, and B.J. Cook, "Humphrey Cole and the Mint." pp.21-26. This misses the fact that an armillary sphere like that provided for Frobisher survives at St Andrews University.

[220]D.W. Waters, *The Art of Navigation in Elizabethan and Early Stuart England,* Hollis and Carter, London, 1958, p.541 cites an advertisment in E.Worsop, *A discouerie of sundrie errors and faults daily committed by Lande meaters ignorant of Arithmeticke and geometrie, London, 1582.* R.T Gunther, "The astrolabes and seals of Humfrey Cole of London," *Illustrated London News,* 14 August 1926. A. Ferguson, *Clio unbound, Perception of the Social and Cultural Past in Renaissance England,* Duke University Press, 1979. M. Hansen, *Narratives of the Land by English Renaissance Antiquarians,* Durham Thomas Harriot Seminar, Occasional Paper No. 13, 1994. B.J. Cook., *op. cit.,* pp25-26.

[221]M.A.S. Hume, *Calendar of State Papers relating to English affairs preserved principally in the archives of Simancas,* vol. II, HMSO, London, 1894, pp. 618 and 621for 7th October and 15th October 1578 mention a marine chart of Frobisher's voyage sent via Seville with Bodenham describing briefly the achievements and the loss of ship in the ice. The better chart and ore samples sent in the owl cup did not arrive in Madrid were acknowledge to have arrived there on 7th February 1579.

[222]G. Connell Smith, "English Merchants trading to the New World in the early 16th century," *Bulletin of the Institute of Historical Research,* vol. XXIV, 1956, pp.53-65. Bodenham's complex career and its several disappointments features in the introduction of P. Croft (ed), *The Spanish Company,* London Records Society, vol.9., London, 1973.

[223] Bodleian Library, Oxford, Ashmole Ms.1419, item 4.

[224]Several factors suggest that the Dyer family interest was sufficient to cover the whole subject matter of the intelligence received in Spain. One of the most obvious features is that Henry Carew, Andrew Dyer's captain aboard the *Hopewell,* had had letters of marque issued by Don Luis de Requesens, once Governor of the Netherlands and Commendator of Castille to cruise against the enemies of King Philip and take any rebel ships found in Spanish waters. In 1578 Henry Carew clearly wanted Andrew Dyer for his pilot, effectively reversing the earlier decisions to displace him from the voyage. Allen's accounts for 1578-79 show "Mr Henry Caru C[aptain] of the *Hopewell*" was paid £35 for his eight months service, "the which gave Mr Caru funds to move." PRO E164/35/ fol. 142. After serving in 1579 with Valentine Pardieu, Governor of Gravelines, Carew was reported on by John Ley on 23 June 1580. See A.J. Butler , ed., *Calendar of State Papers Foreign, 1579-1580* No 336, now SP. 94/51.

[225]By his death in 1607 Sir Edward Dyer, who had inherited thirteen manors from his father in Somerset, providing an income of £130 a year, had borrowed so heavily against them, and from the Crown (over £5,000) that he owed over £11,200. He had only just managed to afford to stay at Court, but to do so needed minor diplomatic tasks and extensive royal grants of the income from concealed lands. See R.M. Sargent, *At the Court of Queen Elizabeth, The Life and Lyrics of Sir Edward Dyer*, Clarendon Press, Oxford, 1935, pp.132-139.

[226]See verso of BL Cotton Augustus I. 1.i, an Atlantic map completed while Frobisher was making his third voyage. Edward Dyer's continued closeness to Dee elicited a letter from him dated 7th September 1597 entitled "Thalattokratia Brettaniki" . It comprised a remarkably coherent piece of legal thinking on "The sea jurisdiction of a British Empire." It harked back to Dee's *General and Rare Memorials* and a Royal claim over Meta Incognita which was only adopted after it had been actively pursued and mapped by Dee between 1576 and 1583.

[227]*Commons Journal*, vol. 1, 1604, 4 June , 1604, pp.231-232. Debate on the "Reformation of Abuses by Informers." Significantly this followed closely on a debate forbidding men to enter into joint stock trading where they had previously been engaged in other trades in a debate that concentrated on the Muscovy Company, but which clearly was informed by Michael Lok's predicament. Ibid. p.220. For more about Edward Dyer see P.W. Hasler, *History of Parliament 1558-1603,* vol. 3, History of Parliament Trust and HMSO, 1990, pp.68-69.

[228] Stefannson, *op.cit.*,Part II, pp. 100, 113, 167, 197, 200.

[229]PRO SP12/122/50 and SP12/126/32. Stefannson, op. cit, vol. II, p.154 and 116 respectively. To put this in context Schutz was paid £25 a quarter but for work at Dartford.. E164/35/36 cites Edmund Stafford's pay as 8 months at £6 a month, and shows the miner were paid just £6 each for the voyage.

[230]BL. Lansdowne 29/1.

[231] B. Allaire and D. Hogarth, "Martin Frobisher, The Spaniards and a Sixteenth Century Northern Spy," *Terrae Incognitae,* vol. 28, 1996, pp.46-58. Hogarth , Mitchell and Borehem, *op. cit.,* p.152 footnote 13. This gives details of his ancestry, life and death. They also suspect that as "Denham of Cheapside, Goldsmith," he was a party to a plot to marry Mary Queen of Scots to the Duke of Norfolk in 1569. He worked between 1583-87 in Cornish mines for the Company of Mines Royal, as documents cited below under Grant Francis (note93) show. From William Carnsewe's death in February 1588 he worked for Sir Thomas Smythe, and then for his son Sir John to about 1600 when Thomas Middleton took over the Cadoxton smelter near Neath. Hogarth and Allaire take little account of the fact Cornwall was very hostile towards the Spaniards and justifiably fearful of invasion in 1587, 1588, 1593, 1595, 1596 and 1598 as Spanish ships actually attempted landings at Mousehole and Mounts Bay in the 1590s terrorising the local community.

[232] Stefansson, *op. cit*, vol.I, p.xcvii. He cites De Guarras writing of Captain Frobisher that he had decided to leave for Flanders in a week to seek his Excellency about services he could render. De Guarras added " *he is the best seaman and the bravest in the country, ...[so] I have promised him a safe conduct to come and go, and free him of debts and consequences of past evils, if no arrangement is made here.* " Frobisher was present on all the voyages, and at the assays mentioned in the report sent to Madrid, and handed over no maps or journals for safe keeping in line with Privy Council instructions of 2nd November 1578.

[233]There is other evidence in support, notably the printer's preface to George Best's work finished in 1578 which states, " *"I have without making privy the Authour, procured this coppie out of the hands of a friend of mine, who had the writing and perusing thereof....and have sought to conceale upon good cuases some secretes, not fit to be published or revealed to the world..."*

[234]J.R. Dasent, *Acts of the Privy Council, 1575-77,* vol. 10, HMSO, London, 1884, p.366.

[235] Ibid, vol. 2, No. 549.

[236]The timing, as Ley gave it, is such that Henry Carew or William Bodenham might have borne the owl cup bearing the map and samples to Spain using the route Carew told Ley about. From there Carew gained a command in the fleet that was to have accompanied Spanish troops first into Lisbon, and then to the Biscayan coast at Corunna where he had to wait for replacement crews from the Straits. Events show they subsequently achieved a landing at Smerwick Bay in Ireland. There the Spaniards under Carew's command were to build a fort using Frobisher's ores from the *Emmanuel of Bridgewater.*

[237] Ibid, vol. 2 No 550.

[238] John Ley on 23 June 1580 in A.J. Butler , ed., *Calendar of State Papers, Foreign, 1579-1580,* No 336, now SP.94/51.

[239] Edward Stafford, seems an unlikely spy in 1578 as he was in Paris on a diplomatic mission when Frobisher sailed.

[240] The Best family with its rural Yorkshire roots both explains George's fine pastoral descriptions and his connection with Martin Frobisher. The genealogy can be examined in C. Best Robinson, (ed) *The Farming and Account Book of Henry Best of Elmswell,* Surtees Society, Durham, 1857. Henry, the son of Richard Best of Wath who died in 1581-2, was a professional scrivener operating

[241] Reade Stafford, the son of Anne Best , tried to break the entails on his inheritance in 1593, even as he entered Parliament as MP for East Grinstead in 1593. See PW. Hasler, *History of Parliament, 1558-1603,* vol. III, HMSO, London, pp. 430-433.

[242] Allaire and Hogarth, *op. cit.,* as footnote 231 above.

[243] Stefansson, *op. cit.* vol. I., pp.7, 22, and 129 explicitly reveal Best's interrelated imperial, agricultural and industrial and strategic thoughts of 1578. At p.22 he notes *"there are great countreys yet remaining withoute Maysters and possessors, which are fertile and bring forth all manner of corne and grayne, infinite sortes of Cattell, as Horse, Elephantes, Kine, Sheepe ... Abundance of fair hilles and vallies, furnished with all manner of woddes and pleasante rivers. Millions of newe fashions, and straunge beastes and fishes, both in sea and fresh waters. Mountains bringing forth all manner of Mettals as gold, silver, yron, &c.*

[244] PRO SP12/112/25 "Mr Lockes Discoors touchng the Ewre, 25 April 1577." This is followed by enclosures of the opinions of Agnello and John Barkeley. See too BL. Cotton Otho EVII fol. 45 which shows the advice Lok sought from Dee, Gilbert, Stephen and William Borough.

[245] Grant Francis, *The smelting of copper in the Swansea District from the time of Elizabeth to the Present day,* H.Southeran, London, 1881, pp.38-62 and Appendix B, pp.1-22,

[246] PRO MPF 11 Amlwch foreshore, formerly located with Elizabeth I's State Papers in SP46/36/9. J.A. Robey, "The Parys Mountain Copper mines and the Amlwch Port, Anglesey." *Staffordshire Industrial Archaeology Bulletin,* vol. 2, No2, December 1970.
J.D. Weston, Parys Mountain copper mine, Anglesey, *Bulletin of the Peak District Mines Historical Society,* vol. 5, No2., October 1972, pp. 109-113.

[247] PRO, SP12/119/8. (This gives yet further reasons to redate SP12/122/9 after it, as explained above.)

[248] N.M. Herbert, op. cit,1996, pp.46-51,61-62, 70-71, 79.

[249] Cumbria Record Office, WD, Rydal Ms. 28 fols. 146-169.
J. McNeil, "Blast: From Blowpipe to Blowing Engine", *Newcomen Society Transactions,* vol. 60, pp.95-106.

[250] C.J. Smith and R.J. Forbes, "Metallurgy and Assaying" in C. Singer (ed) , *The History of Technology from the Renaissance to the Industrial Revolution, 1500-1750.* vol. III, Oxford University Press, 1957, pp.26-71.

Methods of Assaying Ore and their Application in the Frobisher Ventures[1]

Bernard Allaire

Introduction

The results of the analyses of ore from Frobisher's first voyage, as carried out by assayers, were used to justify the second and third voyages, and were instrumental in deciding the fate of this enterprise. The importance of these assays is confirmed by the large number of studies that have been devoted to them. Many writers have mentioned the assays, and some have arrived at very plausible hypotheses[2] but, apart from Donald Hogarth,[3] few have spent time examining the technical aspects of the assayer's art. The efforts to understand the ore itself have focused on the petrography and the geology of the site,[4] on the identification of documentary sources relating to the assays, and on the study of the iron bloom found at Kodlunarn. Curiously, few of the researchers of the history of Martin Frobisher's expeditions have tried to explain the methods and procedures used by the assayers, nor to describe their work environment to the historian.

This is a fundamental topic that deserves to be more deeply elucidated, not only to shed light upon certain events that have remained obscure, but also to allow non-specialists to appreciate one of the more fascinating aspects in the history of Frobisher's voyages, without losing their way in a technical maze. It seems possible, as well, to provide new information about the real abilities of the persons involved in assaying the ore from Meta Incognita. In the following pages, I will present some aspects of the assayers' art: the methods they used to identify precious metals in the ore; and the depictions we have of their work in the sixteenth century. We will conclude with a look at the individuals involved in the analysis of the ore brought back from Meta Incognita.

The assayers of gold and silver in the sixteenth century

The analysis of ore in order to determine its composition has a long history that seems to extend to the very dawn of metallurgy. By the sixteenth century, these techniques had attained a high level of competence, particularly in the domain of precious metals. The techniques were exercised throughout Europe and were the subject of specialized publications. However, our knowledge of the persons who carried out these analyses, the assayers, remains unclear. Despite the number of publications that described the methods, we do not find one that gives us a view of the art as a whole, and its place in the society of its time. In order to understand the usefulness of the assayer's work, it seems necessary to look at all the arts that were involved in the commerce of precious metals. In fact, at this time, the work of numerous artisans touched upon precious metals and, as a result, they could occasionally be called upon to conduct an assay.[5] Besides the assayers, there were the refiners, the goldsmiths and silversmiths, the gold wire-drawers, the goldbeaters, the moneychangers and the coin stampers.

The refiner's place in the trade of precious metals

At the centre of the sixteenth-century trade in precious metals was the art of the refiner of gold and silver. The refiner imported unrefined metal from the countryside into the towns, transformed it and resold it on the metal market. The unrefined metal was transported from ore-producing regions[6] in the form of plates (see Figure 1) measuring, usually, one foot wide (25-30 cm) by one palm thick (2-3 cm),[7] whose precious-metal content was very high.

The refiner's work, under the supervision of the Royal Mint, consisted of separating the impurities from the gold or silver that were contained in the plates. Once the metals were refined, they were melted down into ingots and resold to various trades. In the sixteenth century, precious metals were put to numerous uses. Most importantly, they were used by royal authorities for minting coins, and by gold- and silversmiths for the manufacture of jewellery and silverware. Gold and silver leaf, prepared by beaters, was also used as gilding for statuary, as decoration for buildings and, in printshops, as gilt lettering on the bindings of books. The gold and silver wire-drawers mixed precious metals with silk thread, to make costly items of clothing shot with gold or silver strands. Precious metals were also used, in limited amounts, for inkmaking[8] and for the preparation of medicines that were reputed to cure various ailments.[9] There was also a trade in recycling old coins and silverware, which brought these objects back to the refiners who then re-introduced the metal into the market in ingots (see Figure 2).

The demand for precious metal in the sixteenth century was enormous, due to the fact that public finances were built upon this commodity. Precious metal was used not only in daily transactions, but also as an investment. It was hoarded in coinage and in various other forms. In a time when coins were rare, when savings banks were rudimentarily structured and land ownership was restricted, the merchant class resorted to jewels and silverware as a way of investing commercial profits. This demand alone explains the steady growth in importance of the precious metals trade.

The assayer

The assayer's role in the trade of precious metals was to ensure the quality of ores and finished products, and his skills were called upon at various points in the production process. In the mining regions, he helped to find mineral deposits and to choose the most profitable veins.[10] In the towns, he assayed the plates of raw material purchased by the refiners. After the metal was refined, the assayer took two samples from each ingot (one from the top, one from the bottom), which he then used to conduct his analysis. After the assay, the precious-metal content was etched into the ingot, next to the marks of the Crown and of the assayer, as a guarantee of purity. The coin stampers also called upon

Figure 1: Transport of lead plates containing concentrated precious metals (Agricola, 1556)

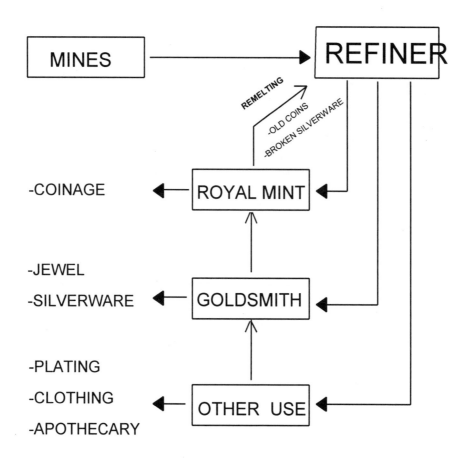

Figure 2: The commerce of gold and silver

the services of the assayer in order to evaluate their purchases of metals, as well as to evaluate the numerous foreign coins circulating in the land.[11] In large towns, the goldsmiths' guilds would retain the services of an assayer who would verify, in the name of the guild, the quality of the metals purchased by the smiths.

On a technical level, there were few differences between the assay and the refinement. The methods were similar and only the scale varied. The assay was carried out by the same method, on a small scale, that was later applied to the transformation of the ore. In his analysis, the assayer used various products without bothering about the costs, while in the large-scale transformation of the ore into plates and the refinement of the metal, the cost of these operations had to be carefully controlled so as to ensure their profitability.

The methods of assaying

The methods of assaying varied, in general terms, according to the type of ore that was being tested. The methods could also be divided into wet and dry procedures. In the dry analysis, the more common of the two, the ore was put in a crucible and melted in a furnace.[12] The intention was to separate the precious metals from the slag that was present in the raw material.[13] This process consisted of capturing a given metal by putting it in contact with another. For example, by pouring lead into molten ore, the gold and silver alloyed and settled at the bottom of the crucible.

The sample to be analysed was, first, ground in a mortar, weighed and placed in a special container (of paper, for example) so as to avoid any loss. A crucible was heated in a furnace, underneath a muffle of fired clay that was heaped with red-hot coals. When the crucible turned red, a small amount of lead was put into it, followed an instant later by the sample. Once the ore was properly melted, the assayer added more lead into the crucible and mixed it in with a glowing coal, which dissolved the silver and gold present in the sample.[14] About an hour later, the assayer withdrew the crucible from the furnace and tapped it on the counter so that the lead and the metal would fall to the bottom. The slag floated on the top and adhered to the sides of the crucible. After cooling, the crucible was broken and the button containing the alloy [lead-gold-silver] was separated from the slag remaining on it.[15]

The lead buttons were weighed because it was already possible to have an approximate idea of the quality of the ore being analysed. They were then put in pre-heated cupels, a kind of container made of compressed bone ash which served as a filter for the molten metals. In a well ventilated furnace, the lead (as well as other metals like iron, copper, zinc or nickel) melted and slowly oxidized. This lead oxide and other oxides then passed into the porous structure of the cupel leaving intact the precious metals.[16] After an hour, the lead put in the alloy completely disappeared, but at the bottom of each cupel remained a shiny little bead of precious metal. An experienced assayer usually knew the value of the ore only by looking at the size of these beads, but the use of a good balance-scale determined more precisely the true content of precious metal present in the sample of raw ore.

But the assay was not yet finished for the metal bead contained both gold and silver, whose proportions had to be determined. To do this, the assayer eliminated the silver with acid. This was possible because gold is untouched by the acids. First, the beads were hammered and flattened into metal leaves to increase the contact surface. The leaves were then put into a nitric acid solution (called *aqua fortis* in the sixteenth century). To speed up the process, the acid could be heated. At the end of the operation, only the gold remained, black in colour, which was weighed to gives the exact proportions of gold and silver of the ore.[17]

There was another method to separate gold and silver with sulphur (or sulphidization) in which silver and copper were transformed into silver and copper sulphide attached together to form a complex substance called matte.[18] The gold present in this mixture precipitated to the bottom of the crucible in which the operation was carried out. The resulting product containing some silver required a treatment using lead in order to remove the copper and the sulphur that were present in the substance.[19] The ore could be analysed with a method using antimony(Sb). In fact, the method made use of antimony sulphide, or stibnite (Sb_2S_3), whose properties had been known since the fifteenth century. This method deserves special attention because it was used by Burchard Kranich to assay the ore coming from Meta Incognita. In this process, silver reacted with sulphur[20] and antimony to produce an alloy with gold.[21] This method had one advantage: it could be used directly upon the ore.[22] At the end, the gold-antimony alloy could be cupelled or simply oxidized in a crucible with a blast of air from the bellows.[23]

To these dry processes, we may add some other methods that made use of various products, like *Saltpetre,*[24] *Vitriol* (solid sulphates, like copper sulphate[25] or iron sulphate[26]). They thus obtained the same chemical reactions as did the other methods using, for example, *aqua fortis*. Agricola gives several recipes without explaining the context of their use. Throughout these operations, the assayer took pains carefully to weigh the samples. The proportions that he calculated at each step gave him the gold and silver content of the ore that was being assayed. It was recommended that several samples should be taken at the point when they were melted in the crucible, so as to reduce the margin of error.

The limits of sixteenth-century chemistry

The methods of analysis used during the Renaissance were relatively complex, but there were, nevertheless, big gaps. Although generally sufficient for evaluating the content of precious metals, the assayers were not able to identify (as is possible today) all the elements present in the ore sample.[27] The methods of the time allowed an assayer to identify numerous metals whose use was widespread, such as gold, silver, iron, copper and lead, but they did not allow him to isolate the other components of a piece of ore.

To get an idea of the knowledge of the time compared to that of today, we need only to glance at a periodic table. In the sixteenth century, chemists knew less than 20 of the 106 basic elements now known to exist in nature.[28] While the chemistry of the sixteenth

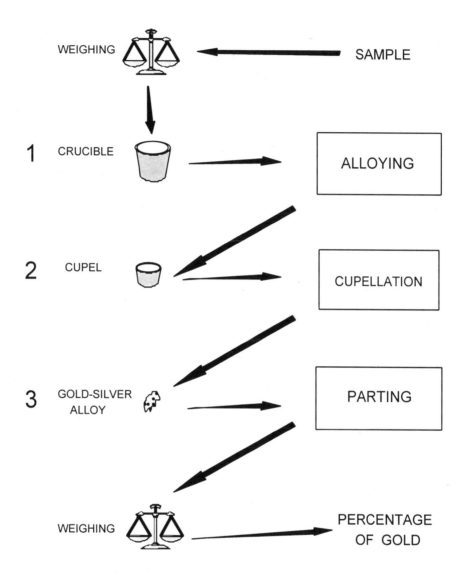

Figure 3: Assaying of precious metal in the sixteenth century

century was relatively developed, at the time it was not supported by clear and incontrovertible principles as subsequently became the case. The chemistry of the Renaissance had only begun to distance itself from the alchemy of the Middle Ages and its ancient Elements of air, fire, earth and water.

The Elements known in the sixteenth century

													C				
															S		
							Fe			Cu	Zn			As			
										Ag			Sn	Sb			
										Au	Hg		Pb	Bi			

In the sixteenth century, the basic elements such as gold or silver were still considered on the same level with chemical compounds such as water (H_2O) or salt (NaCl). There was no real chemistry at that time because alchemists and metallurgists, for instance, shared the same theories to explain the origins of metals. They differed radically however on the empirical level. The chemistry of the time consisted, above all, of practical experience and knowledge linked to a precise art: for instance, pharmacy, metallurgy. A good assayer would have worked at several mines[29] and, over the years, would have encountered different sorts of ore under various conditions. The experience and competence of the assayer were important ingredients in the success or failure of an analysis. Chemists of the time carried out numerous technical operations (amalgamation, precipitation, cupellation, etc.), using a wide array of chemical products, without being able to explain in any great detail how they functioned.

In an operation such as dissolving silver in *aqua fortis*, the assayers of the sixteenth century fully realized the changes that this metal underwent. Some believed that it was possible to substitute, or transmute one dissolved metal with another, such as silver by copper. They could explain, in their own terms, what was occurring at a practical level, but they were still unable to explain the complexity of chemical principles, the valency of the elements, or the links at an atomic level that could explain the results of a given reaction. The methods of assaying ore carried out by the technicians of the sixteenth century incorporated a margin of uncertainty that was much greater than that which exists today. The ingredients used by the assayers were not always pure, and the full composition of the ore sample remained unknown to them. This knowledge represented a certain selection on the part of the assayers, for they were in fact interested only in finding the precious metals. This lack of knowledge of certain chemical principles explains the failure of several assays.

In spite of this uncertainty, the assayer of the sixteenth century certainly did not navigate without landmarks. In fact, there were other, parallel methods of analysis that could help the assayer to identify the elements that were present in his samples. The state and colours of the specimens, as they arrived in the workshop, gave him a general idea of their composition. Blue, for example, meant the presence of *azurite;*[30] yellow meant sulphur or *orpiment;*[31] red meant *realgar;*[32] green meant *chrysocolla;*[33] black meant *bitumen*, and so forth. The assayer could place several pieces on a plate heated white-hot and mix additives to the samples on the hot plate so as to stimulate the melting or, even better, to provoke certain reactions. In this way, he used *litharge,*[34] *ochre,*[35] *minium,*[36] *galena*[37] and *saltpetre.*[38] The fumes that were emitted and the different transformations that he observed gave the assayer additional information.[39]

The assayer possessed a relatively large array of methods, allowing him to identify the composition of the ore that arrived at his door,[40] but none of these was secure from technical error. The only way to counter this uncertainty was to make repeated tests of the samples. Taking the average of these tests was a surer way of obtaining the ore content of the samples and of reducing the margin of error. To reduce the risk of error even more, the samples were sent to more than one assayer. The little piece of ore brought back by Martin Frobisher after the first voyage was not sufficient to perform assays on a large scale. Far from being dupes, the assayers occasionally engaged in fraudulent practices. Legal sources frequently mention this kind of fraudulent practice.[41]

The assayer's work environment

In the past, knowledge of the technical arts was passed orally from master to apprentice in the workplace. Nonetheless, from Antiquity onwards, we find treatises concerning the arts that required a knowledge of technical recipes and of complex procedures.[42] Alchemists, apothecaries, doctors and other artisans possessed specialized treatises to assist them in their work and to instruct them in the knowledge of their art. Beginning in the Middle Ages, we note the appearance of manuals concerning the methods of metallurgy and the treatment of precious metals.[43] However, it is only from the end of the Middle Ages that that we find manuals that are sufficiently precise to be useful for our purposes.[44]

The first half of the sixteenth century

Even though metallurgical treatises existed in the Middle Ages and even in antiquity, it was only around the end of the fifteenth century that they began to be illustrated. The earliest depiction of an assaying workshop is a wood-carving published in Augsburg at the beginning of the sixteenth century in the anonymous *Probierbuchlein auff Gold, Silber, Kupffer and Bley, auch allerley Metall wie Man die zu nutz arbayten une Probieren soll*, the first book of assaying. Other works on the metallurgy of precious metals appeared from 1520 to 1530 in various German cities, under the cloak of anonymity. Of these, three examples merit special mention: *Probirbüchlein tzu Gotteslob* (Magdeburg, 1524), *Probierbuch aller Sächsischer Ertze* (Saxony, 1531) and a *Probierbüchlein* (Augsburg: Steyner, 1534). These works, besides containing recipes and procedures from their regions of origin, repeat the same essential information contained in the first book of assaying, but without republishing the illustrations. Our knowledge of the appearance of the assaying workshops is enriched by the *Pirotechnia* of the Siennese Vannoccio Biringuccio (1480-1539), published in 1540.[45]

The iconography of these two works gives us an idea of the assayers' work environment in the first half of the sixteenth century. For instance, Figure 4 shows an assayer bent over a precision balance, placed inside a case so as to shelter it from air currents. Perched on a three-legged stool, he is weighing the pieces of ore that can be seen on the table next to him. In his left hand, he is holding a piece of paper to contain the samples, so as to avoid losing any material before the ore is fused in the crucible. In the background, we see a small, squarish furnace with a feeder at the bottom. The cover for the furnace is lying on the floor.

The work of Biringuccio shows us two more scenes of activity within an assayer's workshop. The first scene depicts the manufacture of cupels (see Figure 5). The assayer is not, as might be assumed, in the process of crushing the ore with a mortar and pestle, but rather, he is moulding a cupel. He is using a mallet to pound a pestle into a copper mould, in which is contained a paste of ground and charred bone. In front of the assayer we note the tub in which these materials were mixed. On a shelf is an array of cupels of different sizes, where they have been set to dry before being put into use. Behind him we can distinguish the lower part of a furnace with a central feeder or air port, and leaning against the wall, a pallet for arranging the samples.

The second wood-carving from Biringuccio depicts an actual assaying workshop. In front of the furnace is the assayer, in the process of pushing the crucibles into the furnace, or perhaps stirring their contents with a stick (Figure 6). His companion is leaning on a spatula used to place the samples directly into the furnace. On the ground in front of the two is a muffle used to protect the crucibles and the cupels from the coal ashes falling during the operations in the furnace. Behind them on a table is a balance, and off to one side, we notice a three-legged stool. In front of them, on the wall at the right of the picture, is a shelf on which several cupels have been placed to dry. Finally, we see a pile of firewood stacked under the shelf, and another spatula leaning against the furnace.

The second half of the sixteenth century

The quality of the technical works on metallurgy reached a new height with the 1556 publication of *De re metallica*[46] by Georg Bauer, known as Agricola (1494-1555). In his work, Agricola reviewed all the methods used in European metallurgy. The treatise is divided into several chapters, one of which — devoted to assaying in a workshop — is so comprehensive that it served as a reference for metallurgists until the eighteenth century. In addition to describing the methods appearing in previous treatises, Agricola also furnishes a critique that is particularly severe with the alchemists. His work, addressed to specialists and amateurs alike, contains an interesting number of illustrations that show not only the work of the assayer, but also the various tools of his trade.

Figure 4: (Anonymous, *Probierbüchlein...*, beginning of sixteenth century)

Figure 5: (V. Biringuccio, *Pirotechnia*, 1540)

Figure 6: (V. Biringuccio, *Pirotechnia*, 1540)

Figure 7: (G. Agricola, *De re Metallica*, 1556)

Among the woodcuts presented in the chapter on assaying, we find two that show the assayer at work in front of a furnace. This first scene concerns a small assaying furnace circular in form (see Figure 7), in front of which is the assayer, peering through the opening of a protective board so as to protect his eyes and observe the samples as they melt. The furnace is placed upon a counter, on which the assayer can also set the crucibles and hot cupels.

The second woodcut shows us an assayer at work in front of a rectangular furnace with a bottom feeder (Figure 8). The assayer is seated on a three-legged stool and is stirring the molten ore with a stick. As in the previous scene, the furnace is placed on a counter. We note that both assayers are working outdoors, to allow the fumes to dissipate. Their working area is enclosed by a palisade that butts against another building, probably close to the ore entrepot of a mine.

In the text of his work, Agricola provides numerous details concerning the manufacture of the assaying furnaces. He mentions furnaces made from brick, from forged iron and of baked clay. The furnaces made from brick were the easiest and quickest to build, but they were harder to transport than those made of iron or of clay. For small assays, a single furnace sufficed, but sometimes, the assayers required the use of two furnaces.[47] The first of these was generally the larger and the more efficient. Its capacity allowed it to attain the higher temperatures that were required to melt certain ores. The second furnace was used only for cupellation. It could be smaller and it was fuelled by wood coals that covered the muffles in which the samples were protected. At mining sites, or whenever assays were carried out on a large scale, immense cupellation furnaces up to a metre in diameter were constructed. The cupellation furnaces operated on the same principle as did the cupels. Their exterior structure was made from bricks, while the interior or the furnace, especially its floor, was made from bone-ash so as to absorb the lead during the cupellation. At the end of the operation, the cupellation furnace had to be demolished in order to recover the plug of precious metal, and subsequently, to rebuild the bone-ash interior. In order to facilitate this work, carried out by technicians, some versions of the cupellation furnace had metal lids that could be removed after the assay to recover the samples (see Figure 9).

The next depiction of an assaying workshop (Figure 10) comes from the book of Lazarus Erker, *Beschreibung aller Fürnemeisten mineralischen Ertzt und Bergwerks Arten*, an important work on mining and metallurgy published in 1574. This picture enables us to perceive the range of the assayers' activities in even more detail than is offered by Agricola. The first of the two assayers is observing the crucible that he has just placed in a furnace with a pair of pincers, still in his right hand. Next to him is a board (C) to protect his face from the heat and his eyes from the light and sparks (with an observation slot), and a hooked metal rod. To the right of the little furnace of forged iron we clearly see a plate of hot metal on which are arranged sixteen samples.

A little farther along the counter, we recognize the shape of a large crucible, as well as a cellar for another furnace upon which a second assaying furnace could be installed. We

Figure 8: (G. Agricola, *De re Metallica*, 1556)

Figure 9: The cupellation furnace (Agricola, *De re Metallica*, 1556)

Figure 10: (Lazarus Erker, *Beschreibung...*, 1574)

see next the second assayer bent over a water-filled vat (F), weighing auriferous silver in water. He is using a balance to calculate more expeditiously the precious-metal content of an ore sample by determining its density. In the middle of the room we can recognize a flask used to distil the *aqua fortis* (D). On the left, we note a piece of tree trunk on which are an anvil and a hammer used to carry out various operations, and next to it we see again the three-legged stool.

Tools and facilities

The information contained in the treatises is not limited to the assayers in their workshop. These works also contain depictions of the tools and facilities used by the assayers to carry out their task. The books of Biringuccio and Agricola are particularly helpful in this regard. One sees, for example, the large plans of assaying furnaces, including a wealth of details concerning the shape of their different parts. Agricola also gives details concerning the bellows of these furnaces (see Figures 9 and 11), essential for assays at high temperatures. He mentions that the most efficient bellows are those with two chambers, generating a continuous flow of air. As one of the chambers contracted, the other expanded and vice versa.

We also find information concerning the crucibles and cupels used by the assayers in their workshop. From right to left in Figure 12, we see a special oxidizing crucible (A), a large, triangular crucible (B) and a cupel (C). A detailed engraving shows the moulds used to make the cupels, similar in concept to a mortar and a pestle (Figure 13). This picture shows a mould right-side up (A), a mould upside-down (B), the pestle with its rounded base (C and D), and finally the mallet (E). The hole at the base of the positive mould allows the assayer to detach the cupel from the mould at the end of the operation. Agricola also gives us a better idea of the shape of the muffles that were used to protect the ore samples from ashes in the furnace, and to allow the heat to reach the samples (Figure 14). He takes the time as well to identify the main types of weights and measures used by the assayers. Most of the scales were balances hung from a rope, which were used with a series of calibrated weights. In Figure 15 we have, a large (A) and a medium-sized (B) balance and, in the centre (C), a small precision balance sheltered by a cabinet from the air currents that were produced in the workshop. The cabinet has a drawer in which the weights are kept.

The book of Agricola also contains illustrations of other objects such as the boards for protecting the assayer's face and eyes from the intensity of the flames while he observed the samples in the furnace. A specialized tool was the pincer-mould used to make the lead plugs that were essential for the assaying and refining operations (Figure 16). Finally, we have pictures of minor tools such as the metal hook used to manœuvre the samples or to stir the contents of the crucibles, and the tiny ingot mould used to shape the samples of precious metal before they were tested (Figures 17 and 18).

Figure 11: (G. Agricola, *De re Metallica*, 1556)

Figure 12: (G. Agricola, *De re Metallica*, 1556)

Figure 13: (G. Agricola, *De re Metallica*, 1556)

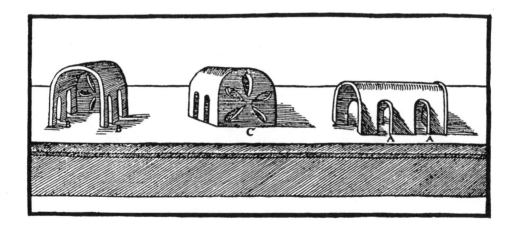

Figure 14: (G. Agricola, *De re Metallica*, 1556)

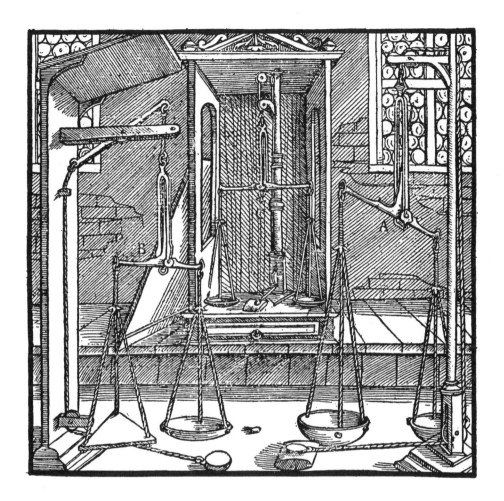

Figure 15: (G. Agricola, *De re Metallica*, 1556)

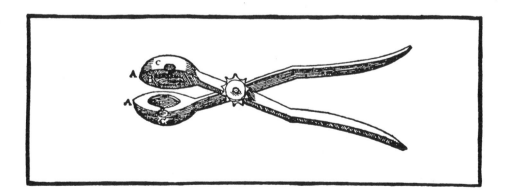

Figure 16: (G. Agricola, *De re Metallica*, 1556)

Figure 17: (G. Agricola, *De re Metallica*, 1556)

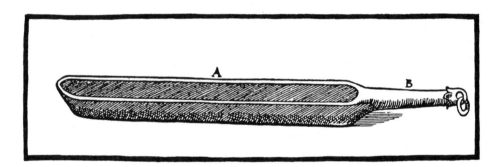

Figure 18: (G. Agricola, *De re Metallica*, 1556)

The Metallurgical Context of the Frobisher Voyages

The methods of assaying the ore of precious metals in the sixteenth century are central to the history of Martin Frobisher's voyages to the Canadian Arctic. This is particularly true for the second voyage which became necessary in order to obtain a sufficient quantity of ore to make conclusive assays, and thence to make a decision concerning the fate of the entire venture. This is however not the case for the third expedition which logically had no reason to exist but was nevertheless sent to Meta Incognita. Several reasons can explain this third and ultimate voyage, among which we shall discuss the international context which, at the time, was favourable to English expeditions towards America.

As far as the metallurgical dimension is concerned, it has often been suggested that there was the possibility of a technical error by the assayers involved in the ore analysis. The most often mentioned mistake was the use of lead that was contaminated with precious metals without the metallurgists' knowledge. Although difficult to demonstrate, this thesis remains plausible, for there is almost no lead on earth which contains no precious metal. This natural phenomenon, known by some sixteenth century metallurgists, not only concerns the metal itself but also the lead oxides which always contain a certain amount of silver. Another thesis that has not been seriously studied but may explain all the positive assays is the possibility of fraud during the assays. The great complexity of the assays, whose limits were sometimes only known by specialists, created an opportunity for this kind of embezzlement.

The commerce of precious metal has always been a sector conducive to fraud where the most common offense consisted of cheating slightly on a sample in order to gain a benefit from the sale of substantial quantities of the metal. The owners of mines or the wholesalers of precious metal could, for instance, inflate the metal content of their samples. Refiners could also commit the same kind of fraud by over-evaluating the metal they sold on the market to the Mint, to goldsmiths, etc., with the same intention of obtaining a larger benefit. Sometimes a metallurgist had to justify his asking price by carrying out an analysis in the presence of a client. In order to artificially improve the results of an assay, the metallurgist could employ one of several techniques. The best known consisted of using additives or lead that contained some precious metal, but other more subtle tricks also existed. The first was the double-bottomed crucible, which consisted of putting gold and silver powder in the bottom of a crucible and covering it with an appropriate clay. During the melting, the powder mixed with the legitimate sample and automatically gave a higher result. An alternative to this subterfuge consisted of putting some precious metal at the bottom of a cupel and covering it with ash. During the firing, the molten lead captured the metal hidden in the double bottom, which then became part of the bead of precious metal that remained at the bottom of the cupel at the end of the procedure.

This double-bottom technique being known by some metallurgists, it happened sometimes that a more vigilant client verified the crucibles and cupels before the assay, or even brought his own assaying containers. In this case, a metallurgist who wanted to falsify and slightly inflate the result could resort to another technique which consisted of hiding precious metal in other materials and instruments used to perform the assays. A piece of charcoal could be excavated and plugged with some gold and silver powder, and then re-closed. During the melting the charcoal burned and its contents would drip into the sample being tested. The same method could also be used with a wooded stirring stick filled with precious metal dust that was released into the crucible during the mixing of hot ingredients. Yet another method consisted of contaminating the paper used to wrap the sample with a liquid silver oxide. A tremendous array of fraudulent practices has been recorded[48] that artificially improved the result of an assay at the time of the sale of a quantity of ore.[49] In fact, to avoid this kind of situation, metal buyers often retained their own assayers who took samples and made their own purity tests, in order to validate the asking price for the metal. This is why we encounter in the Frobisher documentation assayers retained by gold and silver refiners, by the London Mint or by goldsmiths' guilds.

Beside these abuses which aimed simply to add a small profit over a year, there were exceptional cases of fraud that are worthy of mention. The individuals responsible for this kind of offense were often genuine bandits in quest of large sums of money. Preparing their crime in advance, they often presented themselves as magicians or alchemists. They led people to believe in the magical qualities of a substance that could supposedly transmute any metal into gold. To ensnare their victims, some embezzlers did not hesitate to taint all the lead available in a city with precious metal in order to produce positive assays even if the victims provided their own equipment and additives. They might also disguise a genuine golden object by covering it, for instance, with a copper coating that disappeared when bathed in acid, a technique which made the victim believe in the magical power of the pseudo-alchemist.[50]

These relatively rare kinds of fraud were sometimes carried out at the expense of intelligent but naïve and rich persons who were not deeply acquainted with metallurgy. In most cases, the perpetrator disappeared for good immediately after receiving the money he was after. This kind of fraud usually occurred outside metallurgical circles and in remote districts where there were no experts to study the case and detect the trickery. Exceptional situations such as this rarely occurred in the commercial networks of the precious-metal trade, where refiners, goldsmith, or others were able to do a minimum of testing. Flagrant crimes were difficult to commit also because before any important sale of precious metal, the people involved had to lay down a cautionary deposit, procure a mortgage, or find someone to act as guarantor. This is why Francis Walsingham, according to the Frobisher annals, asked Giovanni-Battista Agnello in 1577 to find a guarantor before continuing any further in his project.

Fraud and the Frobisher Voyages

The history of Martin Frobisher is not immune to fraud, but its peculiar context puts it outside these two models of pushing routine results and criminal victimization. The situation which occurred at the end of February 1578 is clearly identified in the sources and was brought to the fore by M.B. Donald in 1950.[51] One of the chief metallurgists in charge of the assays, Burchard Kranich, sent the Commissioners two small ingots of gold and silver that he had smelted from coins of his own pocket, pretending that they were the result of assaying one ton of the ore brought back by Frobisher. Ironically, Kranich did this fraudulent act believing that the ore truly contained some precious metal. He calculated the proportional weights of the two ingots on the basis of an assay of only one pound of ore.[52] What Kranich did not know was that the result of this small test was altered by one of the ingredients he used, the Antimony Sulphide (Sb_2S_3), which was contaminated without his knowledge by precious metal. The other assayer present during the fraud, Robert Denham, subsequently tested the Antimony ore, which confirmed his doubts as to the accuracy of the small test. Burchard Kranich did not intend to rob the English Crown but wanted to obtain the lucrative contract for the treatment of all the ore that Frobisher had brought from the Canadian Arctic. We recall that, at the time, Kranich was in competition with another metallurgist named Jonas Schutz for the direction of the future Dartford plant. He did not commit his fraud in order to pocket a large sum of money and disappear, but to speed up the decision-making process and because he believed in his method using Antimony Sulphide, which was unknown to the English metallurgists of the time. Another aspect must be considered: Burchard Kranich was 63 years old and apparently sick. His fraud saved him the long and exhausting task of manipulating a ton of ore, building a large fining furnace and staying awake for two days in his workshop.

The unfortunate Kranich affair however occurred during a critical period, when several people were promoting a third expedition to Meta Incognita. By creating the illusion that the ore contained gold and silver, the two small ingots that were sent to the Commissioners gave a boost to the preparation of the third expedition and to the building of the Dartford plant. Denounced by Robert Denham at the end of February 1578, Kranich felt into disgrace but, nevertheless, the Frobisher project did not collapse. In the confusion that reigned, several people involved in the expeditions still thought that the ore contained precious metal but that its treatment was difficult. Some may have thought the cost of the treatment might exceed the profit but, nonetheless, they still believed in the ore. Jonas Schutz was named to the direction of assays and another test was performed the 8th of March 1578 which also produced a positive result. At the end of the month, Queen Elizabeth[53] gave her approval to complete the preparations for the massive third expedition which was already well advanced.

The fraud which occurred during this last part of the Frobisher voyages does not conform to the narrow frame of the fraudulent practises normally mentioned in the sources, such as the offense of a gold and silver refiner wanting a bigger benefit over a long term or the crime of a bandit wanting to extort a substantial sum of money. The fraud of Burchard Kranich was that of a man in need of a short-cut who, believing in the quality of the ore, was anxious to obtain a lucrative contract. It was the act of a man exasperated by the slowness of the administrative process and anguished by the idea of being surpassed in his field by a younger competitor.

This flawed crime by one of the most eminent specialists of metallurgy in England at the time (B. Kranich), as well as the mistake repeated by a second specialist, Jonas Schutz, lead us to question the competency of the metallurgists employed by the English authorities. They are all the more obvious, when it is seen that it was precisely the less qualified metallurgists, like the refiners, the goldsmiths, or even the apothecaries, who obtained the best results on their assays of the Frobisher ore. This also brings out a problem encountered in other sciences in the sixteenth century, namely the enormous gap existing between the complex and fragile scientific knowledge of some of the specialists who produced books on metallurgy and the experimental but steady know-how of the average metallurgist, passed on from master to apprentice.

In going through the sources, we have isolated some information concerning the identities of the principals involved in this tale. Among those most easily identifiable, it is clear that William Williams, George Needham and William Humphrey (the young) were assayers who practised this profession. They carry the title of assayer in the sources and they furnished reports of their analyses. Two others however, mentioned as Wheeler and Gregory Bona, were refiners. They transformed precious metals but presumably did not have the necessary knowledge to carry out precise analyses. This was also the case for Robert Denham who was involved in the business of refining. He came from a family of goldsmiths and he seems to have had some experience in mining precious metals. Was Burchard Kranich an assayer? Although we cannot be certain, he is believed to have been an assayer expert in the analysis of ores. He made report of his assays and seems to have had wide-ranging field experience in prospecting for gold and silver ores. Thus, he was the perfect person to test the ore brought back by Frobisher. His reputation was based on his use of antimony procedures, hitherto unknown in England. On the other hand, Jonas Schutz was very critical of Kranich and questioned his ability to examine the ore.

We have very little information concerning Humphrey Cole and John Brode. Were they assayers or were they refiners? We know only that their qualifications were sufficient to allow them to assist Jonas Schutz during his assays. We know little about Sebastian Copland and the four assistants of Hans Staddeler who came from Hamburg to rebuild the furnace and who carried out the assays in Sir William Wynter's house in 1578. It is the case of Giovani-Baptista Agnello that has created the most debate. He seems to have been neither an assayer nor a refiner of precious metal. He was the author of a small treatise on alchemy in 1566[54] and it was perhaps due to this knowledge that he was able to carry out assays on coins.[55] The title that he uses in his first letter to Michael Lok suggests however that he practised the profession. He calls himself "*de la Minera di Tramontana* Maisto nuovo,"[56] or literally, master of the northern mines, in reference to some mines in the north of England or of Meta Incognita. On the other hand, in another letter dated December 1577, he clearly stated to Michael Lok that he was not a specialist in the field. In speaking of the treatment of metals, he said that this "*is not my profession, for in truth, I have never used metals; it is true that, having always been desirous of understanding the secrets of nature, I thought I understood the nature of this ore, as I stated above.*"[57]

The identity of Jonas Schutz, who was present with Agnello from the beginning, is not much clearer. He seems to have possessed good experience in the mines, but was he an assayer as such? In the sources, Schutz is described as a "miner," a "mineral man" and a "master workman in the mineral." This would mean, presumably, that he was above all a specialist in mining techniques, such as the construction of machines for pumping water from mines, the treatment of ore upon its exit from the mine, the construction of cupellation furnaces, etc. While this kind of work was essential for the working of a mine, it does not imply that he possessed the detailed knowledge required for assaying ore. If he were a specialist in assaying and allowed himself to be critical of the work of Burchard Kranich, how could he condone the haphazard methods of Giovani-Baptista Agnello? We recall that Jonas Schutz was introduced to Agnello by John Barkeley so that Schutz could learn "the secret of his techniques."

Conclusion

The third voyage was not justified from a metallurgical point of view. In a normal situation the Commissioners in charge of the decision would have automatically postponed the third expedition and waited for the opening of the new Dartford plant in September before making a decision. There was, after all, enough ore available in London to carry out conclusive assays once the new furnace was operational, at which point they would have realized the non-viability of the project. The history of Martin Frobisher and the Meta Incognita enterprise would have lasted only two years, as was the case for several other exploration projects. The sending of this third and disastrous voyage was not the inevitable denouement to the Frobisher story. Indeed, the obscurantism practiced by the authorities with regard to the assays do not hide the clear anti-Spanish objectives of Queen Elizabeth and her officers who artificially supported the project from 1577 onwards and who transformed the third voyage into a colonial venture in America to their political profit. For Elizabeth, whatever the eventual metallurgical outcome might be, the voyages of Martin Frobisher remained a new occasion to challenge the North American rights and interests of her worst enemy of the time, Philip II king of Spain.

Notes

[1] Thanks are due to Donald Hogarth of the Geology Department of Ottawa University, Lothar Sühling of the Technisches Museum in Mannheim, Fathi Habashi of the Department of Mining and Metallurgy of Laval University and to the members of ARTAF for their assistance in this subject.

[2] See M. B. Donald, "Burchard Kranich (ca. 1515-1578), miner and Queen's physician, Cornish mining stamps, antimony, and Frobisher's gold," in *Annals of Science*, vol. 6 (1950), pp. 308-322.

[3] D. D. Hogarth, P. W. Boreham and J. G. Mitchell, *Martin Frobisher's Northwest Venture (1576-1581): Mines, Minerals, Metallurgy,* Hull, Canadian Museum of Civilization, 1994. See the resumé of assaying methods in Appendix 1, pp. 170-171.

[4] These studies have confirmed, beyond any doubt, that there virtually was no precious metal in the ore from Meta Incognita.

[5] Some very simple analyses could furnish an approximate idea of the precious-metal content in a sample. One of the best known methods, for example, was the touchstone test. This method used a series of granular stones, whose grains varied in size from minute to large. The sample was rubbed across several of these stones, resulting in a striation upon the sample that gave a general idea of its proportion of gold or silver. This method, however, was useful only on objects that contained a large proportion of precious metal.

[6] In the sixteenth century, the precious metals that fed the markets of western Europe came from the Alps, the Carpathian Alps, Africa, India and as well, from Mexico and Peru.

[7] The shape of the plates corresponded to the mould that was situated in the base of the cupelation furnaces put into use near the mines. Their size varied from one place to another because measurement was made using the foot of the man building the cupellation furnace. See Michel Angel, *Mines et fonderies au XVIe siècle*, Paris, Les Belles Lettres, 1989, p. 295 and 298.

[8] Cf. the anonymous *A book of secret shewing divers wais to make and prepare all sorts of inke, and colours [...] also to write with gold and silver [...]* London, A. Islip for E. White, 1596.

[9] Alessio Piemontese (Girolamo Rusuelli), *The secret of [...] Alexis of Piemont, containyng excellente remedies against divers diseases woundes and other accidents [...] translated out of frenche [...] by W. Warde [...]*, 4 vols. London, Kinsgtone, 1558-1569.

[10] Georgius Agricola, *De re metallica*, vol. 2 (1556), p. 40.

[11] The assay was conducted once or twice a year on the principal coinages. See, for example, in the Archives nationales, series K 902, n° 34 (27 May 1590), "Commission d'Henri IV à maître Jean de Carlas essayeur des monnaies pour en vérifier le poids, l'aloi et le titre dans toutes les villes du royaume."

[12] The manual separations (hand cobbing, crushing and cleaning), carried out by mine workers, were also dry methods, but were not considered as such by the authors of assay treatises. This operation, which preceded the forging stages, was important in ensuring the profitability of a mine, especially when the mine did not have extensive equipment.

[13] Roasting the ore in open air could also be used to oxydize sulphur-bearing minerals present in a sample.

[14] Ore + Pb ------> [Pb-Au-Ag] + slag.

[15] Assay can also be possible using the properties of mercury. In this instance, it was not necessary to melt the ore, but only to reduce it to a fine powder and dissolve the precious metals in mercury. The gold or silver was then isolated by mercury evaporation. While this method existed in the sixteenth century, it was not normally used because of the high price of mercury and technical problems in the process. The use of mercury in the extraction of precious metals became general in the seventeenth century, notably in the Americas.

[16] [Pb-Au-Ag] + $\frac{1}{2}O_2$ ------> [Au-Ag] + PbO.

[17] HNO_3 + [Ag-Au] ------> $AgNO_3$ + $\frac{1}{2}H_2$ + Au. This silver in solution was useless for discovering the value of the ore, but this precious metal could be recovered. To make the silver reappear, the gold and silver refiners replaced it with another metal in the residual liquid. In most methods, copper was used, and it should be as pure, or as red, as possible. The copper combined with the nitrate in replacing the silver. The liquid in the basin gradually turned green as the copper nitrate formed and the silver precipitated on the bottom. $2AgNO_3$ + Cu ------> $Cu(NO_3)_2$ + 2Ag. There was also another, less onerous, method consisting of precipitating the silver by adding seawater containing a large proportion of salt (NaCl). Upon contact with the salt, the silver precipitated automatically in the form of silver chloride, insoluble and white in colour. $AgNO_3$ + NaCl ------> AgCl + $NaNO_3$.

[18] 2[Ag-Au] + S + 2Cu ------> [Ag_2S-Cu_2S] + 2Au.

[19] [Ag_2S-Cu_2S] + Pb ------> 2PbS + 2Cu + 2Ag.

[20] Antimony had less affinity than silver for sulphur. See J. Percy, *Metallurgy: the art of extracting metals from their ores* (vol. 3, part 1) *Silver and Gold*, London: John Murray, 1880, p. 367 and 373.

[21] $[6Ag\text{-}2Au] + Sb_2S_3 \text{ ------> } [3Ag_2S] + 2[Au\text{-}Sb]$.

[22] This method is used with ores which have a large precious metal content.

[23] $4[Au\text{-}Sb] + 3O_2 \text{ ------> } 4Au + 2Sb_2O_3$. The silver could be recovered from the silver sulphide by various methods. The lead fusion (with cupellation), for example, gives silver metal and lead sulphide. $Ag_2S + Pb \text{ ------> } 2Ag + PbS$. See more about the antimony process in J. Percy, *Metallugy: the Art of Extracting Metals from their Ores* (vol. 3, part 1) *Silver and Gold*, London, John Murray, 1880.

[24] Potassium nitrate KNO_3.

[25] Chalcauthite ($CuSO_4.5H_2O$). About the commerce of vitriol used for the parting of precious metal see H. J. Kraschewski, "Zur geschichte des Fernhandel mit Blei und Vitriol [...]" in *Braunschweigisches Jahrbuch*, vol. 66 (1985), pp. 115-128 et H. J. Kraschewski, "Vitriolhandel, Termingeschäfte und wechselbriefe [...]" in *Niedersächsisches Jahrbuch für Landesgeschichte*, vol. 59 (1987), pp. 189-211.

[26] Melanterite ($FeSO_4.7H_2O$).

[27] In one of the analyses carried out on the ore brought back by Martin Frobisher, the assayer mentions the difficulty of his task: sometimes, "... il (the ore) est accompaigne de tant dordures et impuretes comme souphres, terre, pierre, loppes et semblables qu'on ne le depart qu'à grant peine...," Geoffroy Le Brumen in V. Stefansson and E. McCaskill, *The three voyages of Sir Martin Frobisher [...]*, London, Argonaut Press, 1938, vol. 2, p. 173.

[28] They knew others, like potassium, chromium, cobalt or phosphorus, but only under their mineral state (sulphide, oxide, nitrate, etc.). Only these 13 elements were partly isolated by 16th century european metallurgists.

[29] Like Georgius Agricola did.

[30] Azurite is a copper carbonate.

[31] Orange to lemon-yellow arsenic trisulfide, As_2S_3.

[32] Arsenic sulfide, AsS.

[33] Copper hydrosilicate, $Cu_2H_2Si_2O_5(OH)_4.nH_2O$, in part; malachite, $Cu_2CO_3(OH)_2$, in part; more commonly white borax, $Na_2B_4O_5(OH)_4.8H_2O$. See E. S. Dana, and J. D. Dana, *The System of Mineralogy*, New York, John Wiley & Sons, 1990 (6th edition), p. 699-700.

[34] Red lead monoxide PbO.

[35] Brown iron hydroxide, $FeO(OH).nH_2O$. See M. Bandy and J. Bandy, (translators & editors) 1955, *De Natura Fossilium* (textbook of Mineralogy) by Georgius Agricola. Geological Society of America, Special Paper 63, p. 34-35 and 198-199.

[36] Red lead oxyde, Pb_3O_4.

[37] Lead sulfide, PbS.

[38] Potassium nitrate, KNO_3.

[39] See M. Angel, 1989, *op. cit.*, p. 141.

[40] They also used transparency, lustre, taste, hardness, specific gravity, flexibility, elasticity, resistance to acids and fusibility.

[41] See, for example, "To the Lord Maiour upon a complainte made by the goldsmithes of London againste their assaier for sundrye yll usage, his lordship is willed withe the assistaunce of this britheren duelie to examyn and heare the cause and to take order therein according to justice so all the parties maye have noe cause of furder complainte," in John Roche Dasent, *Acts of the Privy Council of England, vol. 10 (1577-1578)*, London, Eyre and Spottiswoode, 1895, p. 150 (23 January 1577).

[42] The first evidence of these arts comes from the classical authors, such as Agatharchides of Knidos, Pliny the Elder, Strabo and others. See Bernhard Neumann, "Die Anfänge der Probierkunst und die ältesten

deutschen Probierschriften," in *Metall and Erz: Zetischrift für Metallhüttenwesen and Erzgebau*, Breslau, 1920, vol. 7, pp. 168-169.

[43] See for example Albertus Magnus of Bollstät (1193-1280), *De rebus metallicus et mineralibus*, cited in B. Neumann, *op.cit.*, p. 169.

[44] In a 1977 article, Lothar Sühling of the Mannheim Technisches Museum published a medieval text on metallurgical methods, consisting of the correspondence carried on by Ludwig der Reiche, Duke of Bavaria, with various German experts in metallurgy, around 1468. The correspondence concerns procedures and techniques for the treatment of metals. See, Lothar Sühling, "Herzog Ludwig der Reiche von Bayern als Montanunternehmer am unteren Inn: der Versuch eines Technologietransfers von Nürnberg nach Brixlegg [...]," in *Veroffentlichungen des Museum Fernandeum*, vol. 57 (1977).

[45] Vannoccio Biringuccio, *Pirotechnia*, Cambridge, M. I. T. Press, 1966 (1540).

[46] For an English translation of the 1556 Latin edition, see Herbert Clark Hoover and Lou Henry Hoover, *Georg Agricola: De re Metallica*, London, Dover Publication, 1950 (1912).

[47] We note, in passing, that none of the furnaces depicted in the sixteenth century have a chimney to evacuate the fumes generated by the assays.

[48] Concerning the subject of fraud and precious metal see Michael Maier, *Examen Fucorum Pseudo-Chymicorum* (published in 1617), translated in German by Wolfgang Beck in his Thesis from the *Technische Universitat Munchen*, in 1991.

[49] Voir CSP Dom, CXXVII, n° 78, 1578.

[50] For another example Cf. *Le secret des Alchimistes*, Amsterdam, Time-Life, 1991, p. 99.

[51] M. B. Donald, "Burchard Kranich, miner and Queen's physician..." in *Annals of Science*, vol. 6 (1950), p. 308-322.

[52] "Burcot made proof of but one pound of ore and that according to the proportions of gold and silver found therein he did made upon the rest of the gold and the silver delivered to the commissionners with angel gold and dollar silver of his own." *PRO*, SP12 131-20 cited in M. B. Donald, 1950, *op. cit.*, p. 319.

[53] Walsingham would consult the Lord Treasurer and the Lord Chamberlain. Cf. *PRO* CSP Domestic, vol. CXXIII, N° 5. (11 mars 1578).

[54] Giovanbatista Agnello, *Apocalysis spiritus secreti*, Londra, Gionanni Kingston a instantia di Pietro Angelino, 1566.

[55] D. Hogarth points out that Agnello evaluated the metal content of some coins in 1569. See D. D. Hogarth, P. W. Boreham and J. G. Mitchell, 1994, *op. cit.*, p. 13.

[56] See R. Collinson, 1867, *op. cit.*, p. 99.

[57] "... et tanto più cge questa non à mia professione, per che veramenta io non adoperai mai metalli, glie ben fero che essendo io stato sempre desideroso de intendere i secreti de natura ho pensato de intender la natura di questa minera come di sopra ho detto." See R. Collinson, 1867, *op. cit.*, p. 196.

The Construction of the Dartford Furnaces

James McDermott

Following the return of Frobisher's second (1577) expedition with approximately 160 tons of ore mined from sites on and around the Countess of Warwick's Island (Kodlunarn), the need for larger refining facilities than were currently available to the adventurers became both apparent and urgent. A small furnace-house had been built in the yard of Sir William Winter's warehouse at Tower Hill, in which three "great proofs" of samples of the ore were conducted between November 1577 and March 1578,[1] but neither this nor the smaller furnaces of the assayers Baptista Agnello, Jonas Shutz or Burchard Kranich were able to generate sufficient heat to produce a definitive smelting. Furthermore, the planned scale of the third voyage (even discounting the "illegal" freight ships that were clandestinely hired by Frobisher and Lok) envisaged the mining and return of a quantity of ore that was beyond any existing facility in south-eastern England to refine.

The complex constructed at Bignoures Mill at Dartford to meet these requirements was to be the largest of its kind in England to date. Work commenced in April 1578 and was substantially completed before the expedition returned from Baffin Island at the end of September the same year. Logistically, it was an impressive achievement, financed at a time when other calls upon the adventurers' money were onerous. The intention of this paper is to track the course of construction, adducing the evidence of Michael Lok's account books, to provide an archaeological adjunct to discussions on technical aspects of the assays upon Frobisher's ore.

Sources

Except where stated otherwise, all documentary references are to the two volumes of account books held in the Public Record Office (Exchequer King's Remembrancer, E164/35 & 36), and to the contributions of various individuals contained therein.

Michael Lok himself, as the then treasurer of the pretended Company of Cathay, had charge of the purchase (in London) of most of the materials necessary for the construction of the fabric of the furnaces and the buildings in which they were housed. His own accounts for sums disbursed are contained in E164/36, pp. 177-187, and represent over 50 percent of the stated total costs.

Financial overseer at the Dartford site was John Hales, whose "booke" of accounts is contained in E164/36, pp. 221-292. Hales was primarily responsible for the hiring of labourers taken on locally during the course of preparing the site and erecting the buildings; for the purchase and transportation of timber (other than that supplied by Thomas Kenyon); for the transportation of many of the loads of brick, tiles and mortar purchased in London by Lok; and for the purchase of additional supplies of the same materials outside the capital. A summary of Hales' expenditure during the entire period of construction — compiled by Michael Lok and inserted into the account books as an end-piece to the Dartford expenditures[2] — is reproduced as an appendix to this paper.

The precise role of Thomas Kenyon, another contributor to the account books, is problematic. It is not clear whether he was hired by the Commissioners to arrange for ad hoc purchases of suitable timber in Kent (as, for example, was Robert Thornton), or contracted as an independent agent to seek out and furnish prepared wood directly to site. His personal charges were substantial, representing over 30 percent of the total costs recorded in the accounts he submitted to Michael Lok (which suggests that he was not acting merely in the capacity of employee of the Company).[3] Furthermore, all the timber he provided — over a period of nine weeks between June and August 1578 — was intended solely for the construction of the two "melting houses" built to hold the furnaces; again, this suggests a specific, previously agreed upon service, rather than employment per se. Kenyon also provided (or at least conveyed) the letter of credit in Hamburg which allowed the metallurgist Hans Staedeler to bring four of his compatriots to England to assist at Dartford.[4] In the absence of further evidence, Kenyon's precise status *vis-à-vis* the enterprise remains opaque.[5]

Finally, Edward Castelin's disbursements in respect of amounts still owing at the end of 1578 were placed retrospectively into the account books between Lok's own earlier accounts and those of John Hales.[6] Castelin took on the responsibility for meeting costs relating to the Dartford site following Lok's dismissal as treasurer. Most of these costs were incurred in transporting the ore returned in the third voyage to Dartford and subsequent assays thereon, and not, with few exceptions, to the actual construction work.[7]

A particular feature of the majority of these accounts (compared to those sections of Lok's books relating to the outfitting of the three voyages) is that their entries are quite precisely dated. It is not known why this treatment should be considered appropriate for the Dartford expenditures and not others. In the case of John Hales' accounts, it may have been that the employment of a man who was not an officer of the "Company" — but who was in receipt of large sums therefrom — required a more disciplined record of disbursements; or that the fluctuating need for casual labour on-site throughout the construction period provided too much opportunity for weaknesses (or more deliberate misrepresentations) in accounting for costs.[8] Alternatively, it may have resulted from pressure applied by increasingly disgruntled adventurers who wanted to know how their money was being disbursed. Certainly, this would explain why Lok also set down his transactions for Dartford in a chronological format.

But perhaps the most likely explanation for the form of these entries, however, is the most mundane — that in contrast to the form of the accounts elsewhere in Lok's books, we are looking at primary records of disbursements which were incorporated into the assembled accounts without further posting. There are at least two valid reasons why this should be the case. Firstly, as a significant part of the construction period overlapped with the preparations for the third voyage, time-pressures upon the treasurer may have inclined him to perform no more thorough audit than to collect the day book entries and check totals against receipts from suppliers. Secondly, by the time the construction of the Dartford furnaces was complete, Lok's work was already being scrutinized by the other Commissioners and Privy Council. Within weeks of Frobisher's return, Lok was to be dismissed in the face of several charges against his conduct as treasurer. In view of the personal and logistical problems created by these circumstances, he may simply not have had the subsequent opportunity to post the Dartford transactions into the estate-book format utilized for his other accounts.

Whatever the true reason for their eventual format, the dating of the accounting entries allows for the reconstruction of a "diary" of activity which illuminates much of the actual process of building the Dartford works.[9] It is hoped that this material may contribute to our understanding of the problems experienced in subsequent assays on site, and more generally, to what is known of the archaeology of early-modern building techniques; an issue which the author is content to leave to far more expert scrutiny.

Background

According to the author of the manuscript "A little bundle of the tryeing of the Northwest Ewre by Doctor Burcot, Jonas Shutz, Baptista Agnillo, etc.,"[10] which contains what is probably the definitive account of the early stages of the Dartford works, the Queen's manor at Bignoures was chosen by Jonas Shutz as the most suitable of several sites that he, Lok and Frobisher examined on 16 December 1577, when they rode into Kent at the Commissioners' order.[11] On 12 January, Jonas went back to Dartford with Henrick Williams (who was to construct the brick furnaces) and Sebastian Copland, the German bellows maker, to measure the ground and plan the layout of new buildings to be raised there. Two days later, Jonas presented his structural plans for the refining works to the Commissioners. It is clear, however, that a decision had not been made on the definitive size and nature of the ore-processing works. Certainly, when the Commissioners saw Jonas's proposals they were impressed, but apparently baulked at the estimated cost and time required to meet his specifications, which seemed to preclude the outfitting and despatch of the intended voyage that year. Yet with Jonas continuing to stress that no successful assays upon the ore could be made without significantly larger and better furnaces (and providing assay non-results which apparently proved the point), their prudence became unsustainable. By 22 February, the construction of a major refining plant (probably based largely upon Jonas' original proposals) had been authorized — one of Lok's accounting entries for that date recorded the purchase of freestone "for the furnaces to be bylded at dartford."[12]

Despite the precipitous manner in which this decision to proceed appears to have been made, work did not commence immediately. Funds still had to be secured from the adventurers to finance the building work; on 19 January, in anticipation of this requirement, the second extraordinary assessment, of 20 percent upon existing stock, was authorized and notified to the adventurers.[13] During the following six weeks, Lok recorded only three further transactions in respect of Dartford, and these were peripheral to the actual business of building the works (10s. for the charges of the millwright Robert Hadlow for riding from Rygate to London, 5s. to pay "master killigrew's man" for the receipt of the Queen's portion of the assessment, and 19s. 2d. "for two realmes paper & vi paper book<u>e</u>s"). It was only when Lok, Hadlow, Jonas and Thomas Hitchcock rode to the site on 5 April to measure out the ground once more that work on the Dartford mill could be said to have commenced.[14] Thereafter, the entries for purchases of supplies and, from 23 April, for the hire of labourers, indicate the initially slow (but accelerating) pace of construction.

The following digest traces the profile of this activity, and is drawn entirely from the accounts of Lok, Hales, Kenyon and Castelin.

Construction of the Furnaces

Week ending 26 April 1578:

At Dartford, "The fyrst wekes work began on wedensday being the 23 Aprill 1578 and ended on satturday the 26 Aprill": Workers on site were Robert Hadlow, carpenter (at 2s. per day, with two assistants at 14d. each); two sawyers (one at 16d., one at 12d.); and four labourers, "for waterworkes, to cut a diche to turne the Ryver," their leader at 16d., the others at 12d.

In London, ten hides for making bellows, from Hugh Stanley, currier, at 10s. each.

Week ending 3 May:

At Dartford, Hadlow and two assistants, two sawyers and five labourers "for water workes" (the additional labourer at 10d. per day).

3 tons, & 26 feet of oak timber bought at Dartford wharf.[15] Felling of 4 elm trees of "master goldesmithe;" 1 ton & 24 feet of elm from Sir Francis Knollys' estate at Monk's farm (7 miles from Dartford); elm boards from "Wymfynton."(Wilmington?).

In London, payment for litterage (ie. carriage) of 15 tons of timber to Dartford by Robert Foster (bought from master Barker on 11 April).

Week ending 10 May:

At Dartford, "Hadlow & his ij men were in work, but not reconed withall vntill the xj weke the 5 Julie;"[16] three sawyers, four labourers "for turning the water cours & making a bank thwart the Ryver;"[17] five other labourers (of whom one at 12d., four at 10d.[18]).

3 elm trees (9 loads prepared timber) from Sir Francis Knollys' estate; 3 tons 26 feet of oak timber bought at Dartford wharf; 3 tons 11 feet of oak from Frogland by Sutton (Sutton Hone).[19] Shovel, mattocks, nails "to make whele barowes."

In London, 15 tons of (unspecified) timber carried to Dartford. 2 dozen shovels and a dozen spades; scoops and baskets.

Week ending 17 May:

At Dartford, three carpenters (in addition to Hadlow and his men), four sawyers, thirteen labourers, "to clense the yard for the house plot."

Iron from Dartford to repair cart axles; 3[c]. 26 feet of elm boards from Wilmington; 13 tons and 4.5 loads of elm timber bought from Goldsmith at Wanson Hill (2 miles from Dartford); 1059 feet of oak timber (squared) from Anthony Poulter at Westland (near Sevenoaks), of which 262 feet were delivered to Robert Hadlow "for the watermille workes," and 797 feet "delyvred to hitchcok Carpenter for the frames of the two workhowses" (Hitchcock paid for the transportation of this timber; in the absence of any recorded reimbursement, it is assumed that the cost was rolled up into the total amount he received for building the frames of the workhouses).

In London, iron stampers "to stampe the Ewr at dartford," bought from Harry Matthew, smith.

Week ending 24 May:

At Dartford, no wages paid this week.[20] On site, three carpenters for the millworks (four days only); four sawyers (three for four days only); one labourer.

123 feet of oak from Henry Lane in Hawks Wood (one mile from Sevenoaks). 122 feet of oak from Anthony Poulter. All oak timber squared and delivered to Hitchcock for the workhouses. 14 cartloads of elm (squared) from Coker, Harmon (both of Crayford) and Goldsmith.

In London, ten hides for bellows from Hugh Stanley, at 10s. each.

Week ending 31 May:

At Dartford, three carpenters for the millworks; four sawyers; four labourers "to Clense the yard for the house plote."

Oak, "a great plank" of 19 feet; 5 tons and 20 feet of elm (rough, at 5s. 4d. the ton); 7.5 loads of elm (squared) from Master Vane of Hobery (Hulberry); 15 tons and 11 feet of elm from Coker and Harmon.

In London, no purchases for Dartford in this week

Week ending 7 June:

At Dartford, 9 carpenters for the millworks; 5 sawyers; 11 labourers "for digginge erthe to rayse the ground for the house and myle."

202 feet of squared oak for the millhouses, 209 feet for the watermills (all from Anthony Poulter); 6 tons and 10 feet of elm from Vane at Hulberry.

During this week, and for two subsequent weeks, labourers were also hired to weigh and store the ore returned from the second voyage in the Queen's manor. Their wages were assessed but not paid (the reason for this, unless for want of funds, is not known). On 31 December, according to Edward Castelin's accounts, all these wages remained unpaid.[21] In the seventh week, 23 men worked on this task for five and a half days, at a stated rate of 10d. per day.

No purchases in London for the Dartford works in this week.

––––––––––

At this point, what might be considered as the preliminary period of construction ends. To the end of the seventh week, the main activity appears to have been the preparation of the frames of the buildings to house the furnaces, and of course the bringing to site of the necessary timbers (in the period to 11 June, 150.5 tons of oak timber had been delivered to Dartford for these frames alone). The employment of labourers was confined to the turning of the millstream and cleaning of the foundation sites. Starting in the eighth week, the number of men hired by Hales increased significantly, both to hasten the assembly of the frames for the workhouses, and the raising of their foundations. From 3 June, Thomas Kenyon organized the felling, squaring and transportation of a further 150 tons of timber (for the frames and floors of the watermill) from various sites in the hundreds of Tonbridge and Somerden, and from Sir Francis Knollys' estate at Monk's Farm (Kenyon's entries are not individually dated, and supplies of timber recorded therein are in addition to those stated below).

––––––––––

Week ending 14 June:

At Dartford, 21 carpenters for the workhouses; 8 sawyers; 23 labourers to raise the ground for the workhouse and watermill; in all, 52 men.

122 feet of squared elm for the watermill; 1,046 feet of squared oak from woods about Tonbridge, 76 feet from Knowle Park.

In London, 39 line boards for the bellows.[22]

Week ending 21 June:

At Dartford, 24 carpenters (excluding Hallow and his assistants); 10 sawyers; 46 labourers "to rayes the ground for the house and mille." In all, 80 men; the most labour-intensive week of the construction period. Beginning this week, Richard Clarke and John Wynd (farmers and tenant millers at Bignoures) and the "wydowe Horman" were hired to bring to the site earth, chalk and gravel, for the foundations of the houses and watermill, and also "to make the dame to turne the water;" 13 labourers to weigh and store ore (not paid).

Bolts of iron to repair cart axles; 400 double crossed nails "for the plankes of the milleworkes;" 533 feet of oak (squared) from Sevenoaks and "Lunningstone" (Lullingstone).

In London, no purchases for Dartford this week.

Week ending 28 June:

At Dartford, 17 carpenters (excluding Hadlow); 6 sawyers; 46 labourers to raise the foundations of the workhouses and mill. 20 further labourers weighing and storing ore, not paid.

13 tons of elm (rough) from Crayford.

In London, 51 muffles for the furnaces; also freestone, ladders and baskets "to put nayles in." Charges of Charles Sleed and Thomas Marsh for sums disbursed at Dartford (by bill, unspecified, total 33s. 2d.).

Week ending 5 July:

Hadlowe and his two assistants paid for their work on the watermill; 13 further carpenters; two sawyers; three bricklayers "begininge the 2 of Julye ... to make the foundacone of the housse of hitchecoke carpenter" (1 master at 16d per day, two assistants, one at 14d, one at 12d); 37 labourers "for makinge a diche for the water slewse and for degynge of earthe to skower the river;"[23] 15 further labourers.

To Richard Clarke, £6. 13s. 4d.: "for satisfaccon and recompens for an old sluse of tymber to torne the water, which he made before;" lime from Swanley; 6 loads of sand; rope to draw up the timber of the old mill and sluice; a dozen stopettes "too cast the ryver diche;" 391 feet of squared oak from Lullingstone.

In London, 6,000 bricks (delivered to Dartford wharf on 5 July); lime; ladders; a grindstone and frame; 10 double quarters "to make a frame for the Bellowes."

Week ending 12 July:

5 bricklayers to make foundations for the "house" (3 labourers assisting); 12 carpenters for the millworks (including Hadlow); 2 sawyers; 47 labourers "for leninge" (levelling?) the grounde of the house and Castinge the diche or river" and "scoueringe" (dredging) the river.

10 tons and 20 feet of oak (squared) from Twathe Cross (Tonbridge); 602 feet from Lullingstone; 21 quarters of lime from Swanley.

In London, boards for bellows, 21 square tiles "for saye furnaces;" a "Dansick" chest to carry nails; 5,500 bricks and 500 tiles; £1. 2s. 0d. for caulking, mending and trimming a pinnace to carry supplies to Dartford; 100 bricks and coal to make small proofs at Sir William Winter's "house."

Week ending 19 July:

At Dartford, 10 carpenters for the millworks; 2 sawyers; 4 bricklayers "to tyle the house" (5 labourers assisting); 44 labourers to "skower" the river.

6 tons and 10 feet of elm (rough) from Hulberry; 16 tons of elm (rough) from Sir Francis Knollys' estate at Monk's farm; 151 feet of oak (squared) from Knowle Park; 2,000 tiles from "Moses wydowe of Croken hill;" 13 quarters of lime; 3,500 bricks; Richard Clark and John Wind were paid for the carriage of earth and chalk for foundations (17 days and six days' work respectively).

In London, haulage of 12,000 bricks; 43 line boards, 10 deal boards and "8 powndes of glewe" for bellows; 2 loads of lathes; costs of carriage and repair of "A great paier of bellowes to the tower borrowed of master Lanyson."

Week ending 26 July:

At Dartford, 7 carpenters; 5 tilers "to tyle the great (coal) housse;" 2 sawyers; 45 labourers to "scour" the river (22 discharged after 3 days; all dredging work in the river ended this week).

Iron bolts "for the bemes of the howsse for furnases;" 8,000 tiles (from a mill at Croken Hill) and tile pins; 60 bundles of lathes.

In London, 12,000 bricks;[24] a lantern case "for the saye ballaunce;" charges of Thomas Marsh into Suffolk (2s.) "to the Iron forges for pipes of Iron for the bellowes noses;"[25] 3 loads of lathes and pins; £2. 13s. 4d. "for a nag for Jonas to Ryde to Dartford."[26]

Week ending 2 August:

At Dartford, 7 carpenters for the millworks; 2 sawyers; 8 "tylers for the great housse & plasterares for the walles," 8 labourers assisting.
56 loads of sand from Crayford Heath; 3 loads of lathes from Twathe Cross; 280 loads of clay from Richard Clarke "which claye was vsed in the foundacon of the mill water worke, and ramed in betwene the plankes, and for the slewes."

In London, 14 deale boards for the great bellows; 3,000 bricks; 4 pieces of brass "for myll brasses" weighing 114lb; charges of Charles Sleed into Suffolk "to seake for Iron plates for pipes for the bellowes" (7s. 6d.).

Week ending 9 August:

At Dartford, 6 carpenters; 2 sawyers; 6 tilers and plasterers (14 labourers assisting).

200 lathes, 2 loads "pilles of timber, for the foundacone of the chimnes;" "baste to build the skafoldes;"[27] 12,000 tiles from Herne Hill (Faversham)[28] and 8,000 from Croken Hill; 20,500 tiles bought "at the kiln" at Bawdines (Barn End or a mill of that name);[29] 100 rough tiles for ridging; 11 quarters of lime; 230 feet of oak timber (squared).

In London, 10 tanned hides, an iron pipe and elm planks for bellows; 2 pairs of fine assay balances bought from Robert Denhenley "Frenchman" (one pair at 50s. remaining in London and one at 40 s. sent to Dartford); a small iron furnace for small proofs (£1. 10s. 0d.); carriage of "Jonas Stuffe and Irons for the myll and axeltrees to dartford."

Week ending 16 August:

5 carpenters for the millworks; 2 sawyers; 10 tilers and plasterers "for the ij housses" (11 labourers assisting).

6 pairs of hooks and thimbles "for the 4 greate dores and the 2 howses," 19 pairs of hooks and hinges and latches for 19 windows and "a grete sledge hamer;" 14 tons 26 feet of elm (rough); 258 feet of oak timber (squared).

In London, 12 loads of stones from Cornwall for the furnace at Dartford.[30]

———————

External construction work at Dartford came to an end in this week, with the emphasis passing to interior fittings and dividing walls.

———————

Week ending 23 August:

At Dartford, 5 carpenters for the millworks "within the howse for the stamperes, & the bellowes;" 2 sawyers; 2 bricklayers for the furnaces (Henrick Williams — at 2s. per day — and his assistant),[31] 2 labourers assisting; 5 plasterers "for the walles" with 18 labourers assisting "and doinge other thinges nedfull."

100lbs of iron, to make hooks and hinges for the stampers; 13lbs of iron in hooks "to lincke the stones in the furnasse," and a bar of iron "for the little furnas in the lesser howse;" 21 bushels of "heare" for the plasterers;[32] 14 quarters of lime; 18,500 tiles (and 12 ridge tiles) from the widow Moses; 600 lathes and 5,000 lathe pins; half-tubes "to hold mortar for the bricklers;" 37 sacks of coal; 6lbs each of red ochre and blacking "vsed in the toppe of the Chymney of the furnaces;" 24 loads of clay for binding the sluice; 72 feet of oak (squared).

In London, ash timber and 6lbs of "glewe" for the bellows; charges of Charles Sleed into Sussex for iron plates.

Week ending 30 August:

At Dartford, 5 carpenters for the interior millworks; Williams and 2 assistants building the brickwork of the furnaces; 15 labourers "to driue piles of wode / & to sarve the brickelayers;" 5 plasterers — "william Rice & John beterers and their 3 laborers by taske in great agrement for to finyshe the walles of bothe the howses — £1. 6s. 8d."

155 feet of oak (squared).

In London, 5 pairs of iron plates from George Bullyne "gent." for the bellows, at 33s. 4d. each;[33] 2 loads of freestone; nails for the bellows.

Week ending 6 September:

(The final week in which Hales hired local men for general building work on site)
At Dartford, 5 carpenters; 2 sawyers; Williams and 2 assistants building the furnaces; 10 labourers assisting the bricklayers and making "the fondacons of the furnaces in digginge of earthe and dryving piles of woodde."[34]

Iron used in constructing the furnaces, and for repairs; 50 feet of oak (squared).

In London, 8,000 bricks; 4 calves' skins, 2 elles of canvas, boards, "hogges grese" and glue for the bellows.

Week ending 13 September:

At Dartford, 16lbs of red ochre and blacking for the second furnace chimney; £1 to Harbord More for compensation for turning the course of the stream from his mill; carriage of freestones and 7,000 bricks sent from London.

In London, 5,005lbs of bricks, and 500 tiles from John Clark of St Bartholemew's; picks; nails; 9 deal boards for the bellows, 6 112lb weights (at 6s. 8d each).

Week ending 20 September:

No purchases or wages at Dartford this week.

In London, costs of shipping freestone and bellows to Dartford; glue and (blank) for "the mending and furnishing of the bellowes to (Se)bastian;" £1. 3s. 4d. for the sewing of ten bellows leathers to John Roberts; wages of James, servant to Jonas for 17 weeks (at 5s. per week).

Week ending 27 September:

In this week, John Hales presented his own bill for expenses and wages, as follows:[35]

> *Charges extraordinarie as followeth*
>
> *paid for horse hyer of me John hales, and the Carpentares & other workmen, into the contrye to dyvers places to provyde tymber, and bryk & tyle & other stuffe necessarie for the byldings at dartford mylles, in all this tyme of v monthes*   li 5. 6. 3
>
> *paid for the wagys & dyat & travayll of me John hales, in this tyme of these workes at dartford from the 23 april, vntill the 23 september 1578 / which is for v monthes / at xxd. a daye amounteth li 7. 10. 0*

In London, Lok paid various charges for carriage of materials and minerals, most notably for the freight of 14 tons of marquesite from Newcastle, sent by the instrument maker Humphrey Cole, who had been hired by the Commissioners — for an eventual recompense of £20 — to search out suitable additaments for assays in the new furnaces.

Aftermath

At this point, I have drawn an arbitrary line under the entries for Dartford in the account books. With Hales' submission of his own bill for expenses and wages, the construction of the works drew to a close. Lok continued to disburse amounts relevant to the refining process on site, particularly in respect of the purchase and transportation of lead, "marquesite" and other minerals, and Edward Castelin subsequently recorded significant debts incurred in the hiring of men to attend upon the mills and to transport ore from the wharfside at Dartford to the Queen's House (and from there to the furnaces); but I have considered these matters to be distinct from the actual process of construction, even though the costs are treated by Lok as belonging with the accounts for the "buyldinges at dartford," and comprise part of the total expenditure thereon. Any work subsequently carried out upon the fabric of the buildings or furnaces was to repair the ravages of the assay process, rather than to modify or add to the existing structures.

The refining works were completed a matter of weeks before the return of the third voyage. According to the Auditors' final report (6 May 1581), the complex consisted of "two great workhoussses, & two watter mylles, with fyve great meltinge furnaces in the same housses, & one great Colehous, & other necessarye workhouses erected at beknars mylles neere dartford in kent."[36] The site had hardly been cleared of the detritus of the previous months before the first convoys of carts began to carry their loads of ore from Meta Incognita down the Dartford roads. In the context of that era's seemingly limitless opportunities the image is particularly striking: to the more credulous of the adventurers it must have seemed that they were witnessing the beginning of a commercial exploitation to rival Spain's own New World windfall. If we consider also the difficulties experienced in securing the necessary funds for the first major complex of its type in South-East England, the pace and apparent efficiency of the construction seem laudable, and mirrors the single-minded determination which characterized many aspects of the Frobisher enterprise.

If, however, the accounts illuminate much of the process of creating this facility, they are inevitably unrevealing of its true quality. Appended to Lok's account books is the testimony of Daniel Hochstetter and George Needham, two assayers from Keswick, who in March 1580 attempted to refine quantities of lead and copper ore in the Dartford furnaces.[37] Barely eighteen months after the completion of the works, they describe a scene which might have suffered the neglect of decades; and their report, if intended in part to promote their own skills and processes, was a damning indictment of the abilities of Jonas Schutz:

> (On attempting to refine copper ore) *wherein of smeltinge the same Yewres we spente iij dayes and more by reason the furnace there was not so orderlye made nether the bellowes gave suche apte blaste as they oughte to haue donne ... in the smeltinge of the sayde rosted yewres we founde suche wante in the buildinge of the furnace and the disorderlye placinge of the bellowes that we coulde not by anymeanes possible perfectlye smelte downe all the sayde yewres but muche thereof remayned in the furnace and was turned into a great lumpe commonlye termed a sowe.*

If the copper furnace was poorly fashioned, it was markedly more effective than the great lead furnace:

we did finde the furnace that was made for smeltinge of leade Yewres to be so farre out of order that yt woulde not serve us whereby we were forced to smelte the sayde leade yewres in the furnace where we had smolten our Copper Yewre and stone which furnace was farre out of proportion bothe in forme and in blaste to smelte leade yewres.

Acknowledging the significant attrition caused by the five major assays upon samples of the Meta Incognita ore,[38] it is nevertheless likely that the Dartford furnaces, even newly constructed, were largely inadequate for their intended use. Consider then the relative novelty of the ore's composition and, of course, the extremely low levels of precious metals therein; circumstances more perfectly designed to cause both frustration and confusion could hardly be envisaged.

In hindsight, that the furnaces were so poorly configured seems in large part to be a corollary of Jonas' input to their design. Clearly, the charges of incompetence made against the metallurgist by his former rival Burchard Kranich had much substance; his successive claims for the value of the ore, if not deliberately misleading, evidenced a generally poor level of expertise. Even allowing this point, however, there were surely enough skilled men on site during the construction process to have identified weaknesses in the design of the mills. Unfortunately, the rather inflated contemporary reputation of Saxon metallurgists was not only misplaced in this instance but actively damaging; once Kranich's challenge to his position as lead assayer had been fought off, Jonas' professional abilities were not seriously questioned again until the worthlessness of the ore had become obvious to all. His lack of competence would seem to apply equally to his assaying skills and to a more general lack of understanding of the technology he misused (in extenuation, it is almost certainly the case that the scale of the intended facilities posed technical problems for which there was little contemporary experience in England). Thus, Frobisher's unfavourable opinion of Jonas — characterized by Lok as merely another symptom of their protracted antipathy — had been sound; though Frobisher's own support of Kranich, a man who deliberately salted his assays with silver-bearing additaments, could hardly have produced any more favourable outcome to the business at Dartford.[39]

The site of the Works had been devoted in previous years to milling wheat and malt; within a year of the demise of the Company of Cathay there appears to have been no other activity carried on there. The paper mills that were raised subsequently upon the same site and, more particularly, the gunpowder works established in the early eighteenth century, have erased all trace of the refining facilities and the buildings in which they were housed.[40] For a complex which had been built with such high expectation, its early, complete and inglorious demise seems especially poignant. Ultimately, however, the evidence suggests that the execution of the mills was almost as flawed as the logic which had conceived them.

Appendix: Summary accounts of John Hales & Thomas Kenyon

(PRO; EKR, E164/36, p.299)

Summ of all the paymentes by the booke
of John hales

wekes/	men/	wages/		lefe/		
1	9	li	2. 4. 0	23	li	14. 2. 11/ li 68. 11. 1 for
2	10	li	3. 12. 0	24	li	18. 18. 11 stuffe bought in the
3	12	li	3. 13. 0	24	li	23. 12. 3 Countrie, brike, tyle,
4	20	li	6. 3. 0	25	li	11. 17. 0 lyme, etc./
5/6	11	li	5. 10. 2	26	li	50. 7. 2 / Oke tymber bought.
7	25	li	7. 0. 8	27	li	15. 9. 5 / elme tymbar bought
8	62	li	16. 12. 6	28	li	3. 5. 1 / for cariage of stuffe
						which came from London
9	80	li	23. 9. 6	29	li	1. 1. 4
10	69	li	19. 17. 6	30	li	23. 9. 4 / cariage of Erthe, claye
						to Levell ground.
11	73	li	31. 11. 8	30	li	4. 13. 6 / caraige of brik, tyle,
						& stuffe bought in
						Countrie.
12	69	li	19. 17. 2	33	li	5. 4. 6 / felling & squaring
						elme tymber.
13	65	li	18. 18. 2	35	li	6. 18. 2 / cariage elme tymbar.
14	59	li	14. 10. 0	37	li	4. 13. 1 /
15	25	li	8. 1.10	38	li	7. 7. 1 / li 25. 7. 8 cariage
						oke tymber.
16	28	li	8. 8. 4	39	li	8. 17. 2 /
17	31	li	9. 14. 4	40	li	4. 10. 4 /
18	34	li	10. 15.10	43	li	12. 16. 3 / charges of John Hales
19	28	li	8. 15. 4		li	217. 3. 6 at dartford.
20	20	li	7. 18. 0		li	226. 13. 0
		li	226. 13. 0/		li	443. 16. 6 summ paid by J. hales

Summ of thaccount of thomas kennyon /

Lefe	44	li 10. 3. 10 / for squaring Oke tymbar
	45	li 16. 16. 8 / for cariage Oke tymbar.
	46	li 12. 4. 9 / for charges of thomas kennyon.
		li 39. 5. 3 paid by thomas kennyon /

li 443. 16. 6
li 39. 5. 3

Summ paid   li 483. 1. 9 the 13 september 1578

Notes

[1] PRO, *Exchequer King's Remembrancer* E164/35, p. 152 (hereafter EKR 164/35): "paid to Sir William Winter for bordes bryke and other stufe and Carpentares for workemanshippe, to buldinge the house, for the furnace firste buldede at his house at tower hille - li 8. 7. 8."

[2] *EKR* E164/36, p. 299.

[3] Ibid., pp. 293-298. Kenyon's personal expenses were billed at the rate of £1. 8. 0. per week, or more than double that of John Hales (whose responsibilities for the Dartford works were substantially greater).

[4] Ibid., p. 183.

[5] The manner in which Lok incorporated Kenyon's expenditure into the account books distorted the true cost of the Dartford works. As part of the charges of £948.14.10 reported in his own "booke," Lok includes the amount of £39.5.3 reimbursed to Kenyon "for felling, squaring & cariages of 130 trees/dyvers parcelles of oke Tymber provided by hym in kent, for the buylding of the two melting howses at dartford by his accoumpt geven vpp in august last...." (E164/36, p. 184); yet an almost identical figure — minus the 3d. — is included once more as a discrete item referenced "by booke of kennyon" in the summary of total expenditure (Ibid., p. 187). It appears then that the true total cost of the Dartford works was £1839.18.0, and not £1879.3.0. as stated. The error was not discovered by the auditors, who repeated Lok's total without comment (E164/35, p. 72).

[6] E164/36, pp. 201-211.

[7] Such costs form part of the accounts for "building" work at Dartford, but are distinguished therefrom for the purposes of this paper.

[8] In an arrangement that would be entirely familiar to the twentieth-century contractor, labourers at Dartford were hired on a weekly basis, being paid on Saturday afternoon, following a six day working week.

[9] In many cases, the dates of payment probably do not correspond precisely to those upon which delivery was made, thereby causing some distortion to the reconstruction of a chronology of events. However, in view of the essentially cash on delivery-based arrangements of most, if not all, of the suppliers involved, this is not considered to pose a significant problem.

[10] The hand that set down this document is not Lok's, but its partisan support of Jonas Schutz against the claims of Kranich strongly suggests Lok's influence.

[11] PRO SP/12/122, 62: "And at Deartforde Jonas lyked the mills best of all others for the comodious water and place."

[12] E164/36, p. 177.

[13] The assessment raised £1,080, being based upon the Commissioners' original costing of the Dartford complex (SP/12/122, 9 (19 January 1578)). The amount assessed was significantly less than was eventually to be required; it appears from their deliberations that the Commissioners were originally considering more modest facilities. Although the planned number of large furnaces did not change subsequently, the fact that the site was measured out twice implies a divergence between the original specification and that which was eventually considered appropriate.

[14] Hitchcock, a master carpenter, built the frames of the "two great houses for the milles for the workes at dartford," at a cost of more than £145 (E164/36, p. 184). The fee was noted as part payment, but the (unstated) balance is not recorded as having been paid subsequently (nor shown as outstanding in any of the auditors' reports).

[15] This timber, ready-squared and delivered to Dartford, commanded a premium (at 13s. 4d. the ton) over similar timber purchased where felled (at rates between 2s. "had roughe" and 10s. "redye squared"). The rebate for squaring a particular load was usually 16d. the ton (a "ton" was assumed to provide 40 feet of squared timber). It is not clear whether the general variance in rates paid for timber (especially oak) over the period of construction reflects an inconsistency in quality, the effect of the Dartford works on the local market — all timber came from within a 14 mile radius of the site — or the varying costs incurred in its transportation (throughout the sixteenth-century, transportation of materials was one of the most significant components of the cost thereof).

[16] On 5 July, Hadlow and his two men received wages for nine weeks and two days. Hale does not note the basis upon which he was employed, although, as lead carpenter on site — other than Hitchcock himself — Hadlow was probably contracted (ie. for building the watermill) rather than hired per diem, to be paid at the conclusion of each stage of construction. He continued to work on site beyond the completion of the mills, principally repairing damage wrought by the assaying process.

[17] The course of the stream serving the existing wheat and malt mills was diverted for four weeks to allow the foundations of the new millworks to be laid and set. The tenant of the mill most affected by this, Harbord More, was compensated £1 for his loss of earnings during the period.

[18] There was a distinction in rates paid to labourers employed upon tasks which might be considered semi-skilled, with a premium of about 2d. per day over the basic allowed for basic manual labour.

[19] Oak timber purchased in this and the previous week were paid for at the time of delivery. Subsequent purchases of oak were made under bills of sale, which were settled in the period 2-9 August (E164/36, p. 259: some further, minor purchases of oak were made in August and September, but paid for on delivery). The costs of felling, squaring and transportation — undertaken either by employees of the suppliers of timber, or by independent contractors — were met on a c.o.d. basis. All elm timber was paid for at the time of delivery. The reason for this distinction between the methods of purchasing oak and elm is not clear, unless the significantly greater volume of oak required for the mills caused John Hales to enter into volume-based contracts with his suppliers.

[20] Two weeks' wages were paid to these men in the following week. It is not known whether the failure to pay wages in the fifth week, and the reduced level of activity, reflects a shortfall in funds, although it may be significant that Lok was reporting difficulties in collecting the latest assessment at this time (by the 3 May, £265 of a total of £1,080 assessed remained owing from the adventurers — SP/12/124,2). Certainly, the volume of timber delivered during the previous week indicates there was sufficient work for at least some of the labourers, and the time of year makes it unlikely that poor weather was an issue.

[21] E164/36, pp.206-7.

[22] All the bellows (10 pairs) were constructed in London by, or under the supervision of, Sebastian Copland, and delivered to Dartford complete. Copland was paid £17 for his work (E164/36, p.184).

[23] References to scouring the river probably refer to the dredging of an inlet of the river Darent closest to the Queen's House (where the ore was to be taken upon unloading), rather than to the stretch adjacent to the mill site (approximately one mile further south, and on the river's main channel). Ore subsequently transported from storage in the Queen's House to the mills was brought by cart, rather than water.

[24] These appear to be the same bricks for which Lok paid the haulage costs the previous week. Clearly, brickmakers offered their customers a period of credit in which to pay for their services, wharfingers did not.

[25] Thomas Marsh appears to have been exceedingly busy in this week; the following day he set out to Bristol to oversee the loading of ore returned from the second voyage into the Earl of Leicester's ship (The *White Bear*), but returned immediately "bicause the Shippe would not be redye in Long tyme after" (E164/36, p.179).

[26] At that price, either Jonas was weighting his expense claims or the horse was more than a "nag."

[27] None of the aforementioned items had been paid for as late as 31 December 1578 (E164/36, p. 203).

[28] Delivery of these tiles was tardy; the accounts complain of their being "layed doune the 12 august at a place called hedgehouse shorte of darteford wharfe a mille" (E164/36, p. 267). Richard Clarke was paid to bring them the rest of the way at 16d. per thousand, which seems somewhat expensive (transportation of the ore from the Queen's House to the mills — an equivalent distance — was arranged subsequently at a rate of 10d. per load).

[29] These tiles were 6d - 8d per thousand cheaper for being bought at the production site.

[30] Perhaps sent by Edward Fenton in his search for the "antimonye" used by Burchard Kranibch in his earlier assays.

[31] This was a part-payment; Lok also paid Williams 3 s. per day for the same work in two of the three weeks the bricklayer spent at Dartford constructing the furnaces (E164/36, p. 180).

[32] Hair (probably horse-hair), to bind the plaster.

[33] Considering the cost of iron used elsewhere in the construction work, these plates seem to be inordinately expensive, an indication, perhaps, of their great density, required to protect the bellows from the heat generated in the furnaces.

[34] This work could hardly have been carried out after or whilst Williams finished the brickwork for the furnaces; the entry must refer to work already done in a previous week, or to the preparation of the foundations for the smaller furnaces (the purchase of large number of bricks in London during the same week suggests the latter).

[35] The final amount had been notified to Lok and incorporated into his accounts ten days earlier (E164/36, p. 299).

[36] Ibid., p. 327.

[37] Ibid., pp. 307-313. It is not known why Lok or the auditors should have included these papers with the accounts for the voyages; their conclusions hardly served the apparent purpose of the former treasurer, who was proposing at that time to buy all the ore in return for a quietus est upon the debts of the enterprise. Perhaps he was attempting to absolve himself of responsibility for the failure of the enterprise by adducing evidence of poor technology

[38] According to Edward Castelin's account of monies not paid at 31 December 1578, some 21,000 bricks had been required following the 'completion' of the furnaces; an indication of the destructive nature of the refining process (Ibid., p. 203).

[39] It appears that there was further (but unspecified) technical input from John Dee; in addition to his supplying 24 hundredweight of lead ore for the furnaces, Lok's accounts record at least three visits by the treasurer to Dee's house at Lambeth on "Dartford" business (E164/36, p. 184).

[40] D.D. Hogarth, P.W. Boreham & J.G. Mitchell, *Mines, Minerals, Metallurgy*, Canadian Museum of Civilization, Mercury Series, Directorate Paper 7, 1994, p. 85.

How Strange is a Stranger?
A Survey of Opportunities for Inuit-European Contact in the Davis Strait before 1576

Kirsten A. Seaver

In this place [Frobisher] saw and perceyued sundry tokens of the peoples resorting thither. And being ashore, vpon the toppe of a hill, he perceiued a number of small things fléeting in the Sea a farre off, whyche hée supposed to be Porposes, or Ceales, or some kinde of strange fishe : but comming nearer, he discouered them to be men, in small boates made of leather. And before he could discende downe from the hyll, certain of those people had almost cut off his boate fro him, hauing stollen secretely behinde the rocks for that purpose, where he spéedily hasted to his boate, and bent himselfe to his Holbert, and narrowly escaped the daunger, and saued his bote. Afterwards, he had sundry conferences with them, and they came aborde his ship, and brought him Salmon and raw fleshe and fishe, and gréedily deuoured the same before our mens faces.... They exchaunged coates of Ceale, and Beares skinnes, and suche like, with oure men, and receiued belles, loking glasses, and other toyes in recompence thereof againe.

> George Best, "A True Discourse," in Vilhjalmur Stefansson and
> Eloise McCaskill, *The Three Voyages of Martin Frobisher*, London,
> 1938, pp. 48-49.

Their manner of trafficke is thus, they do vse to lay downe of their marchandise vppon the ground, so muche as they meane to parte withall, and so looking that the other partie, with whome they make trade, shoulde doe the like, they themselues doe departe, and then, if they doe like of their marte, they come againe, and take in exchange the others marchandise, otherwise, if they like not, they take their owne and departe.

> Ibid., pp. 58-59.

[Captain Yorke's men] beheld (to their greatest maruaile) a dublet of Canuas made after the Englishe fashion, a shirt, a girdle, thrée shoes for contrarie féete, and of vnequall bignesse, whiche they well coniectured to be the apparell of our fiue poore countriemen, whiche were intercepted the laste yeare by these Countrie people, aboute fiftye leagues from this place, further within the straightes.

> Ibid., pp. 66-67.

[The fleeing Natives of the Nuuk area of West Greenland] left in their tents all their furniture for haste behinde them, where amongst other things were founde a boxe of small nayles, and certayne redde Hearings, boordes of Fyrre trée well cutte, with dyuers other things artificially wroughte, whereby it appeareth, that they haue trade with some ciuill people, or else are in déede themselues artificiall workemen.

> Ibid., p. 86.

We found also in [the Natives of Meta Incognita's] tents a Guinney Beane, of redde couloure, the which dothe vsually grow in the hote Countreys: whereby it appéereth they trade with other nations which dwell farre off, or else themselues are greate trauellers.

> Ibid., p. 126.

The surviving accounts from Martin Frobisher's three voyages to Baffin Island between 1576 and 1578 provide more than a hint that the Baffin Island Inuit had previous experience with Europeans, as Vilhjalmur Stefansson and Eloise McCaskill frequently noted in their 1938 edition of the Frobisher expeditions reports. Archaeological investigations on both sides of the Davis Strait point the same way, as do written sources, among the earliest and best-known of which are the two "Vinland Sagas."[1] Previous experience with Europeans may well have influenced Inuit behaviour towards Frobisher's men and therefore deserves study within the context of the current Meta Incognita investigations. A presumed earlier presence of Europeans in north-east Canada may also have a bearing on the interpretation of non-Eskimo[2] artefacts found on Frobisher sites.

Here, our focus will be on the five-hundred-year prelude to that first large-scale encounter between well-equipped representatives of Renaissance Europe and their seemingly unpredictable Inuit hosts. Archaeological research done from the Greenland perspective as well as recent studies of the Arctic marine mammals hunted by early European intruders on Dorset and Thule territory will be included, and Norse, English, and Iberian voyagers will be considered by turn, with the greater share of attention being paid to the Greenland Norse because they were the most pervasive European presence in that part of the world until about A.D. 1500. The map in Figure 1 provides a general guide to the locations involved.

Throughout the Middle Ages, the Norse colony in Greenland represented Europe's westernmost outpost and, for a long time, also the north-west frontier of the Roman Church. Church business as well as secular trade in fish, fish oil, blubber, cattle hides, wool, furs of every kind, eiderdown, walrus ivory, and white falcons (ranked by their order on the luxury scale) ensured that for as long as the Norse colony lasted, many mariners knew the route to Greenland and, in time, beyond — a situation which early maps such as the Cantino Map of 1502 and the Ruysch World Map of 1507 make clear.[3] Although contact with Norway eventually ceased,[4] by about 1420-30 south-east Greenland probably was on the regular itinerary of English fishermen and traders already exploiting Iceland and its surrounding waters, who were quickly accumulating a wealth of sailing knowledge about the North Atlantic and the Davis Strait. Those few who appear to have made their way into the deep west Greenland fjords to trade with the Norse were most likely from Bristol, the city from which John Cabot in 1497 made the first documented post-Norse voyage to North America, decades after enterprising fishermen from the same city are likely to have begun exploiting the rich fishing banks off Labrador.[5]

Once it became generally known in Europe, in the late fifteenth and early sixteenth centuries, that the large land mass across the Atlantic continued northwards, the waterway between Greenland and North America known as the Davis Strait (which Renaissance maps often depicted as a bay) became a logical starting point for explorers seeking a north-west passage to Cathay, while the north-eastern American shore soon became a destination in itself for Europeans eager to exploit the rich natural resources of land and sea which the Greenland Norse had discovered centuries before.

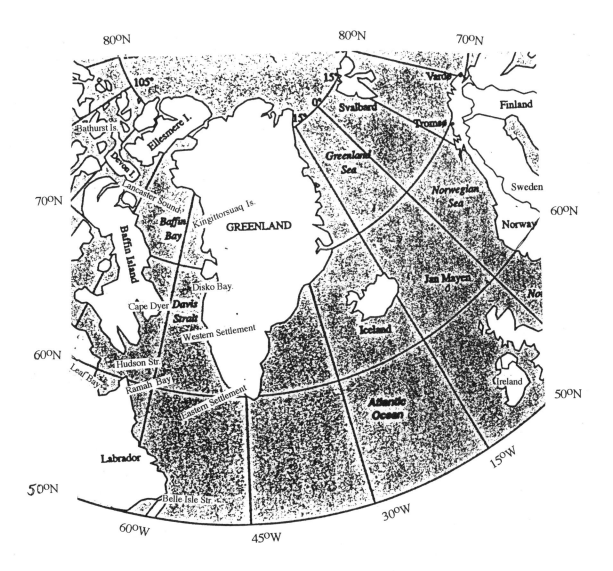

Figure 1: Map marking the chief locations mentioned in this paper.

The Norse

The Norse discovered North America around A.D. 1000. Although the lack of established antecedents for both *Grœnlendinga saga* and *Eiriks saga rauda* has made these sagas (known to us only from their thirteenth-century versions) somewhat suspect as historical sources, we should note that apart from present archaeological proof in Newfoundland that the Norse did cross the Davis Strait soon after settling in Greenland, medieval Icelandic writers and annalists referred more than once to a large and imperfectly known land mass far west of their own country that clearly was not Greenland. This practice may "reflect medieval notions of geography" or even Irish legends, as has been suggested,[6] but direct communication between Greenland and Iceland continued well into the fifteenth century; so given the long stretches of North American coast which the Norse are credited with exploring at a minimum, and considering the likelihood that the Norse Greenlanders continued for several centuries to exploit North America on a limited basis, it is reasonable to suppose that learned men in medieval Iceland took for granted western land beyond their personal ken where any number of events might credibly have taken place.

In *Landnámabók* (The Book of Settlements),whose first written version can be traced back to just before 1300 (but which had been partly compiled by Ari Thorgilsson the Learned, 1068-1148), we find that another Ari, the son of Mar Atlason, reportedly had drifted off to Hvítramannaland or White Men's Country, located west in the ocean near "Vinland the Good" and said to be a six-day sail from Ireland.[7] Through their grandfather Ulf Squinteye, Mar Atlason and Eirik the Red's wife Thjódhild were cousins, and Mar's son Ari was in every way a fellow who would have known his way around the northern seas. The same was true of Gudleif Gudlaugsson from Straumfjord who, according to the *Eyrbyggja saga* (written ca. 1200-1250) drifted out to sea when overtaken by a gale on his way to Ireland. He and his party reportedly drifted west and then southwest, "well out of sight of land," before land finally came into view. The old man who greeted them ashore was conjectured to be the same Björn from Breidavík in Iceland whom Snorri the Priest (d. 1031) had forced to leave home after compromising his (Snorri's) sister.[8]

The fantastic and unbelievable elements in both stories do not obviate the fact that the medieval Icelanders who wrote them down knew more than the set-pieces employed by their learned contemporaries elsewhere in Europe: there was land, and probably lots of it, west in the sea. For example, no explanation about the location of the North American Markland (see below) seems to have been considered necessary as late as in 1347, for which year three different Icelandic annals noted that a small ship with seventeen or eighteen men on board had made it to safety in Iceland after losing its anchor and drifting off course on its way home to Greenland from a voyage to Markland.[9]

There is now growing archaeological evidence that from their Greenland colony, for some centuries after experiencing the hostility of the Natives in the region they called Vinland (Wine Land), the Norse continued to exploit not only the northern hunting region they called Nordrseta (which may have included the Lancaster Sound area as well as the West Greenland coast up to about 73°N), but also the region which they named Markland (Forest Land). Their northernmost forays and those involving the area from Baffin Island south will be treated separately in what follows because, allowing for inevitable overlap, a different social and economic impetus pushed each enterprise in ways that would also have dictated the approximate dates involved and hence their chances of interacting with the ancestors of the Thule people whom the Frobisher parties encountered in Baffin Island.

The lure of the farthest north consisted chiefly in the wealth of export goods obtainable there. To find commodities vital to the Norse Greenlanders' own subsistence economy, it was necessary to sail in the opposite direction to the Labrador region. Their food needs could be met through fish and marine mammals in waters closer to home, but neither land nor sea on the Greenland side provided iron for tools, weapons, and ship's rivets, or lumber suitable for shipbuilding. As the Norse Greenlanders well knew ever since Leif Eiriksson's and Thorfinn karlsefni's famous voyages, both commodities were available in the more southerly areas across the strait.

It is generally accepted that the region Leif dubbed Helluland (Slab Land) is more or less Baffin Island; it probably also included the barren Cape Chidley region, but we do not know what else besides. Markland obviously refers to forested areas in Labrador-Newfoundland, but no agreement attaches to the name Vinland as used in the two "Vinland Sagas." Like so much else concerning early Norse voyages and colonization, including the controversy over Yale's "Vinland Map," the discussion has been hampered by outdated scholarship and a Victorian passion for precise labelling. What year was the first/last voyage? Exactly what was Vinland — Nova Scotia, Maine, or Newfoundland? Exactly where did Nordrseta, Helluland and Markland begin and end?

Attempts to make such a small and early amount of vague, written material fit with modern place names are counter-productive, for many of the names which the medieval Norse assigned during their westward quest and colonization indicated a salient feature of a given region, not a well defined location. Because Iceland (which is far from covered with ice) is an island and therefore finite and definable, we have no trouble associating it with the label assigned by the disgruntled ninth-century explorer Flóki Vilgerdarson after a hard winter spent in the north-western part of the island. Hoping to entice settlers to his own new colony in Greenland more than a century later, Eirik the Red preferred to draw attention to the brilliantly green summer pastures ringing the sheltered inner fjords where the Norse were to establish their farms, while he chose to ignore the preponderance of massive mountains and their ubiquitous ice cap. It is therefore not surprising that when his son Leif took a close look at the lands in the far west which the incurious Bjarni Herjolfsson had glimpsed earlier, he named three regions in ways that to other Norse Greenlanders would have signalled "So-So Area, Useful Area, and Luxury-Goods Area." The general features of Leif's Slab Land, Forest Land, and Wine Land regions are recognizable to this day, but precise definitions are impossible.

Of the Vínland region we know only that it featured grapes, which places it south of the St. Lawrence,[10] and that it was located south of (but not necessarily far beyond) Markland, the forested region which the Greenland Norse continued to visit at least until 1347 and quite likely longer. The hostile Natives described in the "Vinland Sagas" must therefore have been Indians, not the Dorset culture Palaeo-Eskimos who occupied the more northerly coast of Labrador until replaced by the Thule people during the fifteenth century.[11]

Dorset and Thule Eskimos may have overlapped in certain areas and perhaps exchanged information about European encounters, so there is good reason both to push our inquiry back to about A.D. 1000 and to pay close attention to much of the North American coast the Norse would have been likely to cover in their search for American produce, but the southernmost area described as Vinland, which was inhabited by Indians, has no bearing on a study of possible encounters between either Dorset or Thule Eskimos and Norse Greenlanders and will not be considered further. A Dorset-type soapstone lamp associated with the brief Norse occupation of the L'Anse aux Meadows site was most likely obtained by the Norse during direct or indirect contact with Dorset people in Northern Labrador.[12]

While the Greenland Norse often used wooden pegs and lashings made of withies or baleen in their ship construction and replaced metal with antler or bone in articles ranging from arrow-heads to spades, they preferred to build their boats with iron rivets to fasten overlapping strakes of sinewy wood, and they were dependent on iron for good knives and axes. There is ample archaeological evidence that they made such items from reworked crude iron blooms in their farm smithies, despite having no bog iron of their own and despite a scarcity of trees from which to make charcoal. Many scholars right up to the present day therefore believe that the Greenlanders must have imported blooms from Norway or even Iceland. This makes little sense, however, if sailing the relatively short distance across the Davis Strait would have allowed them to smelt their own iron from American ore with charcoal made from American trees. American trees are also much more likely to have been their chief source of ship's timber than random Siberian logs deposited on West Greenland shores.

The open, clinker-built Norse vessels derived their strength, durability, and elasticity from knot-free, pliable planks split lengthwise by axe (never sawed) from the centre of carefully selected trees.[13] These requirements made driftwood an unlikely source, and the gnarled and spindly birches, willows, and mountain ashes of Greenland certainly could not have met them.

While bigger and better trees were to be found farther down into Labrador, the south-west shore of Ungava Bay is a Canadian area likely to have provided both timber and iron without the risk of running into hostile Indians, and within a manageable distance from the Norse settlements in Greenland. Here, the tree line makes a northward swing, while the area lies just far enough north to have been out of Indian territory. White spruce (Picea glauca [Moench] Voss), black spruce (Picea mariana [Mill.] B.S.P.), and larch

(Larix laricinia, also known as tamarack) can all make do with poor, gravelly soil and bogs of the kind common to this stretch of old sea bottom with stratified deposits of clay, silt, sand, and gravel.[14]

Having arrived at this theory on the basis of geological, ethnographical, and topographical maps, I consulted two Canadian scientists with long personal experience with the south-west Ungava region. Both said without hesitation that conditions in south-western Ungava Bay would have been — and still are — right for such a Norse enterprise, but that solid evidence will of course be required. The geomorphologist James Gray further noted that even today the bay itself does not freeze over until November, and that Hudson Strait is usually ice free from the end of July until some time in September or even October, which would have allowed commuting Norse Greenlanders a good working season.[15] In the early part of the eleventh century, which is when the Norse would have been likely to explore this region for the first time, the climate had been warming for over a century, so the ice-free season may even have been somewhat longer.

In the opinion of the geologist Normand Goulet, who has spent the past ten years mapping iron deposits in the Leaf Bay region (south-west Ungava Bay), this sheltered area would have been an ideal place for the Norse to exploit. Here, larch and black spruce grow all the way down to the water's edge, and iron ore in a 35% concentration also reaches down to the shore, in sharp contrast to the Labrador coast on the Atlantic side where there is no iron at all. The top layer of this ore is a carbonate iron formation which the Norse would merely have needed to scoop up and smelt into portable blooms for further work back home. Dr. Goulet added that hematite, jasperlite, and magnetite characterize the local iron ore and suggested that iron samples from Greenland Norse excavations be examined for the tell-tale presence of the chemical olite, which occurs in small, red, circular accretions in Leaf Bay iron from the Labrador iron trough.[16]

Prime specimens of black spruce, an especially common tree in those parts, would have been ideally suited to the Norse Greenlanders' shipbuilding needs. The species grows slowly, producing straight trunks from five to eighteen meters in height, so that small work crews with only axes and no saws to help them would have found the trees both easy to fell and scannable for defects which would make lengthwise splitting of the trunk a waste of time. The bark of the black spruce is thin and its branches short, making easy work of stripping, and the trunk's diameter, which rarely exceeds thirty centimeters, would have produced just the right-sized central plank after splitting. Soft, lightweight, strong, and resilient, at its best such wood would be everything the Norse could have asked for, and the wood trimmings could have been used for smelting bog iron by the technique we know the Norse colonizers of Iceland and Greenland had brought with them from Norway, and which relied on green wood for the fuel.[17]

Preparation of the lumber, charcoal-burning, iron smelting and ship-building would most likely have taken place right on the shore. As will become evident later, the fourteenth-century work *Inventio fortunatae* appears to describe precisely such Norse shoreside ship building activity. Some of Nørlund's 1926 discoveries at Gardar (now:

Igaliko) in the Eastern Settlement suggest that the Norse may also have taken some ore home without turning it into blooms on the Canadian side first, but it is impossible to tell without proper analyses of the samples.[18]

Before we turn to Canadian archaeological discoveries suggesting that medieval Norse expeditions from Greenland to the Ungava Bay region may indeed have taken place for the reasons outlined above, let us look at some other evidence from the Greenland side, where the Norse used wood with surprising lavishness.

Recent wood analyses performed on ten ship's parts found in the Western and Eastern (actually northern and southern) Norse settlements showed six specimens to be of larch, which does not grow in either Greenland or Norway, but which is plentiful in North America. Two specimens were of spruce, and two were of either spruce or larch. The researchers concluded that the wood samples "were probably made out of Siberian driftwood, while it is less likely that the wood employed was felled in Markland (Labrador) or Vinland (Newfoundland)."[19] However, the very fact that these samples of tree species common to north-eastern America came from ship's parts should indicate that the Greenland Norse were unlikely to have obtained them from salt-logged driftwood. Besides being hard to work, such miscellaneous old logs were not apt to yield planks with the resilience required by Norse shipbuilding practices, which (as Crumlin-Pedersen notes[20]) depended on planks obtained from lengthwise splitting by means of axes and wedges. Used in the strakes of the ship's hull, these boards could withstand great stress without splitting, and they lasted a very long time.

Also pertinent to this discussion is an arrow-head found during excavations of the churchyard at Sandnes, the principal farm in the Western Settlement (the inner part of the Nuuk area). Made from chert of a kind usually, but far from exclusively,[21] associated with Ramah Bay on the northern Labrador coast, its style is, according to Robert McGhee, "consistent with that of points used by the Indians of southern Labrador and Newfoundland in the period between A.D. 1000 and 1500" and suggests possible Norse contact with the New World after Christianity was introduced (i.e. after the initial Vinland voyages). Although William W. Fitzhugh ("Palaeo-Eskimos Culture," pp. 29-30) also thinks the point has stylistic ties to Labrador or Newfoundland assemblages of 1000-500 B.P., he believes that further petrographic studies are needed to determine the exact origin of the material itself, which he thinks may have come from Ungava Bay rather than Ramah Bay.[22]

The issue here is not whether a Norseman had been shot by an Indian or an Eskimo before being buried at home, but the fact that an arrow-head which in all probability had been made by an American Native, from material associated with the general Ungava Bay region, was found at a Norse Greenland site. It indicates continued Norse travel to North America along a route which would have taken them right past the Meta Incognita Peninsula in waters where they might encounter Dorset and, in later years, Thule Eskimos.

It is a relatively short trip from Ramah Bay across the base of the Torngat Mountains to Ungava Bay and no great distance around Cape Chidley by sea. Since Ramah Bay is no farther than Ungava Bay from the Norse Greenland settlements, the Norse conceivably had direct contact with the Natives there, but it is just as likely that the arrow-head was obtained through Norse trade through intermediaries, namely the Dorset Eskimos who made their homes in the mountainous tundra regions of northern Labrador as well as along the northern Labrador coast and the shores of Hudson Bay until after A.D. 1400.[23] Archaeological evidence suggests that the Dorset Eskimos in this area traded both with the Norse and with the Indians farther south. Excavations of a twelfth-century Indian site on the Maine coast turned up both Dorset artefacts and a Norwegian coin minted during Olaf Kyrre's reign (1065-80), and in Dorset sites along the coasts of Hudson Bay and Hudson Strait small fragments of smelted metal have been found which McGhee thinks "were probably derived from contact with the Norse."[24] The most interesting of these metal pieces, an amulet made of reworked, European-derived copper, was found in a late Dorset site in Richmond Gulf, radiocarbon-dated to A.D. 1095-1315.[25]

The Norse iron and copper artefacts retrieved during excavations of Dorset sites in the Hudson Bay region are nevertheless so few in number and scattered over such great distances that while they suggest either direct or indirect contact between visiting Norse and the prehistoric Eskimos living in this region, McGhee cautions against concluding that the Norse came here in significant numbers or on anything like a permanent basis, as some have suggested because of large house structures, cairns, and other features of evidently Dorset origin found in the Ungava area. This is sensible advice, especially given the small size of the Norse Greenland population at any time and the fact that the Norse were less likely to antagonize the Natives in the area if they did not build permanent structures for the use of occasional work parties. There is also little reason to believe that the Greenland Norse, whose cultural identity was so closely tied to stock-keeping, would have left their Greenland settlements in any numbers to take up residence in Ungava Bay.

Even so, some of the man-made features in the Ungava region (cairns, for example), may yet turn out to be Norse, and the existence of the Kodlunarn Island iron blooms (but not of the arrowhead and iron wedge found during the 1990 field season at Kodlunarn[26]) indicate a need to expand on McGhee's suggested reasons for why the Norse travelled in these waters.

The flat, triangular wrought iron arrowhead was a surface find in an Thule/Neoeskimo tent ring on the west side of the island; the cast iron wedge was also a surface find, from a tent ring on Tikkoon Point where items clearly associated with the Frobisher expeditions were also found.[27] While the Greenland Norse made cast as well as wrought iron, as demonstrated by the soapstone moulds which Poul Nørlund found at the old episcopal site at Gardar,[28] there is no evidence that the Kodlunarn wedge and arrowhead had anything to do with them. In my view, there is a possibility that the blooms may turn out to be Norse, however, in which case they would provide evidence that on this southern route, Norse hunting and trade were somewhat secondary activities on high-risk voyages undertaken to smelt iron and to obtain ship's timber — perhaps even to build new ships on the American side before heading back north-east across the strait.

All the radiocarbon dates so far obtained on a couple of the crude iron blooms found in conjunction with the Frobisher investigations fall within the time of Norse tenure in Greenland. And to the degree that it has been possible to analyze charcoal fragments in these blooms, there are identifications of four wood species the Norse would have been likely to use if smelting bog iron in the southern Ungava Bay region: spruce, larch, birch, and alder.

The Countess of Warwick Sound was not far from the straight route home for the Norsemen, who in the late summer would have followed the Baffin Island coast before heading home across the narrowing Davis Strait. Then as now, the Sound would have provided shelter from sudden onsets of drift ice in the Davis Strait,[29] and despite fierce tides and other problems, the small and barren Kodlunarn Island would have been a logical place to deposit any heavy, but precious cargo while going off on some other errand — such as to hunt walrus or beluga whales if that had not already been done along the south shore of Ungava Bay. Even today, that south shore is one of the belugas' areas of summer concentration.[30] Especially during their summer molting in shallow water the 12-15 feet belugas "can be secured in large numbers by herding and netting"[31] — a technique which the Norse used with other small whales and with seals also under less favourable circumstances.

Along south-east Baffin Island belugas, whose tasty muktuk skin and large proportion of blubber to meat make them very desirable game, concentrate at the head of Cumberland Sound during summer, especially in the relatively warm and shallow Ranger river estuary at Clearwater Fjord. In smaller numbers they also occur along the south coast of Cumberland Sound, the coast of Hall Peninsula, and inside Frobisher Bay. Their spring and fall migrations, which have only recently been scientifically studied, but of which the Norse as well as the Eskimos would no doubt have been aware, are believed to take them past the coast of Hall Peninsula.[32]

Recent mappings of beluga territory show that while belugas are even now common to a large part of the Arctic, they do not occur along the south-west coast of Greenland where the Norse lived.[33] Beluga remains have nevertheless been identified at Norse sites in Greenland, so it is clear that the Norse brought butchered beluga home from some distance away, although we cannot judge in what quantities. After many years of experience with analyzing bones from Norse Greenland middens, in which whale bones often occur, the American scientist Thomas H. McGovern has noted that "whale bone is often so cut up and modified in Norse contexts as to make species or even genus level identification impossible."[34]

The homeward trip would presumably have taken place in the autumn, when the walrus (present the year round in western Hudson Bay) begin to haul out on the islands in the southern part of Baffin Island[35] and become accessible to hunters in that area. Walrus blubber and hide were essential to the medieval economy of far northern Europe, and their tusks took the place of elephant ivory all over northern Europe. From a voyage to Ungava Bay the Norse may also have carried home furs from muskrat, black or white bear, mink, otter, wolverine, fox, and wolf, all of which animals occur in that general region.[36] Such furs would have been valuable at home as well as abroad. None of these commodities was likely to make a party of Norse Greenlanders forget a cargo of hard-won iron blooms before heading home, however, so if the blooms found on the Baffin Island Frobisher sites are Norse, they are probably a silent testimony to a voyage gone wrong — to a shipwreck, perhaps, or to a deadly skirmish with Eskimos at a hunting site.

Modern scholars do not believe that hostile Thule people drove the Norse out of Greenland (the Dorset had left south-west Greenland by the time Eirik the Red moved in), but in both Eskimo lore and Norse sources there are hints of occasional violence between the two groups, which is not surprising in view of their fondness for the same kind of marine game. Much scholarly ink has flowed over an entry in "Gottskálk's Annals" for 1379, when a Skræling attack is said to have left eighteen Norse Greenlanders dead and two young boys taken "as slaves."[37] There is no word of where this attack is supposed to have taken place, and since the other Icelandic annals do not mention the event despite noting other news about Greenland for this same period, it is tempting to assume that if the attack took place at all, it happened in a distant hunting region, and that the two young boys were intended as hostages rather than as "slaves."[38] Given the late date (1379), any Skrælings the Norse encountered in Greenland or on the American side of Davis Strait as far down as south-east Baffin Island would probably have been Thule people;[39] in the Ungava Bay region they would most likely have been Dorset Eskimos. Of the two cultures, E. Bielanski has suggested that the Thule may have been the more aggressive; a view which Fitzhugh supports.[40]

The opportunity for Norse encounters with both Thule and Dorset Eskimos in the course of American pursuits would theoretically have been present from the beginning of Norse tenure in Greenland. There now appears to be some consensus that the first Thule migration from Alaska had reached parts of the Eastern Canadian Arctic around A.D. 1000, possibly just before the Norse began sailing far to the north of their settlements. Encounters with people of the Thule culture were also a possibility from quite early on even as far down as the Meta Incognita region. The tiny carved figure shown in Figure 2 provides striking evidence of such early contact. It was found by the archaeologist Deborah Sabo in 1977 at a thirteenth-century Thule site near Lake Harbour, located farther up the Hudson Strait on the south coast of Baffin Island.[41]

There seems to be fairly general agreement among experts that the carving most likely is of Thule origin, and that it represents a European dressed in a style commensurate with the thirteenth century. One difficulty is that other Thule carvings of the Norse as well as grave finds in Greenland suggest that this is not clothing normally associated with Norse Greenland farmers, hunters, and fishermen, but whether the tiny figure reflects another kind of European or just a Norseman dressed for something besides logging or hunting, it

Figure 2: A carving in walrus ivory found by Deborah Sabo in 1977 at a thirteenth-century Thule site on the south coast of Baffin Island. It represents a European dressed in the style of the period, but not as a fisherman-farmer in working clothes. The original carving is now at the Canadian Museum of Civilization. Photo: Canadian Museum of Civilization 91-72.

tells us that the inhabitants of Baffin Island had learned to take the occasional European ship's crew in stride long before 1576.

Why and when the Greenland Norse ceased making voyages for timber and iron are complex questions central to any discussion of the final phase of their colony; these questions will be considered here only to the extent that they have a bearing on the chances for interaction with North American Natives.

Since timber and iron were so essential to the Norse Greenlanders' domestic economy, they would still have been needed after trade with Norway was ruptured and traditional export items presumably were no longer in great demand. Although seasonal clashes on the American side by about A.D. 1400 (involving the Thule people pressing southwards, the Indians seeking northwards, and the Dorset caught in the middle[42]) conceivably created inhospitable conditions for small groups of Norsemen far from home in an area which both Susan Kaplan and William W. Fitzhugh convincingly depict as subject to many population changes in the period A.D. 1000-1600, it is also likely that by the 1420s or '30s, English control of the waters around southern Greenland made it increasingly difficult for the Norse to sail outside their own country.[43]

At the same time, English merchants may have alleviated the Greenlanders' need for iron, for in the ruins of a late-phase Norse farm four pieces of unworked iron were found[44] which are neither of medieval Norwegian nor of Norse Greenlandic manufacture, but which correspond to the description of the "osmunds" (iron scraps) which the English bartered in Iceland during the fifteenth century.[45] At a rough guess, therefore, based on indications that the Greenlanders' economy underwent several changes in the first half of the fifteenth century, in part to accommodate the insatiable English market for dried cod,[46] Norse voyages to Baffin Island and Labrador may have come to an end around 1430.

By then, Norse voyages to the northernmost part of the area known collectively as Nordrseta had probably already ceased. It is difficult to distinguish cause from effect in the economic fluctuations brought on by the end of Norse Greenland's contact with Norwegian merchants and church authorities towards the end of the fourteenth century, but the cessation of contact appears to have been preceded by the Greenlanders' refusal to tithe and thus to provide the Norwegian Church authorities with a reason for sending ships to collect the goods. While it is clear that this refusal had much to do with the revolt against increasing taxation which we find in the other Nordic countries at that time, it is also possible that the Greenlanders were finding it more difficult to hunt in Baffin Bay, for instance because of increasing ice in the strait due to climatic fluctuations we are still a long way from understanding.

The definition of Nordrseta is equally imprecise.[47] All we know for certain is that for the two centuries or so that the Roman Church maintained strong links with Norse Greenland, the Norse sailed very far to the north of their settlements in search of walrus ivory, which was valued by secular merchants and Church authorities alike for its value on the European market and for the ease with which it could be transported back to Norway. In addition, we know that trade with Norway was so closely connected with the Roman Church in Greenland (officially established in 1124) that records of Greenland shipping were primarily kept by Church authorities in Norway and Iceland.

Certainly the Norse could eat the marine mammals they hunted in the Nordrseta region, but it was the search for trade and tithe goods that had eventually brought them at least up to about 73°N, at a time when Thule people seem to have been already present in the Lancaster Sound region on the American side and in the Melville Bay region on the Greenland side. When Bishop Arnald arrived in Greenland in 1125, tithing had already been instituted in Iceland and is likely to have been a feature from the first in the Greenland Church, which reached its zenith during the thirteenth and early fourteenth centuries.[48] The thirteenth century is the period to which the majority of Norse finds in High Arctic Thule ruins have been assigned.

In sum, voyages to Nordrseta are likely to have begun a little later than the voyages to Baffin Island and Labrador and to have started petering out by the mid-fourteenth century, when the Norse Greenlanders evidently had second thoughts about paying Peter's Pence and other church taxes, as archaeological evidence from Greenland Norse sites appears to corroborate. McGovern and his team found that, over-all, walrus and polar bear remains associated with the Norse are most common far to the north of the Eastern Settlement, and they cautiously note that late-phase Norse middens appear to contain fewer walrus elements than earlier ones.[49]

While they lasted, however, these northern voyages sufficed to invest a large number of Thule ruin sites in the High Arctic with Norse artefacts ranging from homespun cloth and gaming pieces to objects made of copper and iron. Among the seventy Canadian and Greenlandic Eskimo sites in which Norse items have been found, and which are discussed in the Danish historian and archaeologist Jette Arneborg's comprehensive 1991 survey, from the Norse perspective, of Norse/Eskimo contact in Greenland,[50] eight sites at the northern tip of Ellesmere Island and two in north-east Greenland are so distant from areas where the Norse would have had good reason to go that the Norse objects found there may have been brought by Thule people who had obtained them elsewhere. The possibility that at least some of these items come from a shipwreck grows strong when we know that in a Thule house ruin on Skræling Island in Buchanan Bay, Peter Schledermann uncovered a carpenter's plane with the metal blade missing.[51] It is very unlikely that a Norseman would have parted with such a tool while alive.

Wool cloth found on Skræling Island together with the ship's plane and several pieces of chain mail has been dated to A.D. 1190, while charred oak from the house in which the chain mail was found has produced a radiocarbon date of about A.D. 1260.[52] On the basis of these and several other radiocarbon tests Karen McCullough, who excavated at Skræling Island with Dr. Schledermann, has estimated that the initial "Ruin Island" Thule phase in this Smith Sound region began in the late twelfth or early thirteenth century, or relatively late compared with the dating of Thule sites in the Barrow Strait-Lancaster

Sound area on which we shall focus below. This is a position on which there appears to be some disagreement;[53] there is little hope of determining the latest or earliest dates at which the Norse items could have reached these distant Thule sites until these other data have been sorted out. Meanwhile, it is worth noting that over 80% of the Bache Peninsula Norse objects were found in early or "Ruin Island phase" dwellings.[54]

Even at this high latitude, we cannot rule out direct contact between Thule people and the Norse hunters whom long distances and cold weather clearly did not deter, and who have left behind marks made with their own hands, such as cairns and rune stones. Cairns are built for purposes ranging from celebratory and commemorative to utilitarian, and no one culture, past or present, has the monopoly on their use, so there is much uncertainty about two ancient cairns which the British explorer Captain G.S. Nares found 120 years ago on top of a 900-foot high island near the east coast of Ellesmere Island (above lat. 79°N) overlooking Kane Basin.[55] But the original account of the so-called Kingittorsuaq rune stone found even earlier, next to a cairn in north-western Greenland at almost 73°N, is less controversial as well as illuminating in the present context. Not only has this rune stone long been proof that the Norse made it at least as far north as to the Upernavik district, directly opposite the entrance to Lancaster Sound, but the story told by the missionary P. Kragh[56] may also help with the interpretation of other cairns found along the sea routes the Norse are likely to have used in the Baffin Island and Hudson Bay regions, along which they would have had a chance of encountering either Dorset or Thule Eskimos.

The Kingittorsuaq rune stone was found by the old Greenlander Pelimut in the spring of 1824 and brought to the National Museum in Copenhagen the following autumn. Pelimut found the stone on a mountain peak on Kingittorsuaq Island in the economically important Upernavik region, on which people at that time depended for most of the eiderdown collected in Greenland as well as for narwhal horns, blubber, polar bear skins, and other trade commodities. The barren island itself was reportedly visited by the Greenlanders only occasionally when seals or other desirable marine animals were in the surrounding waters.

The rune stone's message[57] is clearly legible except for the date, which is thought to refer to some time in the mid-thirteenth century.[58] Nothing about the message suggests distress; on the contrary, the stone more likely marks an accomplishment, while three cairns found with it probably constitute a guide to navigation. When Kragh went with Pelimut to see the site for himself, he suffered a long and steep climb up to the highest point of the island, from which there was a wide view of the mainland with the Iceblink some 8-10 Danish miles away, as well as a view to many islands all around. Indeed, Pelimut had climbed the mountain with the cairn the previous spring just to see where the whaling ships lay, because he wanted to buy tobacco; that was when he had found the rune stone near a collapsed, large cairn (which clearly had protected the rune stone until fairly recently) with two smaller cairns next to it.

In the surrounding sea Kragh noted very strong currents and many skerries which made for dangerous sailing. To the northwest, a small island, Naiat, with ruins of old Eskimo houses, had enough grass and soil to make him think the Norse could have pitched their tents there. He reported that on yet another neighbouring island, Kingittortalik, there was a wellspring which never ran dry, and which showed every sign of having been excavated by humans with tools. According to Inuit tradition, the old Kavdlunait (i.e. the Norse) had made it — an interesting piece of information both in view of the water catchment found on Kodlunarn Island[59] and because historical Inuit oral tradition had possibly perpetuated, over a time longer than that which elapsed between the last Norse voyages to Northern Labrador-Baffin Island and the arrival of Frobisher, that Thule people had experience with the Norse at that high latitude in Greenland.

When Kragh climbed his mountain, just 103 years after the European recolonization of Greenland, little was known about the Norse Greenlanders and even less about the Inuit in whose house ruins up and down the West Greenland coast modern archaeologists have turned up so many Norse artefacts suggesting seasonal co-existence as well as later plunder of abandoned Norse sites. Direct contact would hardly have been surprising, given the fact that the two peoples hunted many of the same marine mammals in these and other waters.

Walrus are still common seasonally along the southern coast of Baffin Island and present the year round in the western part of Hudson Bay. Until recently they probably also populated the entire eastern coast of Baffin Island as well as areas to the north. At the Arctic Circle (near Cape Dyer) some 260-70 kilometers separate the Canadian and Greenland shallow coastal areas on which the walrus depend for their food. This is where groups of walrus are most likely to be found in mid-strait, at the edge of the summer pack ice forming somewhere to the north of the narrowing.[60] The summer hunt for walrus would therefore have taken the Norse farther afield the longer they extended their season, for the animals would have retreated north with the ice floes on which they have to haul up when away from land. Especially during the warm climatic period (which is thought to have lasted until about the mid-thirteenth century) the pack ice would have retreated quite far north in an average year.

Pursuing their game along the edge of the ice into the middle of the strait, the Norse would have been travelling west as well as north and could as easily (especially in the earlier, warmer period) have sailed into the opening of Lancaster Sound as down the east coast of Baffin Island. In connection with the former possibility, it is significant that when McGhee excavated several ancient Thule ruins at Brooman Point on the south coast of Bathurst Island (past the terminus of Lancaster Sound), he found Norse objects in Thule house ruins to which he assigned a tentative date of the first couple of decades of the twelfth century — and which both McCullough and David Morrison surmise represent an earlier Thule movement eastwards from Alaska than the one identified as the Ruin Island phase.[61]

The earlier the Brooman Point dates turn out to be, the less likely it is that the Norse artefacts came via Greenland. They may well relate to Norse hunting voyages in the far north just before Einar Sokkason brought a cargo of walrus tusks to Norway to persuade the proper authorities that the Greenlanders could sustain the expense of a proper bishop.[62] We certainly cannot discount direct interchange as the source of the objects McGhee found. For example, one of Poul Nørlund's discoveries at Herjolfsnes in south-west Greenland indicates peaceful contact with Thule Eskimos at an early time. One of the two graves found inside the church (built circa A.D. 1200) contained an oval box with baleen sides and a wooden bottom, typical of the Thule culture.[63] A tow line handle made of walrus ivory found at the Norse farm 064c in 1939 is also clearly identifiable as Thule, and the circumstances of the find suggest that the object had been brought south by the Norse themselves.[64]

We must not assume that all early Norse travel in the Davis Strait had a peaceful purpose, however, for pieces of chain mail have been found in many Thule ruins in the High Arctic as well as possibly on the Norse farm at Nipaatsoq in the Western Settlement — a site which is exceptionally rich in artefacts suggesting long-distance travels to the north as well as to the south.[65] No hunter or fisherman would have worn armour while working, and chain mail was rare and expensive even in Norway, so we cannot exclude the possibility of early armed expeditions in Baffin Bay or the Davis Strait, which would have given prehistoric Eskimos good reason to teach their children that a strange ship might mean trouble.

The English

A "strange ship" in the Davis Strait would not necessarily have been Norwegian or Greenlandic even in the Middle Ages. The much-discussed work *Inventio fortunatae* — of which no copy now survives, but which at one time clearly existed — is said to have recorded the experiences of an English Minorite friar who sailed to Norse Greenland in 1360 and continued north into the Davis Strait on a voyage of exploration. In the form handed down to us (a second- or third-hand account, with many surreal interpolations, of a report "in the Belgic tongue" by one Jacobus Cnoyen) there is straight-forward information which can be checked against other sources, but even after E.G.R. Taylor's heroic work of decoding information gleaned from Geraldus Mercator, John Dee, and Richard Hakluyt, we do not know how far north the friar went. He obviously encountered Eskimos ("pygmies"), however, in a land where no people lived, except "on the last side where in that narrow land [isthmus] there were 23 people not above 4 feet tall ... whereof 16 were women."[66] It stands to reason that if he saw the Eskimos well enough to distinguish the women from the men, they must also have seen him and his companions and known that they did not have these waters to themselves.

The Minorite had evidently started from the Eastern (southernmost) Settlement, where he gave an astrolabe to the Bishop's official at Gardar (identifiable with reasonably certainty through Norwegian documents as the Bergen priest Ivar Bárdarson) shortly before the latter returned to Norway, and where the friar most likely found an experienced crew for his further voyage. From the bare bones of the description left to us we may deduce that he crossed the Davis Strait and went far enough south to reach the tree-growing region with which a Norse Greenland crew would have been familiar, for in two places farther inland from where he had seen the "pygmies" he found "a great piece of ship's planking and other balks which had been used in big ships, besides many trunks of trees which at some earlier date had been hewn down," so that he thought people must have lived there formerly.

It is hard to believe that a well-travelled friar did not know the difference between a pile of driftwood and deliberately logged trees, even if he may have had difficulties with explanations offered him by his Norse guides.[67] Given his reported account of an "Indrawing Sea" of five channels where the "pygmies" lived (before arriving at the shipbuilding sites), there is an intriguing possibility that this area may have included two Norse shipbuilding sites on the shore of Ungava Bay. While his description clearly is a sop to medieval geographical notions about the far northern seas, the fierce tides in Frobisher Bay may also have confirmed his preconceived notions. In that case, the "pygmies" could have been a group of south-east Baffin Island Thule Eskimos watching yet another group of intruders.

The Minorite friar "of Oxford" was not the last Englishman to visit the Davis Strait before the first Frobisher party arrived. English fishermen had exploited Canadian waters long before Frobisher left England in 1576. Most of their activity after about A.D. 1500 appears to have centred on the Newfoundland fishing banks, but given the likelihood that enterprising fishermen had originally come upon the American coast from the Greenland side some time in the fifteenth century, some of them were probably still familiar with the south-east coast of Baffin Island in the early sixteenth century and availed themselves of that knowledge. Although it is doubtful that they would voluntarily have come close enough to the shore to interact with the Natives before exploiting the excellent fishing conditions down the coast of Labrador, they may have done so involuntarily, perhaps to seek shelter from bad weather, but so far there is no evidence of such events. Deliberate English sailings into the upper part of the Davis Strait appear to have been solely concerned with exploration and the hunt for the fabled Northwest Passage.

John Cabot evidently thought that the most promising approach to Cathay lay south of where he had explored in 1497,[68] but his son Sebastian saw a good chance with a northern route along the new coast with which he must have been familiar even as a very young man, and along which he would have known that an experienced Bristol crew had distinct advantages. Cumulative information, most recently obtained and interpreted by Alwyn A. Ruddock and David B. Quinn, shows that Sebastian participated in a voyage of exploration to North America (evidently in Indian-occupied territory) in 1504, which was funded by prominent Bristol merchants. This voyage became confused in the minds of later writers with another voyage of exploration in 1508-9 to a considerably higher latitude. Very recently, Quinn has built further on that research and on documentary discoveries by Margaret Condon and concluded that Sebastian's later voyage to the north probably was not undertaken under the aegis of the English monarch at all, but was financed with money Sebastian had borrowed in Antwerp.[69]

Quinn bases his theory on persuasive documentary evidence, and it seems reasonable also when viewed from other angles. Antwerp was at that time both a banking centre and a general commercial hub, where merchants from all parts of Europe, including England and the Iberian Peninsula, rubbed shoulders with political emissaries and learned men anxious to obtain the latest information resulting from the burgeoning exploitation and exploration of the Americas. Here, as elsewhere, hopes of finding a western short-cut to the silks and spices of Cathay would have been running high while Antwerp merchants continued to thrive on their trade in commodities ranging from salted fish and train oil to silver and copper.[70]

Although Richard Eden had early and direct access to Sebastian Cabot, among the sixteenth-century writers who concerned themselves with Sebastian only Giovanni Battista Ramusio, writing in 1556, claimed to have received written information from Sebastian himself about the 1508-9 voyage. According to Ramusio, Sebastian went "for a long time towards the west and a quarter north along the islands situated by the side of the said land [i.e. 'Nova Francia', or roughly modern Labrador]" and reached a latitude of at least 67°N before he was forced by the cold and ice to turn back. Ramusio also noted that Sebastian was convinced he would have reached "Eastern Cathay ... if the ill-will of the master and sailors, who were mutinous, had not compelled him to turn back."[71]

If Sebastian had an experienced crew, as one must suppose he did, it would have been likely to number several Bristol men who had sailed far up the Canadian coast before, and given his international connections, he had probably also obtained Iberian sailors with similar experience from activities we shall examine more closely in a moment. First, we need to ask why people already accustomed to the inhospitable conditions that often prevail along the Labrador coast decided they had had enough; the answer may be that they had gone beyond familiar waters and were frightened by the ice closing in upon them as they headed ever farther into the unknown. A second question must necessarily be how far they had gone when this rebellion happened.

Sebastian appears to have passed Newfoundland in clear waters on about the tenth of June and to have encountered the daunting ice conditions in July. While no two years are alike in the Davis Strait, it would have been a bad summer (the early part of the sixteenth century was in fact notable for a slight warming trend[72]) which confronted sailors with impenetrable ice south of Cape Dyer by mid- or late July. Taken together with Sebastian's one surviving map, dating from 1544 (by which time even he would surely have been ready to reveal what he actually knew), this information gives us reason to believe that he had crossed the Arctic Circle in the Davis Strait and was on a west-by-northwest course in Baffin Bay when his crew forced him to turn around.[73]

Although reliable longitude observations lay far into the future and cartographical representations were apt to be further distorted by the Tordesillas line imposed in 1494,[74] reasonably accurate calculations of latitude were possible by 1508, and we must suppose that Sebastian was sufficiently well-taught to be able to report on American locations where he had himself sailed, even if his placement of Iceland (entirely above the Arctic circle) and his representation of the rest of the Nordic countries, where he had never been, left much to be desired. Placing the southern tip of Florida at about 24°N he came very close to its true position, and the latitude of what are clearly Newfoundland Island and the entrance to the St. Lawrence also approximates reality. It adds to Sebastian's credibility as an observer that (as Peter Martyr wrote ca. 1516[75]) he reported the currents in what we call the Davis Strait to be flowing westwards — as indeed they do.

Seen in terms of that time's scientific limitations, Sebastian's North American coastline is surprisingly accurate in its eastward trend as far as Cape Bauld. Its somewhat foreshortened nature in some places as well as the exaggeration of its total east-west reach may both be explained by his inability to calculate longitude (east-west distance) with any reasonable certainty. The changeable nature of magnetic deviation, a particularly vexing problem at high latitudes, was also poorly understood and baffled many a polar navigator after Sebastian. After showing the wide "rio duce" (extrapolations from a thawing Hudson Strait glimpsed and bypassed?) at about 60°N, the approximate latitude of Hudson Strait, the 1544 map runs into serious trouble as it continues straight north-east until about 64°N (in Sebastian's terms), where it veers just as sharply west-north-west to some distance above the polar circle.

There is little reason to think that Sebastian went ashore on either the American or Greenland side during the northernmost leg of this voyage, or that he sailed close enough to south-east Baffin Island to be within mutual observation distance of the Natives. Nowhere do the second-hand accounts refer to "pygmies" of any sort, and only polar bears decorate the northernmost portion of Sebastian's representation of Canada. On the basis of modern knowledge, it also needs noting that when the ice moves south in the Davis Strait in the spring and the earlier part of the summer, it hugs the Baffin Island and Labrador shores and leads ships into the middle of the strait, towards Greenland. Only from later summer through the autumn is the south-east Baffin Island coast reasonably free of ice.

There are no records of actual English voyages of northern exploration between Sebastian's 1508-9 attempt to find the Northwest Passage and Martin Frobisher's 1576 arrival in Baffin Island on the same errand. If the bits of clothing and footwear found by Captain Yorke's men the following year did not belong to Frobisher's five hapless men presumed spirited away by the Inuit, we must look elsewhere for the recent source of these as well as of other European objects reported by Best.

The Iberians

The "Guinney Beane of redde couloure" found in the Inuit tent in Meta Incognita was clearly seen by Frobisher's men as non-English. Since the Norse Greenlanders are not known to have raised legumes of any kind, the bean must have reached the Inuit through contact with other Europeans, probably Portuguese or Basque fishermen or whalers using some of their food stores in lieu of trade beads. It is unlikely to have been a relic of the three Corte Real voyages (1500-02), for while we do not know how far north they sailed, or indeed whether it was off the east or west coast of Greenland they met with heavy ice, written accounts and the Cantino Map (1502) suggest that they sailed around Cape Farewell in Greenland and found appealing country with tall trees somewhere in the southern Labrador-Newfoundland-Nova Scotia region.[76]

Portuguese fishermen had been quick to join their English and French colleagues in the New Foundland fisheries.[77] Selma H. Barkham's research has shown that the Basques as well were definitely involved in "Terranova" from 1517 and that the early Davis Strait whaling industry evolved from their cod fishing activities. Basque whaling led to the erection of tryworks in Red Bay (Newfoundland) by the late 1530s, when oil, rather than flesh, had proved the more lucrative part of their prey. Furthermore, it is clear that whaling skippers were given wide latitude as to where in "Terranova" they chose to hunt the bowhead and right whales whose rich blubber they sought.[78]

Of the two species of whale, the bowhead whale was the most economically desirable because of its high fat content and the length of its baleen, and studies of the early Red Bay Basque tryworks have indeed revealed a larger concentration of bowhead bones than of right whale bones.[79] This discovery is important in the context of sailings to Baffin Island and beyond, for just like the walrus, bowhead whales follow the retreating ice north in summer.

According to W. Gillies Ross, an authority on bowhead whaling in the Canadian Arctic after the mid-seventeenth century, most whaling ships would follow the bowheads north along the pack ice edge after a few weeks of hunting along the edge of the pack ice. At the peak of the cold season, this pack ice (carried south by the Labrador Current) would fringe the Canadian coast from south-east Newfoundland to the Hudson Strait. In spring, the wedge of open water between the east and west coasts would widen and the ice belt recede, so that the European bowhead whalers "were close neighbours with the Davis Strait and Baffin Bay pack through the months of May and June, and not infrequently July and August as well."[80]

While Iberian cod fishermen departed for the Newfoundland fisheries in mid-April, the whalers would wait until about mid-June and return home from "Terranova" in about the middle of October, unless they stayed into early January to take in a "second season" of hunting.[81] These "seasons" were dictated by the different migratory patterns of the whales hunted: bowhead whales, right whales, and belugas, in their order of economic importance.

The migrations and habitats of the belugas have already been discussed in connection with Norse voyages; right whales are known to swim slowly along the north shore of Belle Isle Strait between July and October.[82] In earlier days at least, the Davis Strait's discrete stock of bowhead whales wintered northeast of Labrador, at the lower end of the

Davis Strait. In April, May, and June, most would then move north along the west coast of Greenland and cross Baffin Bay when they found a passage through the ice, entering Lancaster Sound and neighbouring waters during June. But many were able to penetrate the so-called Middle Ice farther south and to reach Cumberland Sound and other localities along the Baffin Island coast. In late August, the whales would start migrating south along the east coast of Baffin Island (and to a lesser extent along the west coast of Greenland) to their winter habitat in the lower Davis Strait bordering the open water of the North Atlantic, giving Basque whalers at Red Bay another chance to hunt them in October.[83]

Archaeologists piecing together the life of these mid-sixteenth-century Basque whalers of Red Bay have found few signs of barracks or actual settlements in the rubble of flimsy wooden structures with red-tiled roofs, built to protect the fire boxes with their copper cauldrons, and while this indicates rough camping ashore or on shipboard,[84] a couple of twentieth-century discoveries relating to mid-sixteenth-century whaling in the Davis Strait suggest that some whaling skippers (all of whom worked for private enterprises[85]) decided to follow the whales north in summer rather than wait for the animals to return in October.

"Terranova" was an elastic term, as noted. And, according to Robert Grenier, the whaling ships were so well provisioned when they left home that they could as easily spend their time off the coast of Baffin Island as down in the Strait of Belle Isle, and they were often heavily insured,[86] allowing the skippers (and owners) to take warranted risks. Grenier has also shown that a bowhead whale provided from five to ten more barrels of oil than a right whale, or the equivalent of the annual salaries of two skilled workers in the industry, so we do not need to look far for an incentive to pursue the bowhead north and either tow or carry the catch back to the try works.

Evidence of early Basque sailings past the lower Davis Strait is harder to come by, but it surfaces in the archaeological literature for the Greenland side. Not surprisingly, the three discoveries discussed below were made on the part of the coast facing Cape Dyer, where the strait narrows before becoming Baffin Bay, and where Inuit and Europeans alike would have found the crossing easy. This is where walrus and bowhead whales veer towards the Greenland coast as they follow the receding Davis Strait ice pack in spring and early summer, and where hunters pursuing these animals from the south would also have been forced eastwards.

Although both the "boxe of small nayles, and certayne redde Hearings, boordes of Fyrre trée well cutte, with dyuers other things artificially wroughte" which Frobisher's men found in the Nuuk area, may have been obtained by Greenland Inuit through trade with Canadian Inuit with access to Basque try works farther south,[87] such an explanation does in itself suggest close communication between the two Inuit groups and the sharing of information about pre-Frobisher Europeans in the Davis Strait. More immediately suggestive of mid-century Basque voyages at least as far as to the Cape Dyer region are a

Renaissance bronze medal and the evidence we have of three northern Inuit captured in 1566 and brought back to Europe to be exhibited.

The badly eroded medal (pierced at the top as if to be worn on a neck chain) was found in 1904 at an old Inuit ruin site at Agpamiut (directly across from Cape Dyer) in the Sukkertoppen district.[88] The site itself has never been properly excavated, and up to now the medal — a mid-sixteenth-century reissue of a portrait medal of the Spanish military leader Gonzalo Fernández de Córdoba (1453-1515) — was thought to have been brought to the Davis Strait by a Dutch whaler some time after the mid-seventeenth century. Just why a Dutchman would wear as an amulet a medal commemorating a Spanish military leader a century-and-a-half in his grave was never explained. In his time, however, De Córdoba was revered by all who served under him during his Italian campaigns, and among these men were many Basque mariners. Whoever he was, this man who wore the Great Captain's image inside his shirt, he would not have been likely to leave it with the Inuit except under extreme circumstances, such as a shipwreck.

Nor did the Inuit man, woman, and child brought back to Europe in 1566 come willingly. Central to the modern discussion[89] about these captives is the question of where they were captured. While agreeing with other scholars that the three were probably brought back to Europe by Basque whalers, the Danish Inuit expert H.C. Gulløv argues that these Inuit cannot have been from the Labrador coast as suggested. Relying on the work of Garth Taylor,[90] he observes that in 1566, only Cape Chidley (separating Ungava Bay from the Atlantic) was likely to have had non-Indian Natives, and they would probably have been of the Dorset culture. According to Fitzhugh, however, the Natives on the coast here would have been Thule people.[91]

On the basis of a German woodcut from 1567 showing the Inuit mother and her child in their Native clothes, Gulløv identifies the style of their clothing as one common to the Thule culture on both Baffin Island and in West Greenland at the time. Noting that since contemporary maps show confusion in European minds about whether the name "Terranova" encompassed any one side of the Davis Strait, he says it would be difficult to say whether the 1566 Inuit were captured on Baffin Island or in Greenland, but he does not believe they were taken from farther south than Baffin Island.

Everything we know about European abductions of Inuit reveals desperate anguish and anxiety for the victims' fates among those who were left behind. It would be surprising indeed if the Baffin Island Inuit whom Frobisher and his men encountered in 1576 did not know what had happened to some of their people because of another European ship in those waters just ten years earlier. The defensive manoeuvres and suspiciousness evident in George Best's description of the Englishmen's first encounter with the Inuit suggest that the Baffin Islanders had learned to be wary of white men in big ships.

Conclusion

From the time the first Norse crossed from Greenland and sailed down along the coast of northern Canada a thousand years ago, exploring the land for its economic and settlement potential, encounters with Eskimos were not only possible, but probable. Archaeological discoveries on the American side show that with the passage of time, it became increasingly likely that these Eskimos were Thule people. By the time other Europeans were exploiting the waters north of Labrador, Inuit settlements on both sides of the Davis Strait were likely to have developed both defensive and trading strategies of the kind George Best described.[92] The Frobisher expeditions must nevertheless have wrought another change in how the Baffin Islanders viewed European travellers, because before Martin Frobisher returned to England and the disastrous news about the Meta Incognita "ore" in 1578, his men had built a small and sturdy house on Kodlunarn Island and furnished it with articles designed to show the Inuit how Englishmen lived.[93]

Much current anthropological discussion focusses on the possibility that a desire for European goods may in some way have influenced not only Inuit cultural attitudes, but caused them to migrate to areas where they might scavenge or barter for metal and other manufactured goods.[94] I cannot address this problem myself, but William W. Fitzhugh is surely right to stress the importance of Frobisher's Kodlunarn Island house in assessing the significance of Frobisher's three voyages.[95] A house — especially one so clearly intended to endure — is a powerful symbol of an intention to stay and make oneself at home.

As noted earlier, I do not consider it likely that the Norse coming to Ungava Bay on a seasonal basis would have built large, year-round houses in the face of the Native Americans already there. The likelihood that such a gesture would have been seen as a challenge not only by Dorset people, but also by people from the Thule culture Frobisher and his men later encountered in Meta Incognita, seems borne out by a story now familiar to Greenland archaeologists of the Nuuk region. This is where the Norse had had their northernmost settlement in the inner fjords, and where the Norwegian missionary Hans Egede established his embryonic "Hope Colony" in 1721 in the outermost part of the fjord. The mission was relocated in 1728, and the original site became lost to European knowledge until 1903. Nobody had bothered to ask the local Inuit, who had had a name for the place all along: Illueruunerit — "the place where there used to be houses."[96]

Notes

[1] *Grœnlendinga saga* and *Eiriks saga rauða*.

[2] The term Inuit will be used here specifically to denote Thule Eskimos from ca. A.D. 1500. Before that time, non-Indian American Natives will be referred to as Eskimos or, whenever a distinction is possible, as people of either the Dorset or the Thule culture.

[3] Kirsten A. Seaver, *The Frozen Echo: Greenland and the Exploration of North America ca. A.D. 1000-1500*, Stanford University Press, California, 1996, pp. 135, 213-18, 262-63, 267, 276-80, 284, 287, 362-63, 373.

[4] The last recorded voyage from Greenland to Norway took place in 1410. *Annálar 1400-1800*, Copenhagen (Hið íslenzka bókmenntafélag), 1922, Vol. 1, p. 16.

[5] This development is discussed at length in Kirsten A. Seaver, *The Frozen Echo*, chapters seven, eight, and nine.

[6] Hermann Pálsson and Paul Edwards, translators and editors, "Landnámabók." *University of Manitoba Icelandic Studies*, 1972, vol. 1, p. 61, Note 48.

[7] Ibid., p. 61 (Chapter 122).

[8] Hermann Pálsson and Paul Edwards, translators, *Eyrbyggja saga*, Edinburgh, 1973, pp. 152 (Ch. 48), 193-6 (Ch. 64)

[9] Gustav Storm, *Islandske Annaler indtil 1578*. Oslo, Norsk Historisk Kjeldeskrift-Institutt, 1977 (reprint of 1888 ed.), pp. 213, 353, 403.

[10] Both fruits and metal-worked wood of the white walnut (Juglans cinerea; also called butternut,) were found in a Norse layer at the Viking site L'Anse aux Meadows in Newfoundland. The white walnut, too, grows only south of the St. Lawrence. Birgitta Linderoth Wallace, "L'Anse aux Meadows, the Western Outpost." In Birthe L. Clausen, ed., *Viking Voyages to North America*, Roskilde (The Viking Ship Museum), 1993, p. 39.

[11] Robert McGhee, "The Skraellings of Vinland," in Birthe L. Clausen, ed., *op. cit.*, pp. 45-47; Susan A. Kaplan, "European Goods and Socio-Economic Change in Early Labrador-Inuit Society," in William W. Fitzhugh, ed., *Cultures in Contact*, Washington, D.C., 1985, p. 45. For a comprehensive recent survey of migrations along this part of the Canadian east coast, see William W. Fitzhugh, "Staffe Island and the Northern Labrador-Thule Succession," in David Morrison and Jean-Luc Pilon, eds., *Threads of Arctic Prehistory: Papers in Honour of William E. Taylor Jr.*, Canadian Museum of Civilization Mercury Series, Archaeological Survey of Canada Paper 149, 1994, pp. 239-68.

[12] William W. Fitzhugh, "A Review of Palaeo-Eskimo Culture History in Southern Quebec-Labrador and Newfoundland," *Inuit Studies* 4 :1-2 (1980), especially pp. 29-30.

[13] Ole Crumlin-Pedersen, "Wood Technology and Forest Resources in the Light of Medieval Shipfinds," in Christiane Villain-Gandossi, Salerno Bussutil and Paul Adam, eds., *Medieval Ships and the Birth of Technological Societies*, Foundation for International Studies, Malta, 1989, vol. I, pp. 30-33.

[14] Department of Mines and Technical Surveys, Geographical Branch, *Atlas of Canada*, Ottawa, 1957, Plates 15-17, 35-36, 38, 41-42, 72; R. Cole Harris, gen. ed., *Historical Atlas of Canada*, vol. 1 (R. Louis Gentilcore, ed.), Toronto, Buffalo, London, 1987, pp. 4-6, Plates 4, 9; Bayard Hora, consultant ed., *Oxford Encyclopedia of Trees of the World*, Oxford, New York, Melbourne, 1981, pp. 76-78; Thomas E. Elias, *The Complete Trees of North America: Field Guide and Natural History*, New York, 1980, pp. 80-86; George Rona, gen. ed., *Kulturhistorisk leksikon for nordisk middelalder*, vol. 12, Copenhagen, 1967, pp. 91, 95-96; *Encyclopaedia Britannica Micropaedia*, 15th ed., vol. 5, 1993, p. 330.

[15] Dr. Gray is at the Department of Geography, University of Montreal, Québec. I am very grateful to him for sharing his knowledge of the Ungava Bay region with me in a telephone conversation on April 4, 1996.

[16] Telephone conversation with Dr. Normand Goulet, Dept. des Sciences de la Terre, Université de Québec à Montréal, on April 9, 1996. I am very grateful to Dr. Goulet, who shared his extensive knowledge and also offered his assistance with further analyses of iron samples. Dr. Jette Arneborg at the National Museum in Copenhagen, who recently told me that iron samples from the Western Settlement have been sent to the Danish scientist V.F. Buchwald for analysis aimed at tracing the origin of the ore, agrees with me that the time has clearly come for looking at Norse Greenland iron samples within the widest possible frame. Our hope at present is that it may be possible for Dr. Buchwald and Dr. Goulet to share their experience (and the Greenland samples) with each other.

[17] A good description of black spruce is found in the *Oxford Encyclopedia of Trees of the World*, pp. 80-86. The conclusions about the wood's suitability for Norse shipbuilding are mine. See my later paper in this volume for a discussion of the Norse Greenlanders' manufacture and use of iron. See also E.

Estyn Evans, "Strange Iron Objects from Co. Fermanagh," *Ulster Journal of Archaeology*, Third Series, vol. 11 (1948) : 58-64, p. 63, with reference (note 6) to E. Wyndham Hulme in *Antiquity*, June, 1937, p. 221.

[18] Niels Nielsen, "Evidence on the Extraction of Iron in Greenland by the Norsemen," in Poul Nørlund and Aage Roussell, "Norse Ruins at Gardar, the Espiscopal Seat of Mediaeval Greenland," *Meddelelser om Grønland* 76 (1), 1929, pp. 193-213, especially pp. 199-200.

[19] Erik Andersen and Claus Malmros, "Ship's Parts Found in the Viking Settlements in Greenland," in Birthe L. Clausen, ed., *op. cit.*, pp. 118-22; Seaver, *Frozen Echo*, p. 28.

[20] See reference 13.

[21] Hans Christian Gulløv, "Kong Frederik den Sjettes Kyst — glimt fra tre somres undersøgelser i Østgrønland." In Fra Nationalmuseets Arbejdsmark, Copenhagen, 1993, pp. 70--81, especially p. 80; William W. Fitzhugh, "A Review of Palaeo-Eskimo Culture, pp. 29-30"; ---, personal comm. May 25, 1996.

[22] Radio-carbon datings from archaeological sites located primarily in the coastal region from Nain down to Hamilton Inlet indicate that the so-called Point Revenge Indians occupied central and southern Labrador essentially between A.D. 700 and A.D. 1500. Robert McGhee, "Contact Between Native North Americans and the Medieval Norse: A Review of the Evidence," *American Antiquity* 49 (1984), pp. 6-8, 13; Aage Roussell, "Sandnes and the Neighbouring Farms," *Meddelelser om Grønland* 88 (2), Copenhagen, 1936, pp. 106-08; Seaver, *Frozen Echo*, p. 26.

[23] By about A.D. 1400, the Thule people had reached Hamilton Inlet and ringed the Ungava Bay along with the northern, eastern, and western — but apparently not the southern — shores of Hudson Bay. J.V. Wright, "Cultural Sequences A.D. 500 - European Contact," in *Historical Atlas of Canada*, plate 9; Robert McGhee, "Contact," p. 8; idem, "Peopling the Arctic," in *Historical Atlas of Canada*, plate 11.

[24] Robert McGhee, "Contact," pp. 14-21, in which he singles out discoveries reported by Elmer Harp ("A Late Dorset Copper Amulet from Southeastern Hudson Bay," in *Folk* 16-17, 1975, pp. 33-44) and by Patrick Plumet ("Les maisons longues dorsétiennes de l'Ungava," in Géographie Physique et Quaternaire 36 (3), 1982, pp. 253-89); idem, "The Skrællings," in Birthe L. Clausen, ed., *op. cit.*, pp. 49-50.

[25] "A Late Dorset Copper Amulet from Southeastern Hudson Bay," in Folk 16-17, 1975, pp. 33-44); William W. Fitzhugh, "A Review of Pal;eo-Eskimo Cultures," p. 30. The discovery of the copper amulet was made by Fitzhugh when he took part in Harp's excavations in 1967 (personal comm. May 25, 1996).

[26] I am grateful to William W. Fitzhugh for succinct information about these two items after he had read the draft to this article.

[27] The wedge and the arrow point had high phosphorus contents, providing a link — albeit a very tenuous one — with the blooms recovered from Frobisher sites. Robert M. Ehrenreich and Michael L. Wayman, "Acculturation in the Arctic: The Inuit Meet Martin Frobisher," in Stephen Alsford, ed., *The Meta Incognita Project, Contributions to Field Studies*, Canadian Museum of Civilization Mercury Series, Directorate Paper No. 6, 1993, pp. 142-46. I am also grateful to William W. Fitzhugh for providing me with a closer description of the arrowpoint's shape and method of manufacture.

[28] Poul Nørlund and Aage Roussell, "Norse Ruins at Gardar, the Espiscopal Seat of Mediaeval Greenland," *Meddelelser om Grønland* 76 (1), 1929, especially illustration p. 146.

[29] Réginald Auger, Michel Blackburn, and William W. Fitzhugh, "Martin Frobisher's Base Camp on Kodlunarn Island: A Two-Year Time Capsule in the History of Technology," in Stephen Alsford, ed., *The Meta Incognita Project*, Canadian Museum of Civilization Mercury Series, Directorate Paper No. 6, Hull (Québec), 1993, p. 62.

[30] Kenneth S. Norris and Flip Nicklin,"Beluga: White Whale of the North," *National Geographic*, vol. 185 (1994) no. 6, pp. 2-31, especially map p. 11.

[31] W. Gillies Ross, *Arctic Whalers, Icy Seas: Narratives of the Davis Strait Whale Fishery*, Toronto, c. 1985, p. xv.

[32] P.R. Richard, "Status of the Belugas (Delphinapterus leucas) of Southeast Baffin Island, Northwest Territories," in *Canadian Field Naturalist* 105 (2), Ottawa, 1991, pp. 206-14.

[33] Norris and Nicklin, *op. cit.*, map. p. 11; Erich Hoyt, *The Whales of Canada: An Equinox Wildlife Handbook*, Camden East, Ontario, 1984, map p. 81.

[34] Thomas H. McGovern, Gerald F. Bigelow, Thomas Amorosi, James Woollett and Sophia Perdikaris, "The zooarchaeology of 017a," in C.L. Vebæk, "Narsaq - a Norse landnáma farm," in *Meddelelser om Grønland* (Man & Society), 18, Copenhagen, 1993, pp. 58-74. The quote is from p. 67.

[35] Randall R. Reeves, *Atlantic Walrus (Odobenus rosmarus rosmarus): A literature survey and status report*. U.S. Department of the Interior Fish and Wildlife Service, Research Report No. 10, Washington D.C., 1978, pp. 20-22.

[36] *Atlas of Canada*, plate 42.

[37] Storm, *op. cit.*, p. 364.

[38] Seaver, *Frozen Echo*, p. 141.

[39] Along the coast, the Neo-Eskimo (Thule) culture appears to have reached Northern Labrador by A.D. 1200-1300 and Central Labrador by about A.D. 1500, at the same time as Indians of the Point Revenge Culture were moving north. See William W. Fitzhugh, "Archaeological Ethnicity and the Prehistory of Labrador," in Réginald Auger, Margaret F. Glass, Scott MacEachern, and Peter H. McCartney, eds., *Ethnicity and Culture, Proceedings of the Eighteenth Annual Conference of the Archaeological Association of the University of Calgary*, Alberta, 1987, pp. 147-9.

[40] E. Bielanski, "Contactual Transformation: The Dorset-Thule Succession," in Allen P. McCartney, ed., *Thule Eskimo Culture: An Anthropological Retrospective*, Canadian Museum of Civilization Mercury Series, Paper No. 88, Ottawa, 1979, pp. 100-109, especially pp. 102-3; Fitzhugh, personal comm., May 25, 1996.

[41] The carving shown in fig. 2 now belongs to the Museum of Civilization in Canada. McGhee, "Contact," p. 17 with reference to Deborah and George Sabo, "A Possible Thule Carving of a Viking from Baffin Island, N.W.T.," *Canadian Journal of Archaeology* 2, 1978, pp. 33-42; Hans Christian Gulløv, "Eskimoens syn på europæeren — de såkaldte nordbodukker og andre tvivlsomme udskæringer," *Grønland* 30, 1982, pp. 226-34; Seaver, *Frozen Echo*, p. 39.

[42] Fitzhugh, "Archaeological Ethnicity," pp. 147-50.

[43] In a discussion of this problem with Dr. Fitzhugh in Washington D.C. in March of 1995, he observed that a controlling English presence off the south-west coast of Greenland would have been a more likely deterrent to the Norse than hostilities among American Native populations on the coast of North and Central Labrador.

[44] C.L. Vebæk, "Vatnahverfi: An inland district of the Eastern Settlement in Greenland," *Meddelelser om Grønland* (Man & Society), 17, Copenhagen, 1992, pp. 85-86 (including fig. 119), 120. These four iron pieces, together with several other iron objects found on the same farm, have now been submitted to Dr. V.F. Buchwald for analysis. Jette Arneborg, personal communication, April 9, 1996.

[45] Seaver, *Frozen Echo*, pp. 232-34.

[46] Ibid., pp. 227-253.

[47] Ibid., pp. 28-29.

[48] Ibid., Chapter Three, but especially pp. 61-66.

[49] McGovern, Bigelow, Amorosi, Woollett and Perdikaris, *op. cit.*, pp. 66-67.

[50] Jette Arneborg, *Kulturmødet mellem nordboer og eskimoer — En kritisk analyse af kilderne til belysning af kulturmfdet mellem nordboere og eskimoer i Grønland. Vurderet i norrønt perspektiv.* Unpublished Ph.D. thesis, University of Copenhagen Institute for Prehistoric and Classical Archaeology, 1991. I am grateful to Dr. Arneborg for allowing reference to her research here.

[51] Peter Schledermann, "Notes on Norse Finds from the East Coast of Ellesmere Island, N.W.T," *Arctic* 33, 1980, pp. 454-63; idem, "Norsemen in the High Arctic," in Birthe L. Clausen, op. cit., pp. 54-66 (picture of the plane on p. 54).

[52] Ibid., pp. 59-60.

[53] Karen McCullough, "The Ruin Islanders: Thule Culture Pioneers in the Eastern High Arctic," Canadian Museum of Civilization Mercury Series, Archaeological Survey of Canada Paper 141, Hull, Québec, 1989, especially pp. iii, 8, 239-258.

[54] Ibid., p. 230.

[55] See, e.g., Schledermann, "Notes on Norse Finds," pp. 54-56.

[56] [Rasmus Rask and Finn Magnusen], "Efterretning om en i Grønland funden Runesteen med dens forklaring, forfattet af Professor Rask, og nogle dertil hørende Oplysninger ved Professor F. Magnusen," in *Antiqvariske Annaler* 4, part 2, Copenhagen, 1827, pp. 309-343, with an "Addendum" re the above, containing a report by the missionary P. Kragh, July, 1826, pp. 367-79.

[57] From three young men who said they had carved the runes and raised a cairn over it on Rogation Day (either April 25 or one of the three days before Ascension Day). This exquisitely carved object is exhibited at the National Museum in Copenhagen.

[58] Seaver, *Frozen Echo*, p. 37; Jette Arneborg, "Contact between Eskimos and Norsemen in Greenland," in Else Roesdal and Preben Meulengracht Sørensen, eds., *Beretning fra tolvte tværfaglige vikingesymposium*, Aarhus Universitet, 1993, p. 28. Arneborg refers to a personal 1991 communication from Marie Stoklund for the dating of this rune stone.

[59] Réginald Auger, Michel Blackburn, and William W. Fitzhugh, "Martin Frobisher's Base Camp on Kodlunarn Island." p. 65.

[60] Randall R. Reeves, *Atlantic Walrus (Odobenus rosmarus rosmarus). A Literature Survey and Status report.* U.S. Department of the Interior Fish and Wildlife Service, Research Report no. X (Washington, D.C., 1978), pp. 13-22; Erik W. Born, Mads P. Heide-Jørgensen, and Rolph A. Davis, "The Atlantic walrus (Odobenus rosmarus rosmarus) in West Greenland." *Meddelelser om Grønland: Bioscience* 40, 1994, pp. 12-13, fig. 5; Kirsten A. Seaver, "'A Very Common and Usuall Trade': The Relationship between Cartographic Perceptions and 'Fishing' in the Davis Strait circa 1500-1550," *British Library Journal*, June 1996 (in press).

[61] Robert McGhee, *The Thule Village at Brooman Point, High Arctic Canada*, Canadian Museum of Civilization Mercury Series, Archaeological Survey of Canada Paper No. 125, 1984; McCullough, *op. cit.*, pp. 257-58; David Morrison, "Radio-carbon Dating Thule culture," *Arctic Anthropology* 26 (2), 1989, pp. 48-77.

[62] Seaver, *Frozen Echo*, p. 63; "Grænlendinga páttr" in Gudni Jónsson, ed., *Islendinga sögur*, Reykjavik, 1968, vol. I, p. 395.

[63] The box had been placed under the dead person's head and contained some kind of animal substance. Poul Nørlund, "Buried Norsemen at Herjolfsnes," *Meddelelser om Grønland*, 67 (1), Copenhagen, 1924, pp. 60-67.

[64] C.L. Vebæk, "Vatnahverfi: An inland district of the Eastern Settlement." *Meddelelser om Grønland* (Man & Society), 17, Copenhagen 1992, p. 90; Jette Arneborg, "Greenland, the starting point for voyages to North America," in Birthe L. Clausen, *op. cit.*, p. 18.

[65] Claus Andreasen, "Nipaitsoq og Vesterbygden," *Grønland* 30 (1982), pp. 177-88; Seaver, *Frozen Echo*, pp. 115-22.

[66] E.G.R. Taylor, "A Letter Dated 1577 from Mercator to John Dee," *Imago Mundi* 13, Stockholm, 1956, pp. 56-67.

[67] Seaver, *Frozen Echo*, pp. 122-26, 132-36.

[68] Ibid., pp. 271-74.

[69] Alwyn A. Ruddock, "The Reputation of Sebastian Cabot," *Bulletin of the Institute of Historical Research* 42 (1974), pp. 95-9; David B. Quinn, *North America from Earliest Discoveries to first Settlements*, London, 1977, pp. 121, 129-33; idem, *England and the Discovery of America, 1481-1620*, London, 1974, pp. 142-3; idem, *Sebastian Cabot and Bristol Exploration* (revised ed.), Bristol Branch of The Historical Association, Bristol, 1993, especially pp. 34-40; David B. Quinn, Alison M. Quinn, and Susan Hillier, eds., *New American World: A Documentary History of North America to 1612*, New York, 1979, vol. 1, pp. 103, 121; Seaver, *Frozen Echo*, pp. 300-01, 307. For a useful collection of printed documents and excerpts of various sixteenth-century accounts relating to Sebastian Cabot, see James A. Williamson, *The Cabot Voyages and Bristol Discovery under Henry VII*, Hakluyt Society, Series II, No. 120, 1961, pp. 265-291.

[70] Seaver, "A Very Common and Usuall Trade."

[71] Williamson, *op. cit.*, p. 273.

[72] C.U. Hammer, H.B. Clausen, and W. Dansgaard, "Greenland Ice Sheet Evidence of Post-Glacial Volcanism and its Climatic Impact," *Nature* 288 (1980), pp. 230-5. In commenting on this passage, Fitzhugh wryly noted that they had found impenetrable ice in these waters in the summer of 1992 (personal comm., May 25, 1996).

[73] Seaver, "A Very Common and Usuall Trade." There is an excellent reproduction of Sebastian's map in Kenneth Nebenzahl, *Atlas of Columbus*, Chicago, New York, San Francisco, 1990, pp. 106-7.

[74] The Tordesillas line separated Portuguese possessions and discoveries (to the east of the line) from new Spanish territories (anything west of the line).

[75] Williamson, *op. cit.*, pp. 266-9.

[76] The basic documentary sources are printed in H.P. Biggar, *The Precursors of Cartier, 1497-1534*, Ottawa, 1911, pp. 61-7. David B. Quinn has a useful modern commentary on the Corte Real voyages in *England and Discovery of America*, pp. 111-18. See also Seaver, *Frozen Echo*, pp. 213, 260-63, 269, 274-87, 292-3, 303 ; idem, "A Very Common and Usuall Trade."

[77] Martín Fernandez de Navarrete, *Collección de los viajes y descubrimientos que hicieron por mar los españoles, desde fines del siglo XV*, Madrid, 1825, vol. III, p. 41.

[78] Selma H. Barkham, *Los vascos en el marco Atlantico Norte, siglos XVI y XVII*, vol. III of ITSASOA (Enrique Ayerbe, gen. ed.), Bilbao, 1987, pp. 11-17 (prefatory remarks by Iñaki Zumalde), 28-37, 39, 55-60; idem., "The Basque Whaling Establishments in Labrador 1536-1632 — A Summary," *Arctic* 37 (4), 1984, pp. 515-19; Brian Fagan, "Basques of Red Bay," *Archaeology* 46 (5), 1993, pp. 44-51; Robert Grenier, "Basque Whalers in the New World: The Red Bay Wrecks," in G. Bass, ed., *Ships and Shipwrecks of the Americas*, London, 1988, pp. 69-84, especially p. 69.

[79] Grenier, *op. cit.*, p. 82.

[80] W. Gillies Ross, *Arctic Whalers, Icy Seas: Narratives of the Davis Strait Whale Fishery*, Toronto (ca. 1985), pp. xiii-iv, 4-5.

[81] Grenier, *op. cit.*, pp. 81-2.

[82] Ibid., p. 69.

[83] Ibid., pp. xiii-iv; Fagan, *op. cit.*, p. 46.

[84] Ibid., p. 50.

[85] Selma Huxley Barkham, "Basque Exploration and Discovery," in Silvio A. Bedini, ed., *The Christopher Columbus Encyclopedia*, 1992, vol. 1, pp. 265-6.

[86] Grenier's description (*op. cit.*, pp. 80-2) of provisioning and insurance arrangements make fascinating reading.

[87] For a more detailed discussion, see my paper later in this volume.

[88] The Agpamiut medal is discussed in detail in an article now in the final stages of preparation for *The Medal* (published by The British Museum Department of Coins and Medals): Kirsten A. Seaver, "The Many Faces of the Great Captain." For previous descriptions, see Therkel Mathiassen, "Ancient Eskimo Settlements in the Kangâmiut Area." *Meddelelser om Grønland* 91 (1), Copenhagen, 1931, p. 8, with reference to a three-volume collection intended for English readers: *Greenland, Copenhagen, 1928-30*, vol. III, p. 84. The medal was turned over to the National Museum ten years after the discovery for inclusion in the Royal Coins and Medals Collection. In a 1958 article ("Mønter og medailler i Grønlands jord," *Grønland*, 1958, pp. 1-10), Professor Rudi Thomsen treated the medal as a curiosity, and his description and analysis of the medal are in fact an uncritical and unattributed translation of the opinions of the French scholar Alfred Armand (*Les Médailleurs italiens des quinzième et seizième siècles*, Paris, 1883-87, vol. I, p. 176 and vol. III, p. 77). Armand was unaware that Copenhagen's version of the De Córdoba portrait medal even existed. I recently found the only other known example to be in The British Museum.

[89] For thorough discussions of the 1566 Inuit captives and the drawings made of them, see William C. Sturtevant and David B. Quinn, "This New Prey: Eskimos in Europe in 1567, 1576, and 1577," in Christian F. Feest, ed., *Indians and Europe*, Aachen, 1987; Hans Christian Gulløv, "Noua terra 1566," *Grønland*, 1988 (nos. 5-6), pp. 129-46.

[90] J. Garth Taylor, "The Inuit of Southern Quebec-Labrador: Reviewing the evidence," *Inuit Studies* 4 (1-2), 1980, pp. 185-94; idem., "Historical Ethnography of the Labrador Coast," in David Damas, ed., *Arctic*, [vol. 5 of William C. Sturtevant, ed., Handbook of North American Indians], Washington, D.C., 1984.

[91] William W. Fitzhugh, "Staffe Island 1 and the Northern Labrador Dorset-Thule Succession," p. 239 (abstract).

[92] Fitzhugh discusses this progression of Inuit-European contacts at some length in "Early contacts North of Newfoundland before A.D. 1500: A Review." pp, 23-43 in William W. Fitzhugh, ed.,*Cultures in Contact: The Impact of European Contacts on Native American Cultural Institutions A.D. 1000-1800*, Anthropological Society of Washington Society Series, Smithsonian Institution Press, Washington, D.C., 1985. See esp. pp. 31-38.

[93] Réginald Auger, Michel Blackburn, and William W. Fitzhugh, "Martin Frobisher's Base Camp on Kodlunarn Island," p. 63.

[94] See, e.g., Kaplan, *op. cit.*, pp. 56-8; Réginald Auger, Michel Blackburn, and William W. Fitzhugh, "Martin Frobisher's Base Camp on Kodlunarn Island," p. 76.

[95] William W. Fitzhugh, "Archaeology of the Frobisher voyages and European-Inuit Contact: Overview and 1991 Field Report," in Stephen Alsford, ed., *The Meta Incognita Project: Contributions to Field Studies*, Canadian Museum of Civilization Mercury Series, Directorate Paper No. 6, Hull (Québec), 1993, p. 90, 128.

[96] Hans Christian Gulløv and Hans Kapel, *Haabetz Colonie 1721-1728*, Ethnographical Series 16, Copenhagen, 1979, pp. 5, 20-22. Partly on the basis of two eighteenth-century maps which other investigators had overlooked,Captain Daniel Bruun found the mission's location in 1903.

The Captured "Countrey People": Their Depiction and Medical History

Sir James Watt and Ann Savours

Much has been published by scholars who were particularly concerned with the reception and death of the Eskimos in the strange land of England, so different in climate, customs and speech from their native land. The two men, a woman and her young child all died soon after reaching England and before they could be presented to the Queen, despite a contemporary claim that they were, which was made in an unreliable edition in French of Settle's account of the Second Voyage.[1]

The Inuk of the First Voyage

The Inuk who came to London in early October 1576 is the least known of the three. Michael Lok's pen portrait describes him as being

> very [ ] good sh[ape]... he... [fay]re and strongly pight [built] and made, ...
> his Neck, his Brest,... [with] very brode face, and very fat and fu[lle] [about]
> his Body. But his legs shorter and smaller [than the] [pr]oportion of his
> Body requyred. And his hands... [H]is heare cole Blak, and long hanging and
> tyed [vp a] boue his fore head. His Eyes little and a ... blak Beard. His Culler
> of Skyn all ouer his Bo[dy and fa]ce, was of a dark Sallow, much like to the
> tawny Mores; [or ra]ther to the Tartar Nation, whereof I think he was. [His]
> Countenance sullen or churlish and sharp withall.[2]

However, he is depicted as quite slender by the contemporary Flemish painter, Lucas de Heere, (1534-1584) in a water-colour in Ghent University Library, which appears in Kaj Birket-Smith's "The earliest Eskimo portraits."[3]

Sturtevant and Quinn also reproduce the watercolour in their detailed study of the Frobisher Eskimos entitled *This new prey* (1987).[4] However, as in Birket-Smith, the reproduction is reduced in size and in black and white, not colour. Since one of the present authors (A.M.S.) was able to study the document in Ghent recently, it seems appropriate to add a few more words as a result of that all too brief visit.

The picture of the captured Inuk of 1576 occurs on folio 124 (very nearly at the end) of an unbound volume of 127 folios measuring approximately 12 x 9 inches. The volume comprises a fascinating procession of well executed, unfaded portraits in watercolours of a great variety of men and women, reminding one of Chaucer's Canterbury pilgrims. However, de Heere's characters do not come from any particular century and the portrait of the Inuk (1576) is of a later date than most. In the words of de Heere's beautiful title done in gold paint, his book is a *Theatre De Tous les Peuples et nations de la terre avec leurs habits, et ornements divers, tant anciens que modernes diligemment depeints au naturel Par Luc Dheere, Peintre et Sculpteur Gantois.* He begins with Ancient Romans, then Venetians, Swiss, English, Scots, Irish and others, including Egyptians, Turks and Ethiopians. There is even a Mayor of London.

Like the other portraits, that of the *Homme sauvage amené des pais Septentrionaux par M. Furbisher L'an 1576* is well drawn and delicately coloured, in his case in browns and greys. He stands on a reddish-brown bank or mound, beyond which is the blue-green sea, on which is drawn a manned kayak and a distant sailing vessel. On seeing the picture, one is struck by its freshness, and its softness in comparison with the hard lines of the black and white reproductions. The eminent Eskimologist, Kaj Birket-Smith, has commented on the costume. He also tells us that de Heere was exiled in England from 1568 to 1576, so that he could well have seen the Inuk in London. However, Sturtevant and Quinn suggest that the drawing was done, more likely from another depiction, now lost.[5] We are fortunate that this one has survived.

De Heere ended his fascinating procession of people with thoughts of death and immortality :

> *Or lhomme ayant bien achevé son cours*
> *Apres la mort aura ioye immortelle*
> *Mais au meschant se prepare au retours*
> *(S'il ne s'amende) une paine éternelle*
> (folio 127)

Another Flemish artist, Cornelis Ketel (1548 - 1616) was paid by the Company of Cathay for painting eight pictures of the Inuk, of which one was for the Queen and one for the Company itself. Only Ketel's large portrait in oils of Frobisher appears to be extant and is in the Bodleian Library, Oxford.[6] A similarly well executed portrait by Ketel of Registrar Thomas Pead was sold at Sotheby's recently.[7]

According to Best, the Inuk was scooped out of the sea in his kayak by Frobisher during the first voyage, and "when he founde himself in captivitie, for very choller and disdain, he bit his tong in twayne within his mouth : notwithstanding, he died not thereof, but lived until he came to Englande, and then he died of colde which he had taken at sea."[8] Unfortunately, we are not told of any steps taken by Phillipe Bocket, the surgeon, to arrest the hæmorrhage. Did he employ any of the usual sixteenth century methods, such as styptics, the cautery or stitching? Did he attempt to ligature the lingual arteries or was he content simply to hold the tongue forward until bleeding ceased? In any event, the tongue healed satisfactorily, but the Inuk would have been unable to eat until it did so and this may well have reduced his resistance to the infection from which he died. The financial accounts state that he was buried in the churchyard of St. Olave's Hart Street, London, but the parish registers do not confirm this.[9]

The Trio of the Second Voyage

More is known about the man and unrelated woman and child of the second voyage, who were captured in different incidents. The man, who was seized during an early skirmish, proved to be a tough fighter and might have escaped if he had not been overtaken by Nicholas Conyer, a servant of the Earl of Warwick, who was less encumbered with equipment than his compatriots. Conyer being "a good wrastler, shewed his companion such a Cornishe tricke, that he made his sides ake against the grounde for a moneth after. And being so stayed, he was taken alive, and brought away."[10] The Inuk was clearly roughly handled, thrown to the ground and sustained, at the very least, a chest injury which caused prolonged pain.

The woman was taken, in a later fracas, when she was mistaken for a man hiding behind a rock. An arrow fired at her pierced the arm of the child she was carrying. The surgeon accompanying the reconnoitring party — probably Edward Cooley from the *Ayde*, since Best reported it — applied healing salves which contained various resins and were homeostatic and antiseptic. "But she," said Best, "not acquainted with such kinde of surgerie, plucked those salves away, and, by continual licking with hir own tongue, not much unlike our dogges, healed uppe the child's arme."[11] Saliva may well have been more beneficial than the apothecary's salves, because it contains antimicrobial substances such as lysozymes which dissolve bacteria and factors which help the skin to grow.[12]

In fact, many primitive people achieved rapid healing of wounds simply by keeping them dry and clean, an observation made by Watkin Tench in his description of the Aborigines following the arrival of the First Fleet in Australia in 1788.[13]

Events at Bristol, 1577

Aboard ship, the man and woman displayed the utmost discretion and modesty, each refusing to undress in the presence of the other. Later, they became less distant, but never intimate, the woman waiting on the man and preparing his food.[14] The trio were brought to Bristol in October 1577, where the man died after two months and the woman and her baby soon afterwards. The names have been standardized from different spellings as Kalicho [the man], Arnaq [the woman] and Nutaaq [the child].[15] The three are depicted convincingly by the Elizabethan artist and colonist John White, who is best known for his pictures of Virginia in the 1580s and whose drawing of the fight at "Bloody Point" has survived in an early copy.[16] Cornelis Ketel also portrayed the 1577 Inuit captives, but none of these pictures appear to be extant.

Sturtevant and Quinn have followed up in some detail the illustrations derived from the well known John White drawings of the Esquimaux who came to England in 1577. One of these by William Burch is in the library and archives of Canterbury Cathedral. The picture occurs in a folio volume of miscellaneous pen and ink drawings, very different from Lucas de Heere's finished volume. Its title page reads as follows:

A boke of drawings of the shapes and formes of divers beasts, foules, birds, fishes, monsters, serpents, trees, herbes, plantes, and flowers wth diverse accidents of antiquities and armoury, drawn by me William Burch... this XXth Aug. 1590...

The picture occurs on folio 10 *recto* and is entitled, "The indian man and woman that Sr martin ffrobisser brought into England 1578. A true picture Collinshough & Agnof." To the right of the man, woman and child are drawings of "An indian horse" and "An indian cowe." The volume has no particular associations with Canterbury, having been acquired in the nineteenth century. These Esquimaux were the first, but certainly not the last to visit the British Isles. A number of others followed in the eighteenth and nineteenth centuries, some surviving the change and others not.[17]

Canterbury, however, has a real connection with the Eskimos. One of the Inuhuit from North West Greenland — a group whom Sir John Ross christened the "Arctic Highlanders" — was a student at the missionary college of St Augustine's in the mid nineteenth century. His name was Kallihirua.[18] "Kalli" was much loved and his death as a young man greatly regretted. Later Inuit visitors to Great Britain had the advantage over Frobisher's captives of some familiarity, through explorers and whalers, with the English language and were less of a curiosity to the general public.

Returning now to the trio brought to Bristol by Frobisher in 1577, we find that there are accounts of the preference of the man and woman for raw meat and of Arnaq's way of nursing the infant.[19] The man delighted the mayor and an appreciative audience by his skills with his kayak and his marksmanship with his bird-dart,[20] creating considerable amusement when he attempted to ride a horse facing the tail.[21] By this time, his ribs were no longer troubling him yet, within a month, Kalicho or "Calichough" was dead. A report of his illness and autopsy, written in difficult Latin, was furnished by Dr Edward Dodding, who had recently begun to practise in Bristol.[22] The Latin report was published by Collinson[23] and the first English translation by Neil Cheshire.[24] This is accurate and readable and should be compared with a new translation by William Schupbach, below, which attempts to capture the pedantic and stilted prose of a typical Elizabethan physician.[25]

Dr Edward Dodding's 'Reporte of the Sicknesse and Death of the Man at Bristoll which Capt. Furbisher brought from the North-West.'
On the left side of the dissected cadaver, the first thing which offered itself for my inspection were two ribs, broken by the force of the accident and the blow when he was captured : they were gaping, not stuck together, the care of them had either been neglected as often happens in these most turbulent times and in the narrow confines of naval affairs or, what I rather suspect, had been aroused to inflammation by a disease perceived by no one; and a contusion of the lung in the advance of time had contracted putridity from the same source. Those disorders, creeping freely onwards day by day, had been both stirred up by the ill effect of the external cold, and increased through bad diet, they had

not been mended in the meantime from the outside by the surgeon's art, nor struck back from the inside through drugs, and proceeded to an incurable ulcer of the lung. On top of the evil, putrid pus rushed and piled up a very great flow toward the same, composed of a viscid and sticky material, and the left part of the lung so teemed everywhere that it spat out absolutely nothing through the whole time of the disease, and breathing was held in and constricted.

In addition to this his nature was weakened by the raging of the threatening disease : our diet was more generous than either the evil of this disease can bear or perhaps than the man's daily habit allowed, something which had been effected by the highest concern of the supreme commander and the great generosity of those among whom he was living, everyone having been deceived in their opinion more by the hidden nature of the disease and by stupid indulgence than by malevolence, but that disease clearly expressed by the appearance of shortness of breath shortly before his death and he was not completely free from dropsy. For in the space of the thorax a quantity and abundance of water of a kind that is rarely seen by observant and industrious anatomists was observed to flow. This was shaken about by the movement of the body as the outcome of the affair assured us, and impeded the breathing out of the lung, and finally the lung itself stuck to the ribs more firmly than anyone would think.

Of the wounded and [so to speak] apostemated brain, apart from deafness and the most intense head-pain [with both of which he was always afflicted], infinite and most open signs come forth and emerge, which [lest I be too verbose] are to be wrapped in silence.

The quantity of due weight which Nature had subtracted from his spleen, leaving it very small, she seems to have added with interest to his extremely capacious stomach, which, packed and distended with water, appeared much greater than those of our men, on account of his incurable, I believe, gluttony. In other parts you would say there was a fear of the English which, from his first arrival, although his face was quite cheerful and cleverly simulated, he concealed and lied about, yet his gesture [as I considered the individual features more deeply one by one within myself, suspecting everything], either they openly betrayed and uncovered the same, or as I often maintained, but to deaf ears they forebode an impending lethal disease. These things came to our notice and were confirmed more clearly from his pulse than from himself, for his pulses were always smaller, slower and weaker than they were less frequent, and yet they were less frequent than either his youth or his choleric temperament demanded.

At the first attack of the disease, when his strength was still intact, I was summoned, and with great force urged bloodletting, so that the stings of the inflammation would lie deadened and the matter would be lessened and overcome. But it was forbidden by the barbarous man's stupid, excessively barbarous timidity, and the advice of those with whom he was sailing prevailed with me.

Finally, having been called at the hour which immediately preceded the hour in which he departed this life, I found everything threatening death in a short time: his power of speech interrupted, almost completely cut off; his appetite lowered; no pulse; in a word, all his strength and faculties completely prostrated. Having been refreshed a little, he returned to himself as if from a deep sleep and recognised us, his friends. I turned to medicine and he uttered those few of our words which he had learned, in so far as he could, and responded in turn to questions fairly appositely, he sang forth clearly that same song [as they tell who had heard both] which, standing on the shore, his companions of the same place and rank used to lament or celebrate his final departure, like swans who, foreseeing what good there is in death, die with singing and pleasure. But I had hardly left when he exchanged life for death, breaking forth into these final words, uttered in our tonge : "The Lord be with you."

I was distressed and deeply saddened not so much by his death as because our most serene Queen's great hope of seeing him had now, for a second time fallen as if from our hands. But by a much greater sadness are affected the heroes of this new and solid honour, who are robbed of the prizes and spoils of truly Herculean labour, whom our highest respect awaits by rights [for I say what I feel], for they completed these sea journeys and opened up places which were out of the way, harsh indeed, and unapproached before this time, with great expenses of their own, with labours and dangers, for the greater advantage of the kingdom and of posterity, and to the greatest glory of their own names, so that by the same facility which we who follow may retain these spirits and sinews of the kingdom and of the state [for thus are such riches called, not unknowingly, by philosophers], nor should we accept them before we lost them through our ingratitude [for I do not see what else there is to fear] of what we should repay to the Lord for all the things which he has given to us.

From foreign kings let us hope for nothing good because they do not wish and let us fear nothing bad, because they do not dare. But I do not say these things with the intention of persuading anyone, skulking in the wretchedness of sin, to sleep on either ear, but so that I can free individuals one by one from wickedness, and so that I may drive them all to celebrate divine things more keenly. For what more absurd thing can be said or thought, than that, since God the good and the great is more ready to give, we may be slower to deserve? But there will always be to be recognised that true saying of the true God, "not because you are worthy but because I am merciful."

If the futile and made-up prayers of the chanters, and ineffective ceremonies and games, had any power to drive away disease, immediately this man while he was among the living, "Calichoughe" [for that was his name] would have cut and driven them away though they were pullulating like hydras. For in this art, nobody was more practised, nobody [unless I am mistaken] more trusting in superstition, for he employed magic charms as numerous as the words of pain which emerged.

I showed the cadaver to the woman while she was suffering from spots [which on the following day, when these words are being written, broke out in great numbers on her skin], and she alone, although unwilling, was by my persuasion brought along to the burial which I expressly wished to be carried out without solemnity, lest any fear should be cast into her about men being sacrificed among us, and she was kept there until the body was entirely covered in earth. I showed her human bones dug up, and made her understand that we were all to be buried in the same way, so that I might remove from her mind all worry about the eating of human flesh [which was deeply rooted among them], and that she might learn to shed her fear thenceforth. But either that woman surpasses all our men in prudence and patience, or she is far surpassed in humanity by brute animals themselves, for she was not at all moved by his death and, as far as we understood from her expression, she did not take it badly, so that by this last fact she expressed more clearly what we had long before assumed by conjecture, that she had held him in utter contempt, and that although she was accustomed to sleep in one and the same bed, nothing passed between them except talk, and she abhorred his embraces.

Farewell, Bristol 8 November. Yours as you know, Edward Doddinge. "If hardy Odysseus had seen no danger, Penelope would have been happy, but she would be without praise." [Ovid, *Tristia*, 5.5, lines 51-2]

Implications of Dr. Dodding's Report

Dodding first draws attention to two disunited ribs which he implies had been severely fractured and this may have been the reason for their failure to unite. By this time, however, they would not have been a problem for their ends would have been covered by a protective coating, unlike the problem encountered by William Clowes when serving in the *Ayde* in 1570. In that case, a sharp sliver of rib was penetrating the lung and causing the patient to cough up blood, so an operation to remove it was imperative.[26] Nothing would have been gained and much might have been lost by operating on Calichough and what Dodding thought the surgeons could have achieved by medicines was surely a figment of his imagination, His implied criticism is therefore unjustified. Indeed, on his own admission, the surgeons called him in to examine the patient as soon as his chest infection became apparent. They nevertheless vigorously opposed the blood-letting which Dodding's Galenical outlook demanded, for it appears that Cooley and his colleagues had established an excellent rapport with Calichough and they shewed themselves protective and caring.

Dodding's report, however, plainly established the force which had been used in taking the Inuk captive, for not only had he sustained two severely fractured ribs, but he had also suffered a head injury which Dodding's rather ambiguous account suggests might have been a chronic subdural hæmatoma. He was clearly at a loss to describe what he had found and suggests that the post-mortem appearance of the brain made apparent the reason why Calichough had been suffering from deafness and intense head pains. He had probably been struck on the head by Conyer, his captor, before being thrown on the ground.

A collection of blood can form below the dura mater without any evidence of fracture of the skull and this is what probably occurred. In a small number of cases, this collection of blood forms a thick-walled and discoloured cyst, which appears to have led Dodding to believe it was some form of abscess, since he uses a term usually employed to describe that condition. A subdural hæmatoma, however, would readily explain Calichough's symptoms.

The description of the pathology of the lung could well suggest a left lobar pneumonia, though Dodding is careful to mention that he had not produced any sputum during his illness. What is more likely is that Dodding was describing a lung abscess, with pus flowing towards the liquefied centre of the consolidated lung which was sealed off from the bronchial tubes and therefore producing no sputum. If this were the case, the severely fractured ribs had probably been accompanied by extensive injury of the underlying lung which, becoming infected, developed an abscess with a sympathetic pleural effusion. Both the head and chest conditions were potentially fatal and reflected the violence with which Calichough was apprehended. Calichough died on 7 November 1577 and was buried at St Stephen's church, Bristol, the following day.

Last Days

In his report, Dodding informs us that the woman was suffering from a skin rash when the man died and was covered with blotches the following day. She died a few days later, presumably from measles, and was buried on 13 November, also at St Stephen's church. Under "Burials in Anno 1577" the parish register records :

> *Collichang a heathen man buried the 8th of November. Egnock, a heathen woman buried ther 13th of November.*[27]

The child was then taken in the care of a nurse to London where they lodged in an inn at the expense of the Cathay Company. He was attended by John Gymblet there, when he became ill. There is no history of the illness, but Gymblet was a surgeon, so death may have followed an accident. The boy was buried at St Olave's in Hart Street, in the same churchyard as the Inuk of 1576.[28] So ended, on this tragic note, the first acquaintance of the Inuit with England.

Notes

[1] N. Cheshire, T. Waldron, A. Quinn and D.B. Quinn, "Frobisher's Eskimos in England," *Archivaria*, no 10, 1980, 30.

[2] Transcribed from the original damaged manuscript by W. C. Sturtevant and D.B. Quinn. "This New Prey: Eskimos in Europe 1567, 1576 and 1577," in C. F. Feest, *Indians and Europe,* Aachen : Heredot, 1987, 72. The passage also appears in V. Stefansson and E. McCaskill, *The Three Voyages of Martin Frobisher in search of a passage to Cathay and India by the North-West, A.D. 1576-8,* (1) London : Argonaut Press, 1938, 166.

[3] K. Birket-Smith, "The earliest Eskimo portraits," *Folk,* I, København, 1959,1.

[4] W.C. Sturtevant and D.B. Quinn, *op.cit.*

[5] W C Sturtevant and D.B. Quinn, *op.cit.*, 73-75.

[6] Ibid., 93-94.

[7] Sotheby's, *British paintings 1500-1850,* London, Sotheby's, November 1997, p. 32.

[8] G. Best, A True Discourse of the Late Voyages of Discoverie for finding a Passage to Cathaia by the North-West under the conduct of Martin Frobisher, General, 1578, in R. Collinson, *The Three Voyages of Martin Frobisher in search of a Passage to Cathaia and India by the North-West*, London : Hakluyt Society, 38, 1867, 74.

[9] N. Cheshire et al., *op.cit.*, 24-25.

[10] G. Best, A True Reporte of such things as hapned in the sea voyage of Captayne Frobisher, 1577, in R. Collinson, *op.cit.*, 131.

[11] Ibid., 143.

[12] S.G. Schultz, J.G. Forte and B.R. Rauner, eds., *Handbook of Physiology*, 3, New York : Oxford University Press, 1989, 331-2.

[13] W. Tench, *Sydney's First Four Years*, Sydney; Library of Australian History, 1979, 284-5.

[14] G. Best in Collinson, *op.cit.*, 144-5.

[15] W.C. Sturtevant and D.B. Quinn, *op.cit.*, 80.

[16] P.H. Hulton, "John White's drawings of Eskimos," *The Beaver,* 292, Summer 1961, 16-20. P.H. Hulton and D.B. Quinn, *The American drawings of John White 1577-1590*, 2 vols, London : British Museum, 1964.

[17] A Savours, "Early Eskimo visitors to Britain," *Geographical Magazine*, 36(6), 1963, 336-343.

[18] Ibid., 340-341. A. Bugge, "Kallihirua, polareskimoen i Canterbury," *Grønland*, No 5, 1965, 161-175. P.B. Murray, *Kalli, The Esquimaux Christian : a Memoir*, 2nd edition, London : SPCK, 1857. William C. Sturtevant and Inge Kleivan, "Two early photographs of an Inughuaq (Polar Eskimo)," in ed. J.C.H King and Henrietta Lidchi, *Imaging the Arctic* (London: British Museum Press, 1998), 24-28.

[19] F.F. Fox, ed., *Adams' Chronicle of Bristol*, Bristol, 1910, 115.

[20] Ibid.

[21] V. Stefansson and E. McCaskill, *op.cit.*, 2, 237.

[22] W Munk, *The Roll of the Royal College of Physicians of London*, London : R.C.P., I, 1878, 86-7.

[23] Collinson, *op.cit.*, 189-91 and *CSP, Colonial 59, Domestic Elizabeth, cxviii, No 40,* I.

[24] Cheshire et al., *op.cit.,* 40-42.

[25] W. Schupbach, translation into English of Dr Dodding's *Reporte of the Sicknesse and Death of the Man at Bristoll which Capt. Furbisher brought from the North-West*; published here for the first time. W. Schupbach is curator of Iconography at the Wellcome Institute for the History of Medicine, London.

[26] W Clowes, *A Profitable and Necessarie Booke of Observations for all that are burned with the flame of Gun-powder*, 2nd edition, London : T. Orwyn, 1596, 76-9.

[27] Cheshire et al., *op.cit.,* 17. Tracked down by the tenacity of Alison Quinn.
[28] Ibid, 37-8.

Baffin Island Walrus Mandibles and Iron Blooms

Kirsten A. Seaver

This paper will look at arguments against reaching premature conclusions about two riddles arising from the Meta Incognita project's investigations of Martin Frobisher's voyages of 1576-78. One riddle concerns two carefully arranged accumulations of walrus mandibles (with the teeth extracted) found on Willows Island; the other centers on several medieval-type iron blooms found at Frobisher sites by a succession of investigators, and which appear so closely associated with Frobisher's activities that it is tempting to explain both their origin and their Baffin Island presence within the Frobisher context.

There are many problems associated with two such diverse — and possibly unrelated — archaeological puzzles. We cannot know if a connection does exist between them unless we analyze each problem separately using all the sources at our disposal — sources as rich and diverse as the talents (and sometimes divergent views) of the many scholars contributing to the Meta Incognita Project.

The question of the walrus mandibles is somewhat simpler than the problems surrounding the primitive lumps of bog iron and the charcoal fragments embedded in them and will therefore be addressed first. Although the origin and purpose of the careful, though dissimilar, arrangements of walrus jaws on Willows Island are still unknown, only three cultures are likely candidates for having produced them: the Dorset, the Thule, or the Greenland Norse. Such is not the case with the iron blooms.

Indigenous peoples of the Baffin Island region — Dorset and Thule — are not known to have had any rituals associated with such alignments of walrus mandibles, but Robert McGhee has reminded me that rows of musk ox skulls have been found at an early Palaeo-Eskimo Umingmak site on Banks Island.[1] He therefore associates the Willows Island mandibles with nearby Dorset sites. William W. Fitzhugh, on the other hand, believes that since one of the alignments was found in the midst of a snowhouse [Thule] village and the radiocarbon dating of one skull gave an age of 470 ± 60 years (roughly between 1460-1520), it makes sense to assume that these arrangements were made by Thule people, since Thule people lived in the area within that period.[2]

Quite apart from this lack of agreement, the fact that the Norse Greenland colony still existed within the same time span poses a problem here. Another problem is the approximate nature of radiocarbon datings; yet another is the fact that the Willows Island mandible displays appear to be *sui generis* in northern Canada, despite the considerable number of Dorset and Thule sites excavated there up to now. Nor have deliberate arrangements of even a roughly similar nature been found in Eskimo sites on the other side of the Davis Strait.

What *has* been found in Greenland, however, is a nestling of walrus mandibles explicitly associated with the Norse, who as far as we know were the only other people hunting walrus that far north in the Davis Strait in the fifteenth century. The Greenland Norse had carefully buried more than twenty mandibles (with the teeth extracted) right outside their cathedral wall at Gardar, in soil which they themselves had brought in to provide sufficient fill for a graveyard. The jaws were still undisturbed when the Danish archaeologist Poul Nørlund found them in 1926 and thought they gave the impression of having served some ritualistic or religious purpose.[3] The archaeologist and historian Jette Arneborg (of the Ancient and Medieval Section at the National Museum in Copenhagen) has gone through Nørlund's old field notes and photographs and found nothing to challenge his 1929 descriptions and conclusions regarding these walrus mandibles. For the sake of clarity, she stresses that the actual shape of the Gardar arrangement was different from either of the two Willows Island alignments.[4]

There is no doubt that the Gardar walrus mandibles were placed there by the Norse. In the absence of equally clear evidence that either Dorset or Thule people made the two Willows Island alignments, which despite their differing shapes were arranged with as much deliberation as the Gardar walrus jaws, it seems sensible to allow for the possibility that the Greenland Norse may have made these alignments as well, in the course of voyages across the Davis Strait in search of useful American produce. Another intriguing possibility is that the Norse had observed fellow Eskimo hunters at such a ritual and decided to emulate them, although there are no indications otherwise that sporadic contact between the Norse and either Dorset or Thule people led to cultural change on either side. We must naturally also allow for a third possibility, namely that the mandible arrangements on the Canadian and the Greenlandic sides were made independently of each other, by two different cultures with a similar propitiatory approach to luck in hunting.

A well-founded answer to the Willows Island riddle might add to our knowledge about Native Baffin Islanders' pre-Frobisher contacts with white men; it could also provide useful data for those searching for clues to the physical and economic health of the Norse Greenlanders throughout the fifteenth century. Either way, the information would not materially change the current scholarly perception that the Norse continued to cross the Davis Strait sporadically long after they had investigated *Vinland* at the beginning of the eleventh century.

Vinland — "Wineland" — was the Norsemen's name for the general region in North America where they had found grapes. That discovery suggests that they sailed south of the St. Lawrence, but aside from this, all we know about *Vinland* is that it lay below *Markland* or "Forest Land," which began with the forests of Labrador they saw south of the bleak stretch of Arctic coast they dubbed *Helluland* or "Slab Land." Although the many Norse artifacts found in the Canadian Arctic indicate that the Greenland Norse

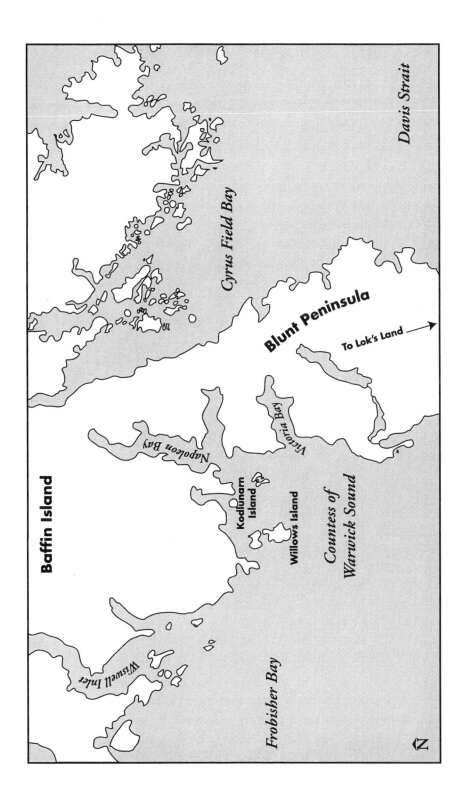

Figure 1: This map is the work of David O. Seaver (Copyright Kirsten A. Seaver).

continued to cross to the American side — an interpretation with which both McGhee and Fitzhugh agree — that is not the same as saying that the Norse continued to go even as far south as Newfoundland. McGhee notes that they would have been no match for adversarial North American Indians, especially in the forested areas of Labrador and Newfoundland, and that they would probably not have found trade with these people particularly useful. In the open, coastal areas farther north, however, the Native Eskimo population had less opportunity for ambush and could offer the Norse such valuable commodities as furs, narwhal horns, and walrus ivory.[5]

We know that narwhal horns, walrus-hide ropes and walrus ivory were the Norse Greenlanders' most prized export articles, and a number of medieval documents and descriptions, as well as archaeological discoveries, reveal that the Norse went very far north of their Greenland settlements in search of their prey. Walrus typically live along coasts and along the edge of the ice, which in the Davis Strait tends to block off the upper part of the strait, turning it into the "bay" seen in many early maps. Confronted with this ice belt, a Norse Greenlander would have had to decide whether to turn back and go home or to keep hunting along the U-shaped ice edge and perhaps end up in Baffin Island.

There were even more compelling reasons for the Norse Greenlanders to cross the Davis Strait than the acquisition of export goods: their domestic economy required timber for ships, which we know they constructed themselves, and iron for various purposes. This brings us to the second problem under discussion here, namely the medieval iron blooms found at Kodlunarn Island and neighboring sites. As we shall see, these blooms may have only a casual connection with the Frobisher ventures. The blooms may well be Norse.

The received wisdom has been that the Greenland Norse imported lumber all the way from Norway as the Icelanders did, but there is in fact no historical or archaeological proof of such imports. Instead, recent research on medieval Norse ship-building has made it very clear that neither salt-soaked driftwood nor the spindly trees and shrubs of Greenland could have met the Norse Greenlanders' ship-building needs.[6] Their nearest and cheapest source of ship's timber would have been in North America, south of the Hamilton Inlet or in southern Ungava Bay.

North America would also have been their most logical source of iron, which they had to import in one form or another. Even if they could spare domestic wood for charcoal with which to smelt bog iron, their own bogs contained no iron ore (small quantities of iron oxide mixed with organic and other matter).[7] To date, a number of Norse Greenland farm smithies have been excavated in both the Western Settlement (defunct ca. 1400 or a little earlier) and the Eastern Settlement (essentially defunct ca. 1500) and have yielded ample evidence that the Greenland Norse *resmelted* crude iron blooms. But not a single hearth pit capable of producing such blooms in the first place has been found, and now we know the reason: they did not have the necessary domestic resources.

The Greenland Norse would nevertheless have been familiar with the medieval Norwegian and Icelandic method of turning bog ore into crude iron blooms to be broken up and reworked in farm smithies. At the beginning of the eleventh century, they brought this skill with them to North America; archaeologists have found a Norse hearth pit furnace at the L'Anse aux Meadows site in northern Newfoundland.[8] But no hearth pit furnace has been located in conjunction with the iron blooms found by Francis Hall and by modern Canadian and American archaeologists investigating the Baffin Island area associated with Frobisher's voyages; indeed, it appears that Baffin Island may be as devoid of bog ore as is Greenland.[9]

These points are significant given a supposition that the Baffin Island blooms were made from bog ore and a fairly general agreement that they have characteristics consistent with medieval hearth pit origins. Disagreement begins with dating the blooms and deducing their provenance. These two problems are obviously related, but they include several subsidiary questions that must be answered independently of each other before we address the larger issue.

The physical and chemical analyses and the radiocarbon datings of a few of these blooms are described in considerable detail, and by several experts, in Fitzhugh and Olin's 1993 book, *Archeology of the Frobisher Voyages*. These sometimes contradictory data gave rise to questions that have since been tackled by the Smithsonian team.

It now appears that both the unusually high sulfur content and the wide spread in radiocarbon dates originally found in the material analyzed by the Smithsonian team were due to unsuccessful attempts to resmelt the crude blooms with coal. This process skewed (aged) the radiocarbon dates in the outer part of the bloom analyzed; it also made the iron brittle and useless. Readings based on the Smithsonian bloom's *core* suggest a date somewhere in the first half of the fifteenth century, which agrees with some of the data listed in the 1993 volume, but not with those that indicated that the blooms might predate the Frobisher voyages by as much as two or three centuries. Projected analysis of a second bloom should shed further light on these problems.[10]

It needs stressing that even with the younger age suggested by the new Smithsonian data, and with the margin one must allow for radiocarbon datings, the blooms appear to predate the Frobisher expeditions. Fitzhugh, too, notes this fact in his 1993 book, along with observing that other people must have visited this region besides those "recorded in the historical literature or in remembered Inuit accounts."[11] It is a timely reminder, for while the bloom dates certainly fall within the period when the Norse were still functioning in Greenland and sailing in the Davis Strait, that is not in itself evidence that the Norse made the Baffin Island blooms.

The account in Fitzhugh's letter makes it clear that attempted resmelting would have involved the Frobisher expedition in some way. Evidence found in the expedition's smithy also suggests that Frobisher's men had broken apart at least one of the blooms.[12] Fitzhugh's information fits with the fact that Frobisher brought sea-coal from England,

and that his expedition's two German specialists were hired because of their experience with a new type of coal-fired smelting oven.[13]

The smashing and attempted resmelting of one or more blooms nevertheless raise the question of whether the Englishmen were merely curious about the blooms or hoped to put them to practical use. In two recent papers, Fitzhugh has addressed the second question.[14] He suggests that survivors from the storm that decimated Frobisher's fleet at the beginning of the last homeward voyage (1578) may have attempted to resmelt the crude iron with coal left behind by the expedition, during efforts to build a ship on Kodlunarn Island in the manner the local Eskimos had described to Francis Hall.[15]

Fitzhugh's theory calls attention to an aspect of the Kodlunarn Island story which has largely been ignored, namely how those enterprising ship wrights found the wherewithal for hull and sail. They would have needed a wrecked ship to cannibalize in the first place, and they would have needed tools of a kind they were unlikely to have carried in a small boat for an intended absence of just a few hours. Had the Kodlunarn boat builders been identical with the five men who disappeared during Frobisher's *first* expedition, they would have done well to cobble together a crude raft and oars with the material and tools at their disposal.

There is every reason to believe that at some point before Hall's arrival in Baffin Island in 1860, ancestors of the Baffin Islanders he met had watched a small number of Europeans construct a ship on Kodlunarn Island and sail away on their second try. But Inuit oral traditions on both sides of the Davis Strait frequently suffer from conflation of events and telescoping of time, and for that and other reasons (to be discussed later), we do not know when the boat building event took place (except that it must have been after the Thule people moved into the area), and we cannot say with certainty that these "white men" were English. They may just as easily have been Norse or some other kind of Europeans.

Fitzhugh's theory may turn out to be the right answer, but while we wait for the continuing archaeological investigations of the Kodlunarn Island sites to provide further evidence, we might consider another possible interpretation of the broken and resmelted blooms. A problem in this connection arises from the fact that we have no clear explanation as yet either for the somewhat wide dispersal of the blooms found or for the fragmentation of some of them.

For example, we need to consider that the Native Baffin Islanders who first found the blooms would quickly have discovered that they were of little use except as heavy (but porous) rocks, because they could not refine the iron themselves.[16] Furthermore, since Frobisher's second and third expeditions were in quest of ore containing precious metal, curiosity about a number of odd-looking stones — so heavy that they might reasonably be suspected of containing significant amounts of some kind of metal — would have been in keeping with that purpose. Both physical fragmentation and attempted smelting would have been reasonable next steps if the nature of the "stones" was not already known to the Englishmen. They may well have tested a couple of these heavy, dark "rocks" in the smithy before deciding that if they had any use, it was as weight on the covers of stores they placed in the Ship's Trench.

This possibility poses another major question, which Fitzhugh's theory about the identity of the shipbuilders does not answer, nor is his theory predicated on an answer. The problem is that if Frobisher's men were unfamiliar with the nature of these "stones," this suggests that the blooms did not arrive with Frobisher's own ships, but had been deposited in Baffin Island by an earlier agent. If the latter, when did the event take place, and through whose agency?

Both McGhee and Fitzhugh are convinced that the original reports and documentation from the Frobisher voyages account for the blooms, but they base their respective convictions on different arguments. In a letter of December 14, 1994 McGhee wrote that "one of the accounts (Edward Sellman??) refers to them as 'our osmonds,' and notes that the Inuit have been taking them." On December 17, Fitzhugh reiterated the position he took in his epilogue to the *Archaeology of the Frobisher Voyages* (where he argued, among other things, that the blooms may have served as ballast): "We also think that the iron was brought to England from the Baltic, perhaps from Russia, and that the blooms are specifically identified in the Frobisher records as 'iron stones of Russia.'"

Before looking at the specific problems associated with either "osmonds" or "iron stones of Russia" we need to consider two general questions, quite apart from the obvious one of why we should ignore altogether the pre-Frobisher radiocarbon dates obtained so far.

The first question is why Frobisher's ships would need extra ballast on their voyage north, especially such useless objects as crude iron blooms. On the contrary, space must have been at a premium on each of the three expeditions. Here, it is important to distinguish between variable ballast and fixed ballast. The latter "was put into the hull just prior to launching or shortly thereafter, before the vessel was masted or rigged. It kept the hull upright in the water and remained in the ship throughout its seagoing life. Smaller amounts of variable ballast were added or subtracted prior to voyages depending on the presence or absence of weighty cargo and armament."[17] It is first of all unlikely that any of Frobisher's ships rode too high in the water when the crew, food, and other provisions including heavy tools and weapons, were safely aboard. Secondly, the shipyard originally responsible for each hull's construction would presumably have chosen the fixed ballast without consulting those using the ship later, and certainly without Frobisher's men inventorying that ballast. Thirdly, regardless of the fixed ballast's composition, it was a permanent part of the ship and would not have been unloaded along with cargo later, *e.g.*, in Baffin Island.

The second question is why any ship arriving in England from an iron-exporting region would take up its own valuable cargo space with crude medieval blooms, when the English were reliable customers for iron that could be put to immediate use.

Since the mid-fifteenth century, England had increased her own production of iron, in part due to the transfer of the water-powered fulling mill technology of the textile industry to bellows for improved bloomeries and to hammer mills that could handle larger blooms. But the need for iron also grew, in step with the expanding population, and good quality iron was imported — sometimes through the Hanse, but often directly — from Normandy, Styria, Sweden, and Catalonia. The latter was of an especially good and malleable quality.[18]

The Swedish (or Baltic) iron, which primarily fell into the category described in the *Oxford English Dictionary* (1976 ed.) as "osmonds," was also much in demand. It came in the form of small pieces and rods and was especially suited to small objects subject to wear and tear. Bristol was a major import center for iron from many countries, and the city's merchants had long used "osmonds" in barter for Icelandic cod, hides, sulfur, and other goods. As Eleanora Mary Carus-Wilson's extensive research in medieval and early renaissance Bristol records demonstrates, outward bound Bristol ships often carried sacks of "osmonds" in their hold along with other merchandise (if the Englishmen needed ballast on their homebound voyage, they opted for Icelandic rocks); she also notes that the term "osmonds" eventually was used for "any similar iron sold in small bars or rods by the barrel or sack (12 barrels to the last) and not by weight."[19]

Since much of the outfitting of Frobisher's ships took place in Bristol, it seems unlikely that those in charge of the business (including Frobisher himself) were ignorant of the barter value of small pieces of iron in the fuel-starved north, or of the common name "osmonds" for these small pieces. And whether Frobisher and his men thought of "osmonds" as "Baltic" or "Russian," they would have known that the word referred to *small* pieces of iron, which lent themselves so readily to the making or repairing of tools and weapons that they surely would have been of practical use to Frobisher's own workmen as well. Such "osmonds" would also have tempted the Baffin Island Inuit in ways that the iron blooms clearly did not.

It therefore seems doubtful that the Baffin Island blooms should be equated with Edward Fenton's Frobisher "osmundes." Might they instead be the "stones of Russia" to which Fitzhugh refers?

Among the many linguistic hurdles historians face, obsolete words such as "osmonds" are easy compared with words that are still in use, but whose meaning has undergone several permutations over time. Both "stones" and "Russia" belong in the latter group. As the many sub-headings in the *Oxford English Dictionary* (1976 ed.) indicate, a "stone" has long been more than a simple rock. Among the definitions applicable both to the late sixteenth century and to heavy, roundish, metallic objects, one stands out: "gun stone." In Frobisher's time, this meant both cannon ball and bullet. In the Frobisher records there is no lack of reference to ammunition of varying size; almost three hundred years later Francis Hall obtained a musket ball on Kodlunarn Island that clearly was associated with the Frobisher expeditions.[20]

If "stones of Russia" refers to ammunition manufactured in "Russia," we would still want to know what the name "Russia" meant to Frobisher, to his advisers, or to those who reported on his Baffin Island voyages. Two maps representing advanced cartographical thought in England at the time — Mercator's world map of 1569 (which greatly influenced Frobisher's thinking) and Sir Humphrey Gilbert's heart-shaped world map of 1576 (the earliest world map printed in England) — suggest that the "Russia" over which the Tsar was known to preside was a rather vague geographical concept in the last quarter of the sixteenth century.

Fitzhugh, who does not believe that the Baffin Island blooms were smelted with local driftwood, observes that the samples of embedded spruce or larch could have come from driftwood from Siberia and been added to birch and alder growing in the Frobisher Bay area. (In 1993, he noted that none of the driftwood samples the Smithsonian team collected from eastern Baffin Island suggested Siberian sources.[21]) On balance, however, he finds the presence of these four woods in the iron more compatible with the theory that the blooms were manufactured in northwestern Russia or the northern Baltic.[22]

The evident lack of bog ore in Baffin Island is good enough reason to suspect that the blooms were manufactured elsewhere, while the composition of the charcoal fragments found in the blooms suggests other points of origin than the Baltic or Siberia. No larch of any kind is indigenous to the Scandinavian Peninsula or to the Baltic (nor to the Iberian peninsula), but all four tree species mentioned in conjunction with the Baffin Island blooms — spruce, larch, birch, and alder — grow in the part of Labrador the Norse called *Markland*, to which we know they were still traveling in 1347. For that year, three different Icelandic annals record that a storm-battered small ship fetched up in Iceland with a crew of seventeen or eighteen, after losing its anchor and drifting off course on its way back from *Markland*.[23] There is no reason to suppose that this was the very last voyage the Greenland Norse made across the Davis Strait, for it was by a mere fluke that any such "post-Vinland" voyage made it into the written record at all.

It would have made excellent sense for the Greenland Norse to burn charcoal and extract bog-iron during any expedition to acquire ship's timber. But their way of life was one of endless physical risk; disasters at sea were all too common among the medieval Icelanders and the Norwegians and must also have cost the Norse Greenlanders dearly in ships and men. All things considered, it is probable that the Baffin Island blooms were aboard a Norse Greenland ship that ran into trouble after a multi-purpose voyage to Labrador, while little argues for their presence aboard one of Frobisher's ship.

Apart from the sturdy blooms, there would be little chance of finding other evidence by this time of a medieval Norse shipwreck in Baffin Island, however. Any wood the Greenlanders brought, including their ship, would have become indistinguishable from other debris in the landscape and would quite likely have been used by the Natives. Any useful objects — especially if made of iron — would also have been picked up by the Eskimos and perhaps taken as far afield as the beautiful Norse carpenter's plane, with the iron plate missing, which the archaeologist Peter Schledermann found on Skræling Island in the Bache Peninsula region in a house ruin that yielded a piece of charred oak radiocarbon dated to about A.D. 1260 and a piece of Norse wool cloth dated to about A.D. 1190.[24]

That is not the same as saying that the Kodlunarn "white men" are likely to have been shipwrecked Greenland Norse rather than desperate Englishmen. For one thing, the Frobisher accounts make it clear that other European ships had preceded the 1576 expedition. In George Best's description of Meta Incognita and its people, he lists a number of reasons why he thinks the Eskimos "vse to traffike and exchange their commodities with some other people," and one of them in particular connects with the evidence we now have of early sixteenth century Basque whaling in the Davis Strait. Best wrote:[25]

> *We found also in their [the Eskimos'] tents a Guinney Beane, of redde coloure, the which dote vsually grow in the hote Countreys : whereby it appéereth they trade with other Nations whiche dwell farre off, or else themselues are greate trauellers.*

The Portuguese had by this time been exploiting Guinea for over a century and a quarter, and they traded various sorts of beads wherever they sailed. An exotic "Guinney Beane, of redde coloure" would also serve as decorative trade goods among people who had never seen a cultivated legume of any sort. Back home, the Basques would have had access to a variety of trinkets to bring along on their northern voyages.

A large number of documents tell about transatlantic fisheries in "Terranova" — a vague term originally referring to the entire coast and all the islands along the coast that is now Canadian and which also includes part of the U.S. Selma H. Barkham notes that the first known Basque document relating to Newfoundland codfish trading dates from 1517. The first one that alludes to a cargo of whale brought from the New World is dated March 22, 1530 in Bordeaux. The whalers, who had clearly been preceded by cod fishers, at first hunted the whales for meat, which was brought home salted in barrels, but shore facilities for rending whale fat may have been constructed by the end of the 1530s. A number of documents prove that whale oil was obtained on a commercial scale from the ports of Labrador before the middle of the sixteenth century and was highly valued all over Europe. All went well until 1550, when hostilities between France and Spain were mounting in Europe, and when not even the harbors of Terranova were exempted from attacks by corsairs.[26]

Especially during those turbulent years, it is not unthinkable that one or more Basque whaling ships (which were quite large, compared with the cod fishing boats) may have ventured far north in the Davis Strait in pursuit of their game as well as of peace and quiet, and that they traded with the Inuit in the process. It would actually be more surprising if future archaeological investigations on both sides of the Davis Strait fail to turn up indications that prior to 1576, the Davis Strait was somewhat busier than we have imagined.

This study could not have been written without the information provided by Jette Arneborg, William W. Fitzhugh, Robert McGhee, and Karsten Secher.

Notes

[1] Letter of December 14, 1994.

[2] William W. Fitzhugh, letter to Sir Ian Gourlay (with copy to K.A. Seaver) dated December 17, 1994.

[3] Poul Nørlund, "Norse Ruins at Gardar." *Meddelelser om Grønland*, vol. 76 no. 1 (1929), esp. p. 137.

[4] Correspondence and telephone communication with Jette Arneborg, Dec. 1994-Feb. 1995.

[5] Robert McGhee, "The *Skraellings* of Vinland," in Birthe L. Clausen, ed., *Viking Voyages to North America*, Roskilde (Denmark), 1993, pp. 50-51.

[6] A recent assessment of several ship's parts from Norse Greenland is interesting in this context. Of the ten pieces of wood diagnosed, six were from larch (*Larix*), two from spruce (*Picea*), and two from either spruce or larch. (Erik Andersen and Claus Malmros, "Ship's parts found in the Viking settlements in Greenland. Preliminary assessments and wood-diagnoses," in Clausen, ed., *Viking Voyages*, pp. 118-22.) The larch does not grow in Norway, and driftwood specimens carried on the East Greenland Current would have been prone to sink before reaching the west coast of Greenland. (For useful comments on this subject, see Fitzhugh and Olin, *Archeology of the Frobisher Voyages*, Washington, D.C., 1993, pp. 91-2, 163.)

[7] Jette Arneborg provided this vital new information to the friends of Norse archaeology in January of 1995. Her informant is Karsten Secher, her husband, who is head of the Danish Polar Center and former geologist / mineralogist at the Geological Survey of Greenland. He described the iron-rich weathering products in Greenland, in which context bog iron is hardly observed. Although hydrated iron oxide (limonite), the primary iron-enriched weathering product, is fairly common in Greenland, sufficient deposits of similar high grade iron ore (brown iron ore) are not known. [His references are to O.B. Boggild, "The Mineralogy of Greenland," *Meddelelser om Grønland*, vol. 149, no. 3, Copenhagen, 1953; O.V. Petersen and K. Secher, "The Minerals of Greenland," *The Mineralogical Record*, vol. 24, no. 2, Arizona, 1993; K. Secher and H. Stendal, "Weathering products of sulfides in the Arctic — with a case history on a Cu-Ni-sulphide occurrence in West Greenland," pp. 499-522 in S.S. Augusthis (ed.), *Weathering: its products and deposits*, vol. 2, Athens, Greece, 1989.] Secher also observed that while it is theoretically possible to trace bog ore to a specific location, it would be very difficult to do so in practice.

[8] Birgitta Wallace, "L'Anse aux Meadows, the western outpost," in Clausen, ed., *Viking Voyages*, pp. 35-37.

[9] Fitzhugh and Olin, eds., *Archeology*, p. 93.

[10] Ibid., pp. 94, 166, 173-80; Fitzhugh, pers. comm. March 1995.

[11] Fitzhugh and Olin, *Archeology*, pp. 95-6.

[12] Ibid., Chapter 11 (by Henry Unglik).

[13] Comment made by Robert Baldwin at the 19 January, 1995, ARTAF meeting in London.

[14] One paper was delivered at a scientific convention, together with Reginald Auger; the other at the American Historical Association's meeting in Chicago, January 1995. Both papers were entitled "Archeology of the Frobisher Voyages, 1981 - 1994: New World Order....Take Two". In addition, we discussed his new theory by telephone on January 27, 1995.

[15] Charles Francis Hall, *Life with the Esquimaux*, London, 1864, vol. I, pp. 271-303; vol. II, pp. 93-152. Hall (vol. II, pp. 77-80) found evidence that coal had been left behind by the Frobisher party.

[16] It is worth noting that the Inuit who told Francis Hall about these blooms appear not to have thought of them as potential sources of iron for their own needs, although they were otherwise quick to spot both manufactured and meteoric iron which they could cold-hammer for tools and weapons.

[17] Roger C. Smith, *Vanguard of Empire: Ships of Exploration in the Age of Columbus*, New York and Oxford, 1993, p. 86. I am grateful to David B. Quinn for pointing out (in his thoughtful commentary to the draft of this report) the need to explain more fully the use of ballast.

[18] Wendy R. Childs, *Anglo-Castilian Trade in the Later Middle Ages*, Manchester, 1978, pp. 62, 112-3, 118; John R.T. Schubert, *History of the British Iron and Steel Industry, c. 450 B.C.-A.D. 1775*, London, 1957, pp. 102-110, 121-2, 145; R.F. Tylecote, *A History of Metallurgy*, London, 1992, pp. 75-76, 103-4.

[19] Eleanora Mary Carus-Wilson, *The Overseas Trade of Bristol*, 2nd ed., London, 1967, pp. 203-53, 337.

[20] Hall, *Life With the Esquimaux*, pp. 283-4.

[21] Fitzhugh and Olin, *Archeology*, pp. 92-3.

[22] Fitzhugh, letter of December 17, 1994. The problems associated with determining the origins of the wood etc. are also discussed at length in Fitzhugh and Olin, *Archeology*.

[23] Gustav Storm, ed., *Islandske Annaler indtil 1578*, Oslo, 1977 [repr. of 1888 ed.], pp. 213, 353, 403.

[24] Peter Schledermann, "Norsemen in the High Arctic?" in Clausen, ed., *Viking Voyages*, pp. 59-63. The spread in dates is a good illustration of the problems archaeologists in that region routinely encounter.

[25] Stefansson and McCaskill, vol. II, p. 126.

[26] Selma Huxley Barkham, *Los vascos en el marco Atlantico Norte. Siglos XVI y XVI*, Vol. III of the series ITSASOA (Enrique Ayerbe, ed.), Bilbao, 1987, pp. 28, 39, 62-5.

Martin Frobisher, the Spaniards and a Sixteenth-Century Northern Spy*

Bernard Allaire and Donald Hogarth

Introduction

Espionage, the art of spying, is hardly a recent activity. The *Oxford English Dictionary* notes the use of the word "*spy*" [*spie*] in an English song of about 1250 and this, in turn, describes an episode of the Biblical Era. From early times, therefore, man has striven to retrieve secret information, but it is only when vital data are involved, or when important national figures or recognized heroes participate, that details are remembered by succeeding generations. The case now considered, grouping together the famous English seafarer, Martin Frobisher, the formidable Spanish diplomat, Don Bernardino de Mendoza, and the all-powerful ruler, King Philip II of Spain, seems worthy of record. It is through the diplomatic correspondence of Mendoza to the King, that the story comes to light.

The potential of diplomatic mail has been demonstrated in historical research, where conventional documentary sources failed.[1] However, part of this documentation has remained inaccessible because of coded messages between ambassadors and their home base. In the sixteenth century, such codes were commonly used in official correspondence by most European embassies, particularly by the nations active in political or military matters.[2] This difficulty has confounded students of the travels of the English navigator, Martin Frobisher, who directed voyages to Baffin Island in 1576, 1577 and 1578, but these researchers were able to benefit from the transcribed correspondence of others. For example, there was the correspondence between the Spanish ambassador in London, Don Bernardino de Mendoza, and Spain, published in 1894,[3] and between the French ambassador in London, Michel Castelnau de la Mauvissière, and France, published in 1926.[4]

It is the Spanish archives, for the last half of the sixteenth century, that are particularly interesting. They constitute an immense holding and comprise a national treasure. The Mendoza correspondence, alone, consists of 16 large bundles in *Archivo General de Simancas* [*AGS*], Valladolid, but many of the letters exist as contemporary copies in *Archivo General de Indias* [*AGI*], Seville. In spite of these comprehensive collections, some letters from the various Spanish embassies appear to have been lost or dispersed, for the history of the Simancas archives is relatively complex. For instance, a large part of the sixteenth century correspondence was seized by Napoleon's army in 1808 as a prize of war, retained in *Les Archives nationales* [*AN*], Paris, and returned to the Spanish authorities by Pétain, only in 1942.[5] Furthermore, an important group of original letters relative to the Spanish Embassy (some in code) is held by the *Public Record Office*

[**PRO**], London. These are assembled in two volumes of the State Papers,[6] the origin of which, at the present time, cannot be given with certainty.

This late sixteenth century correspondence took place during a time of increasing tension between England and Spain, who were clearly on a collision course. By 1577, King Philip II, reacting to the depredations of Spanish possessions, especially those plundered by Francis Drake, had proposed to land mercenaries in England to free the prisoner Mary Stuart and arrange her marriage.[7] England was envisaged as a future Catholic Kingdom with close ties to Spain. The conflict reared into the open in late 1577, when a plot to overthrow the English regime in Ireland, in part orchestrated by the Spanish ambassador in London, the outspoken, Antonio de Guaras, was exposed and thwarted.[8] The English authorities were furious and promptly imprisoned Guaras.[9] In the meantime (1576-79), James Fitzmaurice (Fitzgerald) had left Munster for Paris, Rome, Madrid and Lisbon, in order to gain support for landing a small force in Ireland and driving out the English.[10] Philip II was sympathetic. For her part, Elizabeth tacitly encouraged the Protestants in Holland and Zeeland with money and officers, but mainly with negotiations.[11] The stage was set for a major conflict.

At the beginning of 1578, in the midst of the mounting tension, Don Bernardino de Mendoza, the envoy of Philip II, arrived in London. He was sent to dissuade Elizabeth from encouraging the Protestant cause in the Low Countries, to consolidate the Catholics in England, to promote sympathy for Spain, and to endeavour to set the imprisoned Guaras free. However, Mendoza was to act the diplomat: he was to keep the Queen in good humour and convince her of Philip's enduring friendship, and not to enter into any negotiations with the English Catholics in plots against her.[12] Mendoza complied but, regardless of this conciliatory attitude, the English were suspicious and the new ambassador was constantly watched by informants of Francis Walsingham, England's Secretary of State. His diplomatic pouch was never entirely secure: the courier was sometimes apprehended and material decoded.[13] But, in spite of this harassment, Mendoza did succeed in sending numerous letters to Spain. He had, however, to remain on his guard and his collaborators were given strict instructions on how to act in case of emergency.[14]

The Frobisher voyages and Spanish intelligence

Since the time of the second voyage (1577), the Spanish king had been aware of Frobisher's expeditions. Although Frobisher claimed to be headed to Cathay, the King's informants warned that this routing might be a guise: Frobisher might well intend to thieve in the Indies.[15] This was indeed interesting, as Philip II regarded the West Indies as the special domain of Spain, and Frobisher as an interloper. Later, when it became apparent that Frobisher's goal was gold and silver, interest was maintained: the Spanish controlled a major share of the world's trade in precious metals, and they had no wish to see England become a competitor.

Mendoza, who arrived in England shortly before the departure of the third voyage (1578) was given special instructions to inquire further into the northwest venture.[16] He wasted no time; on March 31, he informed the King of the [Ship's Trench] mine on present-day Kodlunarn (or *Qallunaaq*) Island,[17] and on April 22 he sent small specimens of the "*ores*" to Spain.[18] Mendoza's informant was un-named but was obviously a person closely associated with the project. Correspondence on this subject lasted into May 1579. Martin Hume records 14 letters, here summarized in Table 1, but the collection is incomplete, as Mendoza refers to letters of September 8 and 9,[19] as well as October 26 and November 15, 1578[20] which are not itemized by Hume. In addition, an un-noticed letter of December 23, 1578[21] was discovered in this research, which makes specific reference to the November 15 correspondence, a copy of which was sent with the dispatch.

TABLE 1:
Summary of Martin Hume's Items Pertinent to the Frobisher Voyages

Item	Date	Passage	From	To	Details
484	Mar. 31 1578	3 pages	Mendoza	King	Frobisher's 2nd voyage and mine
489	Apr. 22 1578	19 lines	Mendoza	King	Preparation for 3rd voyage; ore of 2nd voyage dispatched
496	May 16 1578	12 lines	Mendoza	King	Assays of ore in England from 2nd voyage
502	June 03 1578	7 lines	Mendoza	King	Frobisher's voyage to go via Ireland
510	June 13 1578	2 lines	Mendoza	King	Chart of 2nd voyage to be sent to the King
511	June 13 1578	22 lines	King	Mendoza	Assays in Spain gave low returns; new samples requested
513	June 13 1578	2 lines	Mendoza	King	Frobisher ordered first to land in Ireland
528	Sept. 11 1578	5 lines	Mendoza	King	Marine chart to be sent (dispatched September 25?)
529	Sept. 19 1578	4 lines	King	Mendoza	Information on Frobisher's ship acknowledged
532	Oct. 07 1578	18 lines	Mendoza	King	Return of the 3rd voyage; no report of spy
536	Oct. 31 1578	6 lines	King	Mendoza	King awaits report of Mendoza's spy
549	Feb. 07 1579	15 lines	Mendoza	King	The [new] chart and ore samples sent
557	Apr. 11 1579	6 lines	King	Mendoza	Chart received; specimens of little value
571	May 03 1579	4 lines	Mendoza	King	Voyages discontinued; ore worthless; sailors & soldiers unpaid

Of special interest is the installation of a spy on the third voyage. The first notice of this event appeared in Mendoza's letter of October 7, 1578 when he reported that the ships had returned to England but, as yet, he had had no news of his man on the expedition. The King replied that he would be grateful for any news, firsthand, provided the informer returned alive.[22] Presumably, it is through the activities of the successful spy that we owe the information found in the correspondence of November 15, as well as the chart and ore specimens acquired in the third voyage (see Hume's items 549 & 557: Table 1).

The correspondence of November 15 is the focus of the present paper. Why it escaped Hume's scrutiny is unclear, though perhaps Hume dealt only with correspondence that was not written originally in code, or perhaps it had been decoded later by a Spanish archivist.

The decoded and translated document

Don Bernardino de Mendoza to King Philip II, dated November 15 1578, received December 18 1578. [*AGS*, Sección Estado, L831, ff.266-67].

Since I wrote Your Majesty on the seventh ultimo [October], the minerals and duplicate text were sent to France on the twenty-sixth of the same. I saw the arrival of Frobisher and the fleet that carried him, with that which was sent in it [i.e. the cargo], as the ships had arrived at this river [Thames] from the voyage to which I referred, when I spoke to Your Majesty.

Frobisher sailed for Ireland with the 15 ships, conforming to the order of the Queen,[23] left with his armada on the night of June 6 and passed a small island off Cape Durcey in western Ireland. He headed northwest and on the twentieth [of June] touched the Island of Frisland, which they called West Frisland, described thus on map 17 of Ptolemy

[5 lines of cipher, decoded and translated from Latin]

> *"In 1380, the brothers Nicolo and Antonio Genius [Zeno] were shipwrecked, during a severe storm, off the island of Frisland, where Zichmnus was ruler. His customs were those of the Christians."[24]*

At this island, they entered a very large bay or branch of the sea, capable of accommodating 100 ships. Frobisher, with 14 men in a small boat, in a place which he had not been able to reach in the previous years, found two tents and a ship furnished with wood and covered with skins of seal and fish. Inside were some of their people, who, according to other observers, numbered about 20. Their costume and manner were those of the land the English call Cathay or Meta Incognita. At 10 in the morning, in this inlet, a ship, in which was stored part of the wood with which they intended to build the houses and shelters that the Queen had requested and the beer to drink, was lost after having weathered a storm. That same day, at three in the afternoon, in order to have the most favorable winds, they sailed towards the northwest, in order to see the cape. The second of July they espied the land of the Queens Foreland and Meta Incognita.[25] Here they encountered an abundance of ice and at night, because of the force of the west wind, all the ships found themselves ice-bound and in a great danger. They lost one vessel which was wrecked by the ice, for having full sails; the others travelled at half sail during the following day at sea.

The third [of July], they wished to enter into one of the two mouths which could be accomplished because the wind had grown so much stronger in the strait where they had been in the previous year. Land 12 leagues away was inaccessible, due to wind, which kept the ice from going out to the open sea, and the extremly foggy weather, which prevented them from recognizing the two capes and being able to take to sea. With the force of the tides, the ship headed for the western part of the strait where they seemed more secure from stormy weather and mists that were at the entrance.[26] Then they travelled 14 days and 50 leagues into a strait towards the western region,[27] where they found a calm sea, finally arriving at a cape or island, which they called St. George's and where they set off in a bark to reconnoiter. They found many islands, all of which were small and on which they were unable to land any boat due to surrounding ice. Clear weather permitted these discoveries, they having been unable to enter this bay or strait the preceding year. For this reason they took a route along the coast of Labrador, heading southwest[28] for more than 40 leagues without seeing land but, on July 22, sailed towards the strait and cape which he had explored earlier. They encountered much ice and a severe storm, which stormy and windy conditions never changed and kept the ice and high tide from escaping. Thus the tide of the strait constrained the sea in it with such fury that they were lifted to a great height by the waves and their sails became entangled, one with the other. Because of this, when they arrived at their destination, they were in temporary ruin; the sailors were soaked. Now that the wind had grown so much stronger, on July 26 Frobisher resolved to enter with five ships, the largest of the two entrances. This took place July 30 in an arm of the sea or sound, named the previous year the Countess of Warwick Sound.[29]

Now the remaining five ships of the eight, were outside the entrances to the strait, where they spent 12 days and, being delayed, entered in good weather into the same sound, where they found the others. This was off a small island [Kodlunarn]. Here, at the very location where they had mined last year, they extracted three kinds of ore from two places.[30] They found similar ore, in the area surrounding, to be less rich. Here was a stone like white sapphire, though not as hard, and another like ruby, but with a depth of colour inferior to jacinth.[31] All of this land is very austere and sterile.

From this sound, they travelled five leagues into the land. A mountain appeared where they observed the sea on the opposite side. They distinguished a separate island, but were unable to discern what lay in the land beyond it.[32]

The men and women they saw were tiny and fled to the mountains. The land is very sterile and no trees can be seen, nor can it be said to be well inhabited. The men are small and of bad color; the women wore lines on their faces [tatoos?] like Indians. They are clothed in seal skins in the manner of the savages of the land of Labrador. They [the English] put mirrors, little knives and other things on the ground in order to bring them to trade. They [the Inuit] took them and left, in exchange at the same place, skins and other things of little value. Then they departed in their small barks of leather with which they fished.

While they [the English] loaded their ships, they built a small stone house, where they left a quantity of gifts and little candles, buried the wood, with which they intended to build houses, and 30 barrels of flour and salted meat, dry cod and pork, the provisions which 100 men, during 18 months, were supposed to consume.[33] This plan was cancelled after they lost the ship which carried the beer, brought as drink for the colony, and part of the wood for their houses.[34]

The salt they had buried the year before was found in ice, because the land is so frigid that it was snowing and freezing on Santiago Day,[35] so that they had to be diligent in removing the snow from ropes and ships, to prevent it from freezing in place.

The 13 charged ships sailed at low tide from their port, the beginning of September, although one of them could not leave with the others and remained behind; the crescent moon, which was thinly curled, came and they waited for the [next propitious?] tide. This tide changed every six hours, and six hours later most of the ships were en route. By September 28 they had returned to England, without receiving any news of the one that stayed behind with ore.[36]

Four miles from here, they discharged ore from the 12 ships into a house, which the Queen had ordered built for the purpose [storage].[37] The bulk of this rock (of which I sent Your Majesty a sample) resembles marcasite, with the other two types containing either white sapphire or mediocre ruby.[38]

There is no one capable or reliable and I am therefore not, at present, sending Your Majesty the navigation chart, which shows the disposition of the newly discovered territory and island.

He [our agent?] made an assay of the rocks, which does not agree, in the manner that one man had taken from it,[39] from which they [the assayers] claimed they could subtract the cost from the profit. Now, it appears that the expense [of handling the ore] will exceed even that of navigation. This makes me wonder why someone who took part in this venture, a gentleman and a scholar, should sell that which they returned[40] and then suggest that they could extract gold profitably. It is incomprehensible that a land so cold as this can produce anything,[41] though Frobisher has supported it as much as possible. Though fearful of discovery, they [the metallurgists] augmented assay results of the previous years,[42] in order to encourage interested parties, who maintain that it is the will and within the power of the Queen to make a return voyage next year. It would be useful to learn, at no cost, which of the ships, in particular, remains behind in the summer [of 1579?]. Under threat of pain of death and confiscation of goods, no one dares write about the navigation chart, about the voyages, the assays, nor anything about the new metallurgical plant[43] because, according to Frobisher, the French with six ships, went this summer [1578] to discover the land [Baffin Island] but due to ice, they did not advance sufficiently far. Then they sailed to Newfoundland, where they fought with an Englishman.[44]

Humphrey Gilbert, about whom I wrote to Your Majesty, left with eight great and small ships and a row boat [pinnace?], with a rumor that he went to explore a rich island [Newfoundland?]. I took difference with a well known son of the Treasurer of the house of the Queen, who has armed three ships for the voyage, from which some mariners fled.[45] It came out that they were not paid, and in compensation, first took to sea and captured two French ships carrying wine. It is said that for dire need, the mariners disarmed some ships to reinforce others, in which were carried perhaps 50 men and 140 pieces of artillery, clearly public property, which the officers wished to steal. In the same manner, the other ships which armed themselves in the western part, are feared not to be headed for the Portuguese Indies, because it is rumored since the death of the diassi[46] they are destined for the eastern part of this realm, such as along the coast of France.

Xarpa[47] is a pirate in those possessions of Your Majesty, where two voices have persuaded some at this court, that it would be wise for his ship to ambush those of Captain Drake, who is now among the Camarrones[48] and very rich with vessels captured since he left [England] the previous year. They have armed three ships, one of 150 tons, one of 80 and another small boat [pinnace?].

The ships plan yet another trip to Muscovy this summer, to the land of a mona,[49] which a monk showed them, with whom some persons of this court have negotiated successfully. I have had some information from her, which I sent to Your Majesty along with the rest.

[The remainder of this document is in Spanish, unciphered, and translates as follows:]

From the Lord (S.C.R.P.) that your Royal Highness may increase in many kingdoms and territories, as your vassals and servants wish and Christendom requires. In London, November 15 1578.
Your humble vassal and servant, who kisses your royal hand
[signed] donbernardino
To this Sacred Catholic Royal Majesty (S.C.R.M.). By the hand of Gabriel Zaras, Secretary of State.

Discussion

The foregoing account of Mendoza's agent is surprisingly accurate and gives a good summary of the activities of the voyagers in Baffin and Greenland. The few inaccuracies are minor and can be explained mainly by errors in understanding, transcription and coding, during the preparation of the drafts. Thus the dates of the sinking of the *Dennis*, the July snowstorm, and the departure of the ships from Baffin Island, are slightly but understandably in error. On the other hand, a few details (all plausible) not found in other accounts, appear in the Mendoza transcript, such as some concerning the landfall at Greenland and the digression into Hudson Strait.

In addition, description was given of the Baffin ore, and of the inhabitants of Greenland and Baffin. The Dartford storage depot and Bignores metallurgical plant were mentioned, though not named. Other than saying that the ore from Kodlunarn was superior to that of other mines nearby, no mention was made of on-site assays. Failure to record the results of these assays was indeed unfortunate, as no data of the on-site tests have survived in other manuscripts or in the published accounts.

Who was this man, Mendoza's agent? He must have been intelligent, capable of assembling important facts and transmitting them in an understandable manner. Detailed information suggests he was aboard one of the nine ships that sailed into Hudson Strait, but most likely in the *Ayde*, captained by Frobisher, in order to gather information authoritatively.

The first key to his identity comes with the statement that he took part in one of the large assays in London. This test, reportedly made to check the previous high-grade assays was, no doubt, the "*third great proof*," a confidential trial completed March 8, 1578 and known to Mendoza on or before March 31.[50] The only assayer of this test who was present in the third voyage was none other than Robert Denham, Frobisher's chief assayer on the expedition assigned to the ship *Ayde*. Possibly Denham, who was also assayer in the second voyage, was responsible for the March 31 transmission, probably hastily recorded by Mendoza or repeated from memory, thus explaining the mixture of truths, inaccuracies and inconsistencies throughout. The latter is in sharp contrast with the correspondence of November 15, which is factual, methodical and accurate.

What did Denham hope to gain in this transmission to Mendoza? He was already well established as a London goldsmith and he was paid £3 a month on the third expedition, as

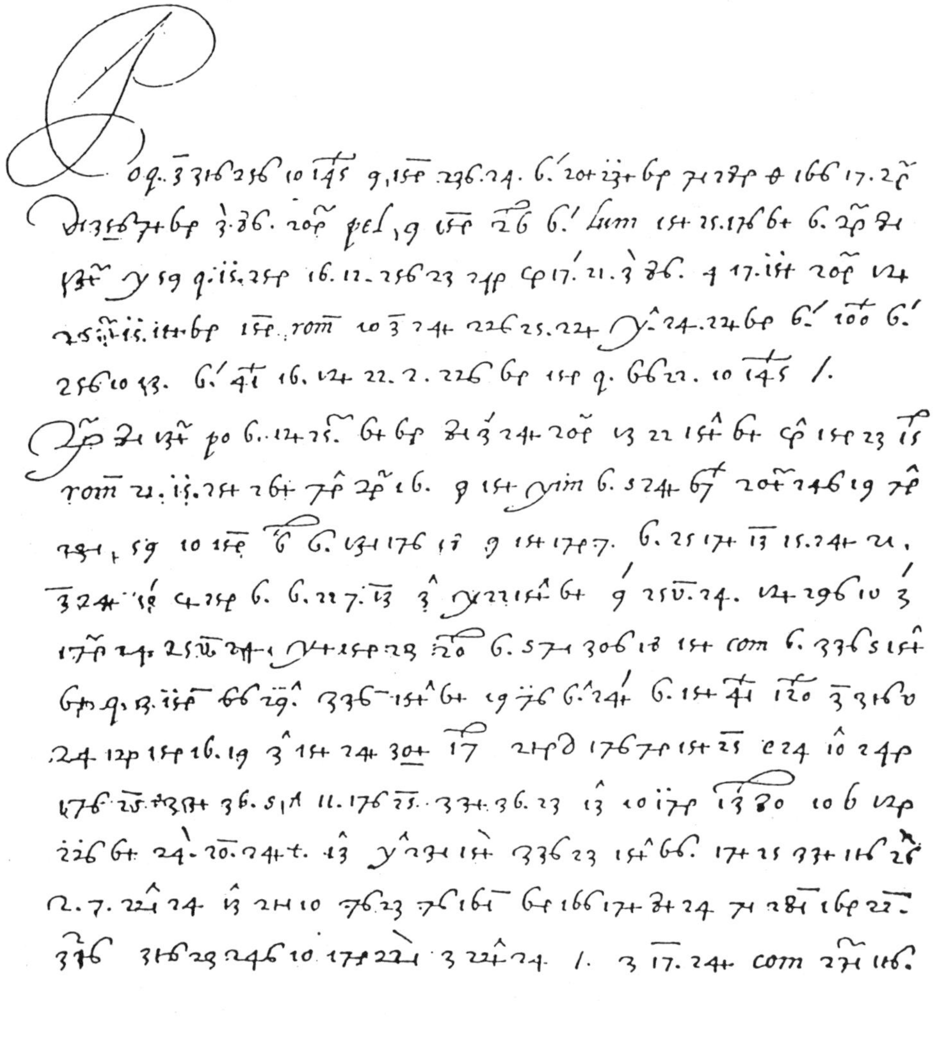

Figure 1a: The first page of the coded manuscript of November 15, 1578 (*AGS*, Estado, leg. 381, f. 266). Published with permission of *Archivo General de Simancas*, (*Ministerio de Cultura de España*).

Despues que escribi a Vuestra Merced a los siete del pasado cuyo mine for
duplicado envie por Francia a los 26 del mismo la venida de Forbu
jar y armada que llevo me he visto con el que envie en ella por ha
bar llegado los navios a esta rivera y enterado del [Tamesis] del
viaje del qual me ha referido lo que dire a Vuestra Merced.
Forbujar despues de haber dado vuelta por Irlanda con los 15
navios que llevava conforme a la orden desta reyna partio con
su armada a los 6 de junio a la noche de vna isleta que
esta al cabo de Dereceis en Yrlanda al ueuste hacia el
norte-ueuste y a los 20 descubrio la isla de Frislan-
da que ellos dicen Frislanda occidental de laqual tierra escrir
Teholomeo en la tabla 17 Quod Nicolaus et Anto
nius Geni. Fratres in anno 1380 ab ho
rrida tempestate in insula Frislandia naufragium
fecerunt in qua Zichmnus dominabat cuius mores
cristianorum erant. En esta isla surgi

Figure 1b: The first page of the coded manuscript deciphered.

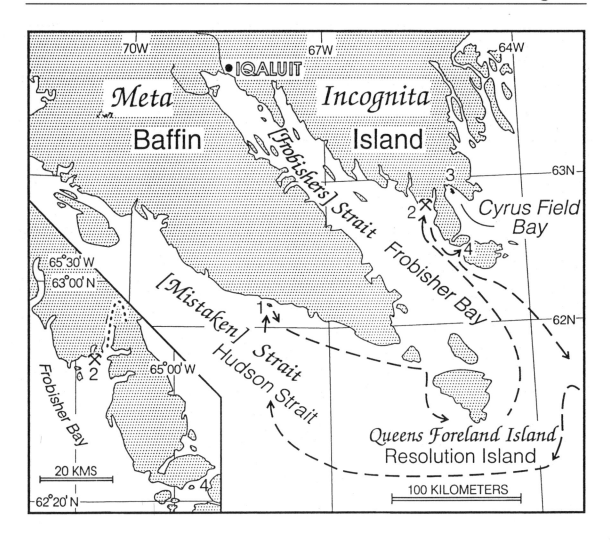

Figure 2. Route taken by the *Ayde* in the third Frobisher voyage, in the Baffin island area, 1578 (dashed lines). Excursion of Edward Fenton and Thomas Morris to the pass between Napoleon Bay (north-south inlet) and Cyrus Field Bay, August 27 1578 (dotted line). Localities mentioned in the manuscript are in old, italic, script; those in present-day usage are modern, roman, script. Specific localities are 1, *St. George's Island* [Saddleback Island(?)]; 2, mine on small island [Kodlunarn] in *Countess of Warwick Sound*; 3, un-named island [George Henry Island]; 4, final port [Beare Sound].

well as a £50 annual pension for life for services rendered in the Frobisher enterprise. He was Protestant and, therefore, had no special allegiance with Catholic Spain,[51] and the penalty for discovery in such espionage would, almost certainly, be death. On the other hand, his loyalty could be questioned after he had secretly obtained a test sample of stibnite, used as an additive in the assaying process, from his erstwhile employer, Burchard Kranich.[52] Furthermore, an unidentified Denham, an assayer of London, was implicated in the uprising of the Northumberland earls (1569).[53]

Another possibility was that Denham, as a double agent, acted on behalf of the Queen: he fed Mendoza with just enough facts to interest him and gain his confidence, later to throw him off track and persuade the King that it was futile to pursue the matter further. The ore specimens might truly have been atypical and the map concocted (neither can be found today). Certainly, such details as precise locations and size and grade of the ore deposits are completely lacking in the account (as they were in the censored contemporary publications). We must conclude that, although Denham appears to have supplied Mendoza with information on the Frobisher enterprise, his motivation remains obscure.

Regardless, King Philip's interest persisted up to the time when the ore specimens were tested in Spain.[54] When the abysmally low results became available, his curiosity vanished and the year-long espionage caper came abruptly to an end. Diplomatic correspondence has already shed light on the Frobisher enterprise and holds promise as a source of further information. For example, the identity of Mendoza's agent(s) could possibly be verified if the preliminary notes, from which the ciphered letters were composed, were discovered and studied. Possibly these notes might lie amongst the documents relating to Spain in *PRO*, SP94. This source should be searched thoroughly. As a precaution of secrecy, names of agents may have been omitted *deliberately* from the ciphered manuscript.

A more comprehensive, and perhaps more rewarding, exercise would be to check *all* documents in Spain and elsewhere,[55] ciphered and unciphered, pertaining to Bernardino de Mendoza, composed from 1578 through 1579. They could then be catalogued and summarized, in anticipation of future retrieval. The Spanish national archives (*AGS*) may, themselves, hold undiscovered treasures, as they were reassembled only in the 1940s and, as yet, have not been calendared in their present system. Concerning the Frobisher voyages, some valuable data might appear in this investigation. For example, reference might be made to the exclusive Baffin assays or a sketch might be found, locating lost mines (see Table 1, items 528, 549, 557). Such information could shed further light on two perpetually aggravating mysteries: where exactly did Martin Frobisher dig and what did he really think was there?

* We would like to thank François Allaire (*GRIX, Montréal*), the Archival Task Force UK and Ian Gourlay [*ARTAF*], Denis Brearley (*University of Ottawa*), Gayle Brunelle (*Fullerton University, California*), Edward Dahl (*National Archives of Canada*), Brad Loewen (*Parks Canada*) and Juana Munoz-Liceras (*University of Ottawa*) for their help in this research.

Notes

---

[1] For example, see documents concerning preparation of Jacques Cartier's voyages to Canada, found in Vienna, by R. Hapke (R. Hapke, "Der erste Kolonisationversuch in Kanada," *Hansische Geschichtsblätter*, N° 2 (1911), pp. 447-450); text repeated by Charles de la Roncière, *Notre première tentative de colonisation au Canada* (Paris, 1912), extrait de la Bibliothèque de l'École des Chartes.

[2] In contrast to ambassadors of Spain who, in the sixteenth century, ciphered most of their correspondence, the French ambassador in London at the same time coded only a small part of his letters. This attitude, no doubt, reflected the spirit of cooperation that reigned between France and England. For more information about the cipher see, David Shulman, *An annotated Bibliography of Cryptography* (London, Garland, 1976).

[3] Martin A. S. Hume, *Calendar of Letters and State Papers Relating to English Affairs preserved principally in the Archives of Simancas*, vol. 2: Elizabeth, 1568-1579 (London, Her Majesty's Stationery Office, 1894).

[4] Conyers Read, "The despatches of Castelnau de la Mauvissière (on Frobisher, Gilbert, La Roche and Drake) 1577-1581." *American Historical Review*, vol. 31 (1925-1926), pp. 285-296.

[5] Presently available on microfilm in Paris. See *AN*, K Series.

[6] See *PRO*, SP94. Possibly this holding represents confiscated letters.

[7] See M. Hume, *op. cit.*, Introduction, esp. pp. xlv-xlvii.

[8] Mendoza to Zayas, July 19, 1578, in M. Hume, 1894, *op. cit.*, item 519.

[9] Antonio de Guaras was arrested October 19, 1577, imprisoned 18 months in the Tower, released May 5, 1579, passport returned May 11, 1579, and expelled from England. Hume, *op. cit.*, Introduction, p. xlvi; Mendoza to Zayas, May 8, 14 1579; item 574, 575. See also, Alfred Morel-Fatio. "Bernardino de Mendoza" *Bulletin Hispanique* (Annales de la faculté des Lettres de Bordeaux), tome 8 (1906), pp. 20-70, 127-147.

[10] See especially H. C. Hamilton, ed., *Calendar of State Papers Relating to Ireland in the Reign of Elizabeth 1574-1585*. (London, Public Record Office, 1867), p. 112. The unsuccessful landing took place in July 1579.

[11] M. Hume, *op. cit.*, Introduction, esp. pp. xlvii-l.

[12] The King to Mendoza, Instructions. January 8 & 26, 1578. M. Hume, *op. cit.*, items 475 & 476.

[13] See A. Haynes, *Invisible Power: the Elizabethan secret services, 1570-1603*, (Stroud [Gloucestershire], Alan Sutton, 1992), esp. chapters 2 and 3.

[14] Mendoza to the King, April 22, 1578, in M. Hume, *op. cit.*, item 489. The agent transporting mail and "ore" specimens was directed to throw both into the sea if his ship was apprehended en route to Spain.

[15] Ldo. Antolinez, Ldo. Salazar, Muñoz Esparedo, Diego de Zuñiga and Lopez de Sarr[abia] to the King, June 25 1577. *AGI*, Indiferente 739, N° 28.

[16] A memorandum attached to Mendoza's "Instructions" is noted in Hume's translation (M. Hume, *op. cit.*, item 484). This memorandum is missing from Hume's printed "Instructions" (*Idem*, items 475 & 476).

[17] Mendoza to the King, March 31, 1578, in M. Hume, *op. cit.*, item 484. In this letter, Frobisher's landfall was located in Labrador [Persemua] at "62 degrees north latitude." The width and depth of the mine, here described, correspond closely to the dimensions of the "Ship's Trench" on Kodlunarn (Baffin Island area). See D. D. Hogarth, "Mining and metallurgy of the Frobisher ores," in W. W. Fitzhugh and J. S. Olin, eds., *Archeology of the Frobisher Voyages* (Washington, Smithsonian Institution Press, 1993), Fig. 7.3.

[18] Mendoza to the King, March 31, April 22, 1578. M. Hume, *op. cit.*, items 484 & 489. One specimen was said to represent highgrade ore, worth "60 crowns the quintal nett." This presumably represented the "Third great proof" (assay sheet of March 6, 1578), of ore from the second voyage, which indicated a clear

profit of £60 for each 100 lb ore. See V. Stefansson and E. McCaskill, eds., *The three Voyages of Martin Frobisher* (London, The Argonaut Press, vol. 2, 1938), pp. 131-132.

[19] Mendoza to the King, September 11, 1578, in M. Hume, *op. cit.*, item 528. Copies of letters referred to therein, were sent in this despatch.

[20] Mendoza to the King, February 7, 1579, in M. Hume, *op. cit.*, item 549.

[21] Mendoza to the King, December 23, 1578, in *AGI*, Patronato 265, R35(2).

[22] The King to Mendoza, October 31, 1578, in M. Hume, *op. cit.*, item 536.

[23] Frobisher sailed with ten authorized vessels (commissioned and company ships) and five obtained without warrant. One of the latter group (*Beare Leicester*) was later given the same privileges as authorized ships. See D. D. Hogarth, P. W. Boreham and J. G. Mitchell, *Martin Frobisher's Northwest Venture 1576-81: Mines, Minerals and Metallurgy*, Canadian Museum of Civilization, Mercury Directorate Paper, N° 7, 1994, p. 38.

[24] A text describing the Zeno voyage, is printed on the obverse of this map, *viz.* map 26 or additional map 17. Mendoza's quotation was apparently, abstracted from the text of the Latin edition of the augmented Ptolemy atlas, published in Venice by Vincento Valgrisius in 1562 (or as a reprint in 1564). In his navigation, Frobisher used the 1569 world map of Mercator, which outlined Frisland of the Zeno brothers. Frobisher's West Frisland was southern Greenland. See K. R. Andrews, *Trade, Plunder and Settlement, Maritime Enterprise and Genesis of the British Empire, 1480-1630* (Cambridge, Cambridge University Press, 1984), pp. 169-171.

[25] The chronology is confused here. Frobisher left Greenland June 21 but the ship (*Dennis*) sank in the mouth of Frobisher Bay July 2. This is mentioned, correctly, two sentences below. Frobisher's route, in Southeastern Baffin island, is shown in Figure 2.

[26] Full sails were hoisted 8 pm, July 3, in order to get clear of the ice (Log of Christopher Hall, *British Library* [BL], Harley MS 167, N° 42).

[27] Frobisher passed the south side of Resolution Island July 6, entered Hudson Strait and proceeded Northwest July 7, and retraced his route towards Resolution Island from July 18. See E. Sellman in Stefansson and McCaskill, *op. cit.*, pp. 59-60.

[28] Labrador, at that time, was poorly defined and included Ungava as well as coastal Labrador. This was the return journey, out of Hudson Strait, and Frobisher would be travelling east-southeast (not southwest).

[29] The *Armonell*, *Ayde*, *Beare*, *Emanuel* and *Hopewell* attempted to enter "Frobisher Strait" on July 26, but, finding the passage blocked with ice, returned to the open sea. Finally, on the night of July 30, these ships, and the *Francis* of Foy and *Salomon* entered the "Strait," attained Countess of Warwick Sound within, and found the *Judith* and *Michael* awaiting. See E. Sellman in Stefansson & McCaskill, *op. cit.*, pp. 62-64.

[30] Three types of ore on Kodlunarn, which the miners and assayers were capable of distinguishing, may have been homogeneous, spotted and micaceous, all "black ores" and corresponding to types *A1*, *C1* & *C2* of D. D. Hogarth *et al.*, 1994, *op. cit.*, p. 123. The two mines comprised a seaward trench (now known as the "Ships Trench"), mined principally in 1577, and an inland trench (now known as the "Reservoir Trench"), apparently mined in 1578 only.

[31] The pseudo-sapphire was probably well crystallized quartz, though it could have been apatite or white feldspar, all of which are known in the region. The false ruby was, no doubt, red garnet, very common throughout this area. Jacinth is a red zircon, known as hyacinth today.

[32] On August 27, Edward Fenton and Thomas Morris travelled to the end of Napoleon Bay and went through a pass to the east-southeast viewing Cyrus Field Bay and George Henry Island within it, to the eastward from the high point of the pass. See W. A. Kenyon, "The Canadian Artic Journal of Captain Edward Fenton, 1578" *Archivaria*, N° 11, 1981, p. 199.

[33] An early estimate of provisions for the colony, which includes the items noted, is given in the journal of Edward Fenton (*Pepys Library*, Magdalene College, Cambridge, MS 2133, 1578).

[34] Half of the framed house went down with the *Dennis* on July 2; half the brick and most of the lime for its exterior were in the *Thomas*, which deserted about August 8; 84 tons of beer were in these two ships and the *Mone* and *Anne Francis*, which did not arrive until the time of departure for England. See D. D. Hogarth *et al.*, *op. cit.*, p. 44.

[35] This is equivalent to St. James Day, July 25. The snowstorm, however, came the following day. See Christopher Hall's Journal, *BL*, Harley MS 167, N° 42, 1578.

[36] The *Emanuel, Gabriel* and *Michael* finished loading September 1 and left Baffin Island September 2. The *Emanuel* tarried behind, was separated from the fleet, and beached as a wreck in Ireland, where she unloaded her ore. Payment to her seven miners, presumably back in England, is recorded on March 10, 1579[OS]. See D. D. Hogarth *et al.*, *op. cit.*, pp. 58-72.

[37] Ore from the third voyage was stored in the Dartford Manor House, built by Henry VIII in 1542, but renovated for ore storage in July 1578 (*Acts of the Privy Council*, vol. 10, 1578, pp. 271-272).

[38] Here, white sapphire may represent plagioclase feldspar from Countess of Warwick Mine (Kodlunarn Island), ruby may represent garnet from Countess of Sussex Mine (Baffin Island), both constituents of certain "black ores." Marcasite (and other sulphides) is atypical and rare in the Baffin excavations. See D. D. Hogarth *et al.*, *op. cit.*, pp. 101-141.

[39] This test must refer to the "third great proof," representing ore from the *Ayde* (second voyage). Details of this test are given in Stefansson and McCaskill, *op. cit.*, vol. 2, pp. 131-132. The disputed test was completed February 21, 1578[OS] by Burchard Kranich, see *idem*, vol.2, pp.127-129.

[40] This must refer to Michael Lok, initially the principal promoter of the enterprise, who in 1578, sold half his stock in the northwest venture (worth £1000) to Edward de Vere, Earl of Oxford. See C. Shammas, "The invisible merchant and property rights; the misadventures of an Elizabethan joint stock company" *Business History*, vol. 17, 1975, pp. 95-108.

[41] It was then widely held that gold was most common in countries with hot climates and, conversely, was absent in very cold regions. This strange notion pervaded geological literature until the mid-eighteenth century. See F. D. Adams, *The Birth and Development of the Geological Sciences*, (New York, Dover Publications, 1954), pp. 282-283.

[42] This suggests purposely adding gold metal to the furnace charge or "salting," an allegation, with data at hand, that can be neither proved nor disproved.

[43] The metallurgical plant where gold and silver were to be extracted was built on the Bignores estate, 2 km south of the ore storage depot (Dartford Manor House). See D. D. Hogarth *et al.*, *op. cit.*, pp. 86-92.

[44] In a report, Frobisher is said to have intercepted a letter, in which the King of France disclosed plans to arm 12 ships and take possession of the territory. See *BL*, Landsdowne MS 100, N° 1, 1582, fol. 7r. This affirmation of Frobisher may also refer to the colonization venture to Canada of Troilus de La Roche in June 1578, when the main ship fought with four English vessels. See A. J. Butler, *Calendar of State Papers, Foreign Series of the Reign of Elizabeth vol. 13: (1578-1579)* (London, State Papers Office, 1903), p. 53.

[45] The allusion is made to Henry Knollys, who took off with some of Gilbert's ships on an adventure of piracy in 1578. See D. B. Quinn, "Humphrey Gilbert," *Dictionary of Canadian Biography*, vol. 1, 1979, p. 332. Henry was the son of Sir Francis Knollys, treasurer of the Royal Household from 1572 to 1596.

[46] This word *diassi* is not clear, but must refer to the King Sebastian (*De Aviz*) of Portugal who died August 4, 1578, in Morocco, during the battle of Alcaçar-Quivir.

[47] This word *Xarpa* may be Zarpa, "the Claw."

[48] Camarrones may refer to Cimarrones: slaves who, having fled their Spanish master, were living in the West Indies, Guiana and Central America.

[49] Mona, pretentious woman.

[50] *Supra*, N° 39.

[51] D. D. Hogarth *et al.*, *op. cit.*, pp. 55 (N° 13) and 152 (N° 13).

[52] Ibid., p. 82.

[53] Ibid., p. 152 (N° 13).

[54] The King to Mendoza, April 11, 1579, in M. Hume, *op. cit.*, item 557 and, Mendoza to the King, May 3, 1579, in item 571.

[55] Some letters from Bernardino de Mendoza were found recently in a private collection in France. These private archives comprise several documents seized from the Spanish ambassador, now belonging to M. Jacques de Monts whose ancestor was Louis de Revol, Secretary of State of the Kings of France Henry III and Henry IV. See Jacques de Monts, 38930 Lalley, France.

French Reactions to the Northwest Voyages and the Assays by Geoffroy Le Brumen of the Frobisher Ore (1576-1584)

Bernard Allaire[1]

Introduction

At least three Frenchmen were interested in the fate of Martin Frobisher's ventures to the Canadian Arctic: the French ambassador to London, Castelnau de la Mauvissière, who sent reports to the King of France; the King's cosmographer in Paris, André Thevet, who publicly took a stance against the Northwest Passage theory; and a French Huguenot apothecary exiled in London, Geoffroy Le Brumen, who performed assays on the ore Frobisher brought back to England in 1577 and 1578. These assays of ore are certainly the most complex but exciting dimension of this history which involved a wide range of people. After Frobisher's return from his first voyage (1576), about a dozen artisans assayed and re-assayed samples taken from a single small piece of ore. Some of the assayers were specialists in this trade, but others belonged to related professions (such as goldsmiths and refiners) and undertook this kind of operation with reasonable success. The Frenchman, Geoffroy Le Brumen, was among these non-specialists employed to analyse the ore. Le Brumen not only performed more than one analysis of the ore brought back from northern Canada, but was also one of the few assayers who left written records of his assays.

It may surprise some that a Frenchman was among those consulted for ore analyses by the Secretary of the Privy Council, Francis Walsingham. However, given the Anglo-French context and the relations between these two men at the time, Walsingham's choice of Le Brumen becomes more understandable. Researchers interested in the Frobisher voyages have traditionally devoted little attention to this man or to his role, concentrating instead on the individuals in the foreground of the story.[2] The history of this quiet Frenchman who, at times, worked in France as a spy for the English intelligence service, offers a good opportunity to explore the French perception of the Frobisher expeditions. A look at Anglo-French diplomatic relations[3] at the time will finally bring to light the state of tension that existed in the English Channel and the "troubled waters" upon which Martin Frobisher was sailing. This study not only explores the place of a French technician in the Frobisher story, it also investigates the personal relations which linked the three principal groups involved in the decision-making process: the court, the administrators and the assayers. Indeed, within this confidential network details appear which challenge both the competence of various persons and the methodology of the assays in and of themselves.

Anglo-French Relations and the Northwest Voyages (1576-1584)

At the time of the voyages of Martin Frobisher, France was experiencing a civil war between Catholics and Protestants which had been raging sporadically since the Massacre of Wassy (1562). To this background problem which so divided the French can be added the Anglo-Spanish conflict. The struggle between Elizabeth I and Philip II moved to the continent in the 1570s and materialised in English and Spanish financial and military help to Huguenot and Catholic belligerents respectively. This situation only weakened the already declining French royal power. While Elizabethan financial assistance to the Protestants actually dates from before this period, after the Saint Bartholomew's Day Massacre (August 1572) the sums of money from the English crown increased dramatically.[4] In large part this was due both to the encouragement coming from the Protestant communities exiled in London[5] and to the legitimization provided by Philip II's financial aid to the Catholic partisans in France.

The diplomatic correspondence of the ambassadors in London and Paris at this time brings to light three obvious and recurrent themes: the fate of Mary Stuart, the conflict in Flanders, and the problem with the Duc d'Alençon. These three issues, and the last one in particular, constantly threatened the fragile balance of Anglo-French affairs. Hoping to gain another ally in the fight against Spain, the English attempted to win France to their cause. An alliance was formed at the time of the Frobisher voyages, sealed by the marriage pact between Queen Elizabeth I and François, Duc d'Alençon, the younger brother of the King of France. From 1577 on, however, the Duc sought to assume leadership of the French Protestants (the Huguenots) in order to intervene in the Low Countries. While Elizabeth I originally welcomed this idea,[6] the initiative was later rejected on the grounds that it might lead not only to the resumption of the latent war with Spain, which was then occupying Flanders, but even worse, might lead to a blockade of Antwerp, the most important market on the continent for English commerce.

Against this political backdrop which characterized Elizabethan foreign policy, the years 1576 to 1578 saw many events which were likely to create tensions between English and French authorities. One matter which preoccupied both French and English ambassadors was the Lansac affair,[7] which degenerated into a series of small conflicts at the end of the summer of 1577. In fact, at the time of Frobisher's return from his second voyage to Canada, about fifty English ships had been captured in France by Sieur de Lansac,[8] who was under the orders of King Henri III to arrest ships outfitted in England supplying Protestants in La Rochelle.[9] The Peace of Bergerac (September 17, 1577) should have put an end to all the problems in this region, but this was not the case. By way of reprisal, English authorities captured sixteen French ships in their ports which were loaded with valuable merchandise.[10] A few merchants of Dieppe responded by seizing other English ships and imprisoning various London merchants. In this context, Elizabeth decided to stop the English wine fleet (200 ships) which made its yearly voyages to France.[11] French pirates and privateers presented a permanent problem to shipping, particularly in the English Channel, and it was by mere chance that Frobisher escaped this threat.

Another matter which possibly lit the powder keg between England and France was the intrigues of Fitzmaurice who wanted to invade Ireland.[12] French authorities neither encouraged nor prevented the preparation for this invasion. At the same time, the English strongly suspected that a Frenchman from Brittany, the Marquis de La Roche,[13] was collaborating with Fitzmaurice in the invasion. The English were convinced that La Roche was using a colonisation venture to Canada to conceal his participation in the Irish invasion. To counter this possibility, in 1577 Elizabeth ordered English ships[14] to keep constant watch over the English Channel and, in 1578, asked Frobisher to sail with her surveillance fleet up to Ireland before he continued on towards northern Canada. The English ambassador in France closely surveyed La Roche and complained to the King of France. Neither the good word of the Queen-Mother Catherine de Medici to Amyas Paulet[15] nor any promises the French ambassador in England gave to Elizabeth[16] reduced English anxieties. Called to the Paris court by Catherine de Medici, the Marquis de La Roche even met personally with the English ambassador in an attempt to convince him of his good intentions towards England.[17] The effort was futile, as Amyas Paulet remained convinced that La Roche's venture was linked to Fitzgerald's plot to invade Ireland.[18] Nevertheless, even if his enterprise was not concealing help to Fitzgerald, he sailed in the same direction (and with the same intention: colonisation) as did Martin Frobisher or Humphrey Gilbert, which was a potential danger.[19]

The French diplomat Castelnau de La Mauvissière and the Frobisher voyages

It was in this climate of tension and distrust between England and France that Castelnau de la Mauvissière told his superiors of the voyages of Martin Frobisher. The ambassador first brought up the subject in a dispatch of 9 October 1577 to the King :

Someone called Forbichet is back from his voyage and new navigation with a certain quantity of gold[bearing] ore, which they say they will extract a great profit and that the English want to settle in the country that he has discovered on the north side [of America] in the direction of Cathay, with the intention of establishing a New England.[20]

The same day Castelnau wrote another dispatch, this one addressed to Catherine de Médici, in which he elaborated upon the voyage of Frobisher:

Someone called Forbichet, as I mentioned in the letter to the King, wants to enlarge the frontiers of England in a country newly discovered near the north where the lands are so large and spacious and full of gold[bearing] ore as he reported after his return and if Your Majesties want to take part to this venture it will be very easy to do so without hindering the Spaniards and Portuguese conquests and the land given to them as a gift by the Pope. I think it is the voyage that someone called d'Albaigne, which was in La Rochelle proposed one day to the late King Charles, your brother, and to you, where there is place to build

*empires and monarchies of more than seven or eight hundred leagues of land easy
to conquer and to keep and with a possibility to reach by land the lands
conquered by the Spaniards and Portugueses, but after the assays they will make
on the great quantity of ore they brought back I will inform Your Majesty of the
results and of the preparations they will do to return over there.*[21]

Although this affair was important enough to be mentioned in diplomatic correspondence,
it does not seem to have been an official state secret since the French ambassador did not
even take the time to transform into code the part of the dispatch which spoke of the
affair.[22] Castelnau was informed of Frobisher well before the Spaniards, despite the latter
being more concerned with English maritime expeditions. This is not difficult to
understand considering that the Spanish envoy in England at that time was in jail for
plotting against Elizabeth's life.[23]

In the following dispatches to the King and the Queen Mother, Castelnau de la
Mauvissière clarified the location of the mining colony as being "someplace in
Newfoundland towards Estotilant and the islands called Grenelant and Yslant,"[24] and
talked about the difficulties Frobisher met with because of the ice and the cold climate.
He then warned the French King about the English desire to winter on site, and the size of
the third expedition which was being financed by several merchants and members of the
Privy Council.[25] A few days later, Castelnau spoke of the assays of ore and mentioned
that according to what he heard, "a pound and a half returned two ounces" of gold.[26] On
October 17, 1578 he alerted Henri III of the return of Frobisher's ships which were
loaded with ore which had to be tested before going further.[27]

A long silence follows and we must wait almost three years before the French
ambassador in London again writes to the King of France on this subject. He tells us then
that he met Martin Frobisher in April 1581 at a party given south of London, near the
Thames, in honour of Francis Drake's return to England; Queen Elizabeth I and several
other important English personages were in attendance. On this occasion, Frobisher
mentioned to Castelnau that he still wanted to search for the passage to Cathay through
the Northwest and spoke to him of

*the profit that the Queen would find if by the same means he shortens by two-
thirds the way needed to reach the West-Indies and Peru and by the same way to
all Asia, but he never has the time to begin his voyage as he wants to do another
time because he lost time searching for gold mines in which the profit is small and
the expenses too high.*[28]

The King's cosmographer André Thevet

News concerning the voyages of Frobisher did not circulate just in the upper echelons of
diplomacy. The information also spread through the royal court and the story became
widely known when, in 1578, Nicolas Pithou published a French version of the Frobisher
voyages written by Dionyse Settle. The cosmographer, André Thevet, in Paris was one

of those who lent an interested ear to the Frobisher project.[29] This was, however, not just a one-way interest, for we know that the English authorities consulted Thevet in 1577 through their embassy in Paris in order to sound out the cosmographer's opinion concerning the Northwest Passage.[30] The English interest in Thevet is all the more notable since some of Thevet's works were among the books Martin Frobisher brought with him on the first voyage. The sources concerning this voyage mention, among other things, the presence of two of Thevet's printed books, one of which appears to be *La Cosmographie Universelle*[31] published in 1575. These books were most likely chosen because of the overrated reputation of the French cosmographer, but perhaps also owing to their recent publication.[32]

It is, however, curious to find these works among Frobisher's books, for Thevet had argued since at least the 1570s against the idea of reaching China through a passage in northwest America. Thevet believed that not just the absence of a sea route[33] but also the polar climate in this region made the passage impossible. The French cosmographer was familiar with this hypothesis and had known for quite some time that the English wanted to reach the Far East by avoiding Spain or Spanish colonies. He cited Richard Chancellor's failures in the 1550s to reach China by way of the northeast and in the 1560s by way of Florida.[34] Thevet in fact persistently opposed the views of Humphrey Gilbert, who since the 1560s had been claiming the existence of a northern passage.

However, as Franck Lestringant rightly points out, Thevet's strongest criticism against the voyages of Frobisher comes much later[35] in a book called *Les vrais pourtraits et vies des hommes illustres*[36] and in his unfinished work *Le Grand Insulaire;*[37] both were written well after Nicolas Pithou's French version of Dionyse Settle's account of the voyages of Frobisher.[38] According to Thevet, Frobisher "is wrong because for five years he has lost his time with great cost and danger to cross from the Atlantic to the Pacific ocean" without giving good results.[39] He essentially reproached the English for treating the North American Inuit with the same kind of cruelty for which they reproached the Spaniards[40] and, what is worse, for their "lust for the treasures of this unknown country."[41]

His opinion about these treasures, especially the precious metals which could be found in Canada, had not wavered since 1575. In his *Cosmographie Universelle*, he mentions, among other things,

> *I think we can easily find gold and silver mines, like those found in France, but what kind of ore? rough and more full of sulphur than of fine gold and which would cost more to clean than twice the profit we can pull out of it*[42]

A little bit later in the same book, he adds...

> *Rocks can be found which in weight and color look a lot like gold ore, but when we wanted to test them to know if they were good, they could not survive the fire and were automatically dissolved and converted into ashes.*[43]

We should not assume that Thevet wrote with conviction here or even based his conclusions on first-hand experience. By no means an expert in precious metals from North America, Thevet was merely repeating what others had said on the subject and what had been written about Jacques Cartier's voyages to Canada in the 1530s and 1540s. After the end of the Frobisher voyages to the Canadian Arctic, information, manuscripts, prints and even North American minerals continued to circulate on both sides of the English channel. Indeed, in 1584 the French merchant from Rouen, Estienne Bellenger, gave a piece of rock he took during his voyage to North America to Richard Hakluyt, who was at the time a member of the English embassy in Paris.

Geoffroy Le Brumen, the Apothecary

These references to the value of the North American ore brings us back to the focus of our subject: the assays performed by a Frenchman named Geoffroy Le Brumen. We have little information concerning the precise identity of this man. His date of birth, the year of his death or even the day he left France[44] are unknown. But with information drawn from the correspondence of Francis Walsingham and the writings of other contemporaries, it is possible to rebuild partially Le Brumen's story.[45] Geoffroy Le Brumen was French,[46] and was probably the same Geoffroy Le Brumen who belonged to the Parisian militia in 1567,[47] and was relieved of his command two years later for perjury[48] during the imprisonment of a Protestant merchant of Lyon.[49]

We do not know the date of Le Brumen's arrival in England but he was certainly among those exiles who fled France during the Wars of Religion. The Huguenot emigration to England reached its peak after the Saint Bartholomew massacre (August 23-24, 1572), and is thus probably the period of his arrival. While the exact date he came to England remains uncertain, we do know that he was in London by the beginning of 1577 and we are left to believe that Walsingham had known him for quite a while. We do not know, however, if they perhaps met in Paris sometime between 1570 and 1573 when Walsingham was the English ambassador at the court of Charles IX. Le Brumen cannot be found among the archives of French Protestants living in London at that time. He is also absent from the acts of naturalization of sixteenth century England.[50] In a document of 1587, he is mentioned as a "stranger" which could signify that he was living in England as a stranger merchant without English citizenship, and thus would explain his absence from the official records.

While some believe that Le Brumen was a doctor[51] or surgeon,[52] he was in fact an apothecary interested in all that touched upon medicine. Despite his London exile, Geoffroy Le Brumen travelled frequently to the continent to maintain contact with the French medical world, and he often returned from these visits bearing printed materials concerning medicine.[53] As a specialist in the medical community, he often informed Sir Francis Walsingham about the health of people at the court or living in Queen Elizabeth I's entourage.[54] Although we lack evidence, it is probable that he was also taking care of Francis Walsingham's health, whose disease made him incapable of completing his daily business.[55]

The Technical Expert and the Spy

Sir Francis Walsingham employed Geoffroy Le Brumen for other diverse tasks in England. Le Brumen acted, for instance, as a technical adviser on scientific and military questions. He evaluated products and substances with a critical eye so as to determine the future success of inventions. He had a role in bringing to England a man who knew how to build a new model of arquebus;[56] Le Brumen worked to provide this craftsman with tools and implements and helped to fund the experiments needed to perfect the weapon.[57] In another interesting case, Le Brumen negotiated in Walsingham's name with a man called Joachim about the possibility of obtaining the privilege to make all saltpetre sold in London[58] using a new and more economical process.[59] The work done for the secretary of the Privy Council was not limited only to medical consultations and technical advice. Indeed, our Huguenot apothecary, as one of the numerous spies of Francis Walsingham[60] and William Cecil, worked undercover on the continent. Called "Monsieur Geoffroy" by correspondents,[61] Le Brumen often went to France, Flanders, and even Spain and Portugal,[62] to receive important letters[63] and to make contact with informants working for the Protestants.

Often under surveillance,[64] and frequently fed with false rumours, early modern embassies relied upon parallel networks capable of quickly confirming or invalidating important information. In fact, the English recruitment of agents on the continent only lessened after the defeat of the Great Armada (1588) and the death of Walsingham (1590). It is interesting to note that Le Brumen was serving as an agent under the cover of being an apothecary, which facilitated his constant voyages between England and France. For example, in 1579 when assayers in Dartford were trying to recover precious metal from the last shipment of ore brought back by Martin Frobisher, Geoffroy Le Brumen was on a mission to Antwerp.[65] Six months later he was in Ghent, still in the service of Walsingham. From September to November 1582, Le Brumen travelled to Paris[66] and contacted several people, all the while completing his professional tasks. He returned to France in early 1583 with merchandise and passports obtained by Walsingham in order to get in touch this time with Henri de Navarre (future Henri the IV, King of France) in the name of Queen Elizabeth I. Geoffroy Le Brumen did not meet the "Béarnais" directly, but did negotiate with a gentleman living at his court in Nerac. Le Brumen was back in London in June 1583. We see him more deeply involved in espionage in 1587 when he left Greenwich with 50 canons to be sent abroad, probably to French Huguenots in France.[67]

It is quite surprising that Le Brumen's powerful contacts in England and France and his multifaceted career had so long escaped the attention of scholars. Conyers Read, for instance, familiar with Walsingham's agents in France (Jacomo Manucci, Thomas Wilkes), doubts the existence of Le Brumen. He instead believes that Le Brumen was simply conjured up by Michel de La Huguerye, a Protestant envoy of Henri de Navarre.[68] The same omission is striking in the recent book of Alison Plowden[69] who nevertheless takes time to study other minor agents. The better quality works of Alan Haynes[70] and

De Lamar Jensen,[71] specialists on espionage, also fail to discuss Geoffroy Le Brumen who remains unknown.[72]

The Assays of the Frobisher Ore

It is therefore in his role as technical expert for Sir Francis Walsingham that Le Brumen was asked to advise upon the piece of ore Martin Frobisher brought back from the voyage to the northwest. This despite the fact that Le Brumen was neither an assayer nor a precious metal refiner, but rather an apothecary. In the sixteenth century this profession was not completely unrelated to the metallurgy of precious metals. Apothecaries, with their wide-ranging knowledge of chemistry, were familiar with gold and silver and at this time were the only craftsmen capable of evaluating certain complex substances (drugs, oil, etc.), and understanding their nature. Apothecaries also possessed workshops equipped with tools and implements similar to those of assayers (furnaces, flasks, etc), which they used to identify products or distil pharmaceutical substances, much in the same way that assayers prepared substances necessary for their analysis (acids, for instance). Finally, apothecaries had a solid knowledge of precious metals, since they used them for pharmaceutical purposes. In fact, apothecaries sold remedies containing metallic gold or silver which were used at this time in medical treatments.[73] The preparation of these expensive remedies therefore meant that apothecaries frequently dealt with and refined gold or silver.

Geoffroy Le Brumen was called upon twice to work on the Frobisher ore. First, in the months which followed the return of Frobisher's initial voyage, and later in the months preceding the departure for the third and last voyage. The story of that first piece of ore, as great as a "halfe pennye loaf" begins, of course, in the Arctic at the end of the summer of 1576. It was at this time that Robert Garrard[74] and other sailors on Frobisher's ship came across a rock, which they described as being "much like sea-coal," on the beach of the country later named Meta Incognita. Back in London the piece was given to the chief administrator of the voyage, Michael Lok, in the presence of other people, each of whom broke off a piece as a souvenir of this exotic voyage. From November 1576 to January 1577, Lok gave several people samples to analyze: William Williams, a man called Whelar who was contacted by Lok in November 1576, and George Nedam, who was contacted in December, each received a piece. All their assays of the rock revealed a total absence of precious metals. But in January 1577 Lok got in touch with a certain Giovanni-Batista Agnello, who finally obtained positive results on the ore. Lok, quite the sceptic, asked Agnello to perform new analyses, and insisted upon seeing the results with his own eyes. Lok became convinced of the precious metal in this rock upon seeing both additional positive assays, and Agnello's strong interest in organizing another expedition to procure more ore. At the end of this same month, Lok informed Francis Walsingham of the analysis result. Walsingham, even more incredulous than Lok, requested that rock samples be given to other assayers for additional analysis. Between January 28 and mid-February, samples were distributed to Edward Dyer and three other people; all of these assays turned out to be negative. On March 23, 1577, Walsingham and Lok asked Geoffroy Le Brumen to perform assays on the piece of ore. Le Brumen seems to have been the last person to examine it before Frobisher's departure for the second voyage to the Northwest.

The choice of the people consulted to perform the assays is not a coincidence. Although they seem arbitrary, these choices bring to the fore the existing network of human relations behind the decisions. Indeed, several people who were qualified and available to perform assays in 1576 were only invited to do so after the return of the second voyage in 1577. Initially, Lok chose the experts and did not mention the real origin of the samples he gave to these expert assayers so as to ensure the validity of the assays. He first consulted the most well-known specialist in London, William Williams, a coin assayer working at the Tower of London; after the negative analysis Williams suggested that Lok consult a gold and silver refiner called Whelar.[75] Williams certainly knew this Whelar through his connection with the Mint. We have few clues about Georges Nedam, but perhaps it was also upon Williams' suggestion that he was contacted. As far as Giovanni-Batista Agnello is concerned, it is almost certain that Lok knew Agnello beforehand, owing to the former's connection with Italians merchants living in London.[76]

All the assays which followed those of Agnello were performed by people connected to Francis Walsingham, including the Frenchman Geoffroy Le Brumen. In March 1577 Michael Lok, acting under Walsingham's instructions, gave Le Brumen the first piece of ore. Of course, to keep the first assays impartial, Walsingham and Lok decided to lie about the real origin of the ore:

> *The xxii day, I came to Mr. Secretarie, and brought hym another pece of the ore. He wylled me in his name to carrye it to one Geffrey, a Frenchman, and to tell hym that it came out of Ireland, and to wyl hym to make a proffe therof, and he to bringe reporte to hym.[77]*

It seems that there are no written traces of the initial analysis performed after March 22, 1577. The result was probably transmitted verbally by Le Brumen to Walsingham, who then informed Lok. We do know, however, that no precious metal was found in the sample, or at most a tiny trace of silver was detected.

The second analysis performed ten months later, on January 24, 1578, was somewhat different because Le Brumen was aware this time that the sample came from Martin Frobisher's ships. Although the assay was negative, a document from the analysis contains some interesting details (written reports usually only emerged from positive assays). Here, Le Brumen not only announced his findings, but for some unexplained reason also took time to explain the nature of the ore to the secretary of the Privy Council, even suggesting other methods to use in later assays. This text probably answered Walsingham's specific questions concerning the ore. The document, originally found in the Walsingham correspondence, was gathered in the collection of the *State Papers*[78] and first published by Richard Collinson in 1867.[79] It was never translated from French to English, which certainly explains its absence from most studies concerning the Frobisher ore.

Translated version of the letter to Walsingham from Geoffroy Le Brumen
PRO: SP12-122, N° 17 [24 January 1578[NS]]

Jan.24th, 1577. FROM MASTER GEOFFREY LA BRUM, TRYAL METAL FALLING NOT OWT.

A *Sir I have considered all the kinds of mineral you had the pleasure to give me and I found that most of them are only marchasites and not minerals the said marchasites ordinarily contains so much sulphur that even if there were some good metals we could not extract it without great pain and loss and to establish a proof and perform a real assay it would be necessary to*

B *have much more of it and not trust only two or three proofs only because some pieces that we believe to be good and full of gold and silver contain nothing or very little, more often in contrast, some that we dislike can be found the best sometimes with the existing diverse method of extracting the pure metal and it must be tried diverse ways because in any mineral the*

C *metal is so raw that it disappears and can be lost during the melting if it is not held by cementations and fixatives, in others it is accompained by so much dirt and impurities like sulphur, earth, rock, filth and similar things that we separate it only with great pain in certain way that we must prove sometimes with salt, sometimes with mercury, sometimes by roasting,*

D *sometimes by cementing it or melting it with soap, lead, salpeter, borax and others substances which are great in numbers and too long to be written[.] Concerning those of the Captain Forbischer they really need diverse preparations and if I had received enough I would have tried several methods but with so few we can be sure of nothing I can only tell you that I have*

E *roasted washed and rinsed some of it and mixed it with lead and put it in ash or cupel which left nothing of fine at the end which makes me think that there is no big profit because the other way and means of extracting the fine metal are of great cost and require work on quantity[.] It is true that if I had one pound or two I would try a preparation with commun salt made with other*

F *ingredients which I have reduced before some strongly calcinated metal which the borax made from niter-glass and other similar were unable to reduce[.] I have not given to Monsieur Marchant the said ore to give back to you because I do not know if he wants them [or] if I can receive more of the ore of the Captain Frobisher I would make better proofs. I have waited*

G *before writing you until I saw the end of some work that I began a long time ago for the medicine and also until I could talk with you about it as a gift of all the courtesy and goodness that I have received from you and for which I am and will forever be obliged to your Lord but the said work not being finished and Monsieur Marchant having informed me at noon of your order I*

H *have done the present to excuse myself and to beg you to hold me among your very humble and loyal servants I pray God Monseigneur that he raise*

your Lord and keep you in a long and very happy health to serve more and
more for his glory Amen from London this Saturday 24TH day of January
1578[.]

I   *Your very humble and obeying*
                               servant Geoffroy Le Brumen

Like many other people involved in the assays, Geoffroy Le Brumen described the ore as
being a "marcasite stone," originally an Arab word (markaschâtsa)[80] which at the time
generally signified all minerals containing iron. Today the term marcasite concerns a
kind of iron sulphide, often mistaken for pyrite,[81] whose yellow crystals somewhat
resemble metallic gold.[82] This was a mistake frequently made by non-specialists, which
was only accentuated by the mineral's presence throughout Europe. In order to identify if
the ore contained iron, professional assayers as well as other artisans involved in the gold
trade (goldsmiths, refiners, etc) performed some very simple operations. If the visual
analysis and the test of its density proved to be insufficient, analysers used a magnet to
identify the presence of metallic iron.[83] However, in the case of marcassite (or pyrite)
they would roast a piece of ore under a flame. Instead of melting (as gold metal would)
the yellow crystals of iron sulphide would burn and yield a strong odor of sulphur
dioxide.

Geoffroy Le Brumen's report to Walsingham is quite ambiguous on this aspect. While
the quality of his analysis is questionable, it seems that he went beyond the simple
operations described above. He begins by declaring that the ore is marcasite and then
discusses the presence of sulphur (see text, section A). Since we know today from
analyses made by Donald Hogarth that Frobisher's ore contained little sulphur,[84] we can
suspect that Le Brumen did not really test the sample. However, it is unclear as to
whether Le Brumen was talking about the presence of sulphur in the rock brought back
by Frobisher or in marcasite rock in general, whatever its origins. The fact that he refers
later to the rock of "the Captain Forbischer" (section D) seems to make clear that he was
talking about the marcasite. The one thing that is sure is that Le Brumen, like the
others,[85] had difficulties detecting the difference between the marcasite (or pyrite) and the
ores which contain metallic iron.

Le Brumen's description of the steps involved in the assays of the samples (lead fusion,
cupellation) shows that as an apothecary he had a certain knowledge of the analysis of
precious metal. He was critical of his own assays and insisted upon performing several
analyses to confirm the results. He complained, of course, about the small size of the ore
the Secretary of the Privy Council gave to him. Le Brumen then mentioned to Francis
Walsingham an important fact that would become one of the explanations for the failure
of the assays: there might perhaps be quantities of precious metals in the Frobisher ore,
but the techniques used to extract it would cost more than the value of the gold or silver
which could be found. He went on to propose undertaking other assays using different
and improved methods, and ended the letter by personally thanking Walsingham for his
financial support.

The involvement of Le Brumen in works related to precious metal for Francis Walsingham does not end with the Frobisher voyages. Indeed, we meet him a last time in January 1589 when he makes with a friend several assays on another piece of ore sent by Walsingham. This assay does not seem to be related to the ore brought back from the Canadian Arctic but rather to the fabrication of some "or potable," a remedy containing precious metal, supposed to cure diseases and bring eternal life.

Conclusion

Among the three Frenchmen interested in the fate of Martin Frobisher's ventures to the Canadian Arctic — Castelnau de la Mauvissière, André Thevet and Geoffroy Le Brumen — the first two give us an image of the French point of view, the study of the third individual — Le Brumen — brings to light the ramifications of the network within which decisions concerning the future of Martin Frobisher's voyages were taken. This network, under the supervision of the principal secretary of the Privy Council, Francis Walsingham, demonstrates the serious attention paid to the organisation of these discovery ventures.

Like several other people involved in this story, Le Brumen was not really a qualified assayer. This aspect, noted earlier on in our investigation, becomes all the more significant in the case of Le Brumen. Although he was only an apothecary, the description of the ore Le Brumen left in his second analysis shows that he was well acquainted with the metallurgy of precious metals, a conviction reinforced by the results of his two assays which declared the ore almost worthless. From Walsingham's point of view, it seems that Le Brumen's competency as an assayer was secondary in importance; Le Brumen was above all a man Walsingham could trust. That is why Walsingham twice requested that he perform the assays. There were two advantages in enlisting Le Brumen's help: first, he did not belong to one of the parties fighting to obtain the lucrative contract to treat all the ore coming from the Arctic; and, secondly, he was not financially involved in this venture. Well-occupied by other tasks (medical, technical or diplomatic), Geoffroy Le Brumen was outside this debate, and thus better placed to render an objective judgment.

Even if we dispose of several general or specific explanations of the cause of the organisation of the futile third voyage to Meta Incognita, the assays of the ore remain the principal clue. In regards to this precise aspect, we still do not know the level of competence of most of the people involved in the assays, nor do we have a good idea of the context in which decisions about the analyses were taken. Any reconstitution of this context must first undertake the difficult but necessary investigation of each participant in the assays;[86] this is difficult owing to the scarce[87] and dispersed sources, but feasible with the technical and financial means which did not exist in the nineteenth century when the exact site of Frobisher's Headquarters on Baffin Island was rediscovered by Charles Francis Hall.

Appendix: Transcription of the letter to Walsingham from Geoffroy Le Brumen

1　　　*Monseigneur jay considere toutes les espesses de*
　　　mineres quil vous ha pleu me bailler et ay trouve que
　　　la pluspart ne sont que marchasites et non mineres
　　　lesquelles marchasites ont ordinairement tant de souphre
5　　　*que qua[n]t il auroit quelque peu de bon metal on*
　　　ne le pourroit tirer sans gra[n]t peine et perte qua[n]t
　　　a en faire preuve et essay certain il en faudroit
　　　bien davantage et ne se fault fier a deux ny troys
　　　preuves seulleme[n]t car tel morceau quon pense estre
10　　　*bon et habonder dor ou dargent il ne sy trouve rien*
　　　ou peu de chose le plus souvent et au co[n]traire tel
　　　quon mesprise se trouve le meille[u]r quelquesfoys avec
　　　ce quil y ha divers moyens pour extraire
　　　le pur metal et le fault tenter par diverses voyes
15　　　*par ce qu'en aulcunes minieres le metal est encore*
　　　ta[n]t crud quil sesvanuit et perd en la fusion sil
　　　nest retenu p[ar] cementations fixatives en aultres il
　　　est accompaigne de ta[n]t dordures et impurtes comme
　　　de souphre terre pierre loppes et semblables qu'on ne
20　　　*le depart qu'a gra[n]t peine de facon qu'on le doyt*
　　　esprouver tantost avec selz tantost avec vifarge[n]t
　　　tantost la brusla[n]t tantost la cementa[n]t ou fonda[n]t avec
　　　savon plomb selpitre borax ou autres qui sont en
　　　gra[n]t nombre et trop longs a escrire. Qua[n]t a celle
25　　　*du Capp[itain]e Forbisher elle merite bien ta[n]t de diverses*
　　　preparations et sy jen eusse eu no[m]bre j'en eusse tente
　　　plusieurs facons mais po[u]r sy peu on nose asseurer
　　　de rien seulleme[n]t je vous peux tesmoigner que jen
　　　ay brusle lave et purge puis joint avec du plomb et
30　　　*mis en cendre ou couppelle qui nha rien laisse de*
　　　fin qui me faict juger quil ny ha gra[n]t p[ro]fit par ce
　　　que les aultres voyes et moyens dextraire le fin so[n]t
　　　de gra[n]t coust et labeur sur qua[n]tite. Vray est que
　　　sy j'en avois ugne livre ou deux jessairoys quelque
35　　　*preparation par sel c[om]mun p[re]pare avec aultres ingrediens*
　　　par lequel jay aultreffoys reduit des metaux fort
　　　calcines que le borax faict de verre nitre et aultres
　　　semblables ne pouvoient reduire. Je nay baille a
　　　Mons[ieu]r Marcha[n]t les susd[it]es mineres a vous reporter
40　　　*par ce que je ne scay sy les desires sy je peux*
　　　recouvrer dava[n]tage de celle du Capp[itain]e Forbischer
　　　jen feray plus amples preuves. Jattendois a vous en
　　　escrire jusque a ce que jeusse veu la fin de quelq[ue]s

oeuvres que jay co[m]mencees y a ja longtemps po[u]r
45   la medecine affin de vous en faire part en
       tesmoignage de ta[n]t de courtoysies et bienfaictz que
       jay receuz de vous pour lesquels je suis et seray
       a tousjours oblige a vostre grandeur mais lesd[it]es
       oeuvres nesta[n]tz parfaites et mons[ieu]r Marcha[n]t maia[n]t
50   adverty a midi de vostre co[m]mandeme[n]t jay fait
       la presente po[u]r mexcuser et vous suplier me tenir
       au rang de voz treshumbles et tresfideles
       serviteurs je prie Dieu
       Monseigneur quil augmente vostre grandeur et
55   lentretienne en longue et tres heureuse sante pour
       de plus en plus servir a sa gloire. Amen de
       Londres ce samedi 24^e jo[u]r de janvier 1578

                       Vostre treshumble et obeissa[n]t
                       servit[eu]r Geoffroy Le Brumen

Notes

[1] I would like to thank Professor David Quinn (University of Liverpool), Sir Ian Gourlay, Lt. Cdr. D. W. Waters, Ann Shirley, Kirsten Seaver (ARTAF), Stephanie Whitlock (University of Chicago), Silvia Marzagalli (Université de Bordeaux), Gayle Brunelle (University of Fullerton), Donald Hogarth (University of Ottawa), Robert Descimon (École des Hautes Études en Sciences Sociales), and Franck Lestringant (Université de Lille).

[2] Additional difficulties encountered when studying Le Brumen are that most of the documents concerning him are dispersed throughout the collection of *State Papers* and are written exclusively in French.

[3] At the time of the Frobisher voyages the ambassadors were Amyas Paulet, ambassador of England in Paris (1576-79), and Castelnau de la Mauvissière, ambassador of France in London (1575-85).

[4] In 1577, Elizabeth wanted to group all the Protestant factions (Calvinists, Lutherans, etc.) within a European Protestant alliance. Cf. Conyers Read, *Mr. Secretary Walsingham*, Oxford, Clarendon Press, 1967 (©1925), vol. 1, p. 299.

[5] There has been a French Huguenot community in England since the 1540s. From 1550 they have been established with a church in London. Cf. Bernard Cottret, *Terre d'exil, l'Angleterre et ses réfugiés 16ᵉ-17ᵉ siècles*, Paris, Aubier, 1985.

[6] C. Read, *op. cit.*, vol. 1, p. 285.

[7] Guy de Lusignan de Saint-Gelais, sieur of Lansac, son of Louis de Lusignan, a French military serviceman devoted to the king of France and the queen mother Catherine de Medici.

[8] Most of these English ships were officially coming to France to buy salt at Brouage.

[9] Cf. for more details, Agrippa D'Aubigné, *Histoire Universelle*, (ed. A. de Ruble), Paris, Renouard, 1891, vol. 5, p. 294.

[10] Bibliothèque Nationale [Hereafter *BN*], manuscript department, series *Les Cinq Cents de Colbert* N° 337 [hereafter *CCC*], Letter from Castelnau to King Henri III (14 October 1577).

[11] Discussions lasted several months before an agreement was finally reached. Henri III and Catherine de Médicis demanded in exchange that Elizabeth cease financial aid to the Prince of Casimir, who was sending German mercenaries to France to help the Protestant cause, and that the Queen stop sending supplies to La Rochelle. Cf. *Lettres de Catherine de Médici, vol. 5 (1574-1577)*, [Hereafter *LCM*] (ed. H. de la Ferrière), Paris, Imprimerie Nationale, 1895, (Letter of 20 June and 1 August 1577).

[12] James Fitzmaurice Fitzgerald, pretender to the throne of Ireland. With financial help from the king of Spain and the Pope, Fitzgerald had been gathering troops since 1574 to invade Ireland (in 1579) and overthrow the English.

[13] Troïlus du Mesgouez, Marquis de La Roche.

[14] "Instructions by the Council to Mr Geo. Winter to take command of *the Lyon, the Foresight* and *the Dreadnought*, to cruise off the Irish coast, and to watch La Roche, a Frenchman, who was fitting out certain ships, in conjunction with James Fitzmorris, an Irish rebel," in Robert Lemon, *Calendar of State Papers, Domestic series (1547-1580)*, [Hereafter *CSP, Domestic*] London, Longman, Brown, Green, Longmans and Robert, 1856, p. 552, [July 1577].

[15] *LCM*, vol. 5 (1574-1577), (20 June, 1 August and 3 August 1577).

[16] *BN*, *CCC* N° 337, Letters to Henri III (7 July 1578).

[17] Arthur John Butler, *Calendar of State Papers, Foreign (1577-1578)*, [Hereafter *CSP, Foreign*], London, Eyre et Spotiswoode, 1901, p. 506, N° 652 and p. 509, N° 654.

[18] The English authorities only realised their mistake several months later in July 1578. Cf. *CSP, Foreign (1578-1579)*, 1903, p. 53, N° 71.

[19] Frobisher must have been referring to La Roche when he affirmed that some Frenchmen were preparing a voyage to Meta Incognita. Cf. Letter of Bernardino de Mendoza to Philip II of Spain (15 November 1578), in B. Allaire & D. D. Hogarth, "Martin Frobisher, the Spaniards, and a Sixteenth-Century Northern Spy," published in this volume. Also published in *Terræ Incognitæ: the Journal for the History of Discoveries*, Arlington, Texas, vol. 28 (1996).

[20] BN, *CCC* N° 337 (09 November 1577). Some of the letters from Castelnau have been published (in French) by Conyers Read, in *American Historical Review*, [Hereafter *AHR*], vol. 31 (1925-26), pp. 285-296.

[21] BN, *CCC* N° 337 (9 October 1577).

[22] The parts coded in the letters from Castelnau always referred to Mary Stuart or the conflict in Flanders. Cf. for instance, BN, *CCC* N° 337, (23 September 1577).

[23] In fact, De Guaras was in jail for 18 months, from the end of October 1577 to May 1579. The new envoy of Philip II, Bernardino de Mendoza, only arrived in London on March 1578, after which time he permanently watched over Frobisher's voyages.

[24] BN, *CCC* N° 337, Letter to the King (4 July 1578).

[25] *Idem.*

[26] BN, *CCC* N° 337, (7 July 1578). In this dispatch Castelnau seems to confuse the voyage of Frobisher with the voyage Humphrey Gilbert organized to Newfoundland in 1578.

[27] BN, *CCC* N° 337, (17 October 1578).

[28] BN, *CCC* N° 337, (9 April 1581).

[29] The best study on this subject is that of M. Franck Lestringant, the French specialist on the cosmographer André Thevet. Cf. among others, F. Lestringant, *Le Huguenot et le Sauvage. L'Amérique et la controverse coloniale, en France, au temps des guerres de Religions (1555-1589)*, Paris, Aux amateurs de livres, diffusion Klincksieck, 1990, pp. 217, 219-220 and 239-241.

[30] Thevet, André, *Les vrais pourtraits et vies des hommes illustres...*, Paris, J. Kervert et G. Chaudiere, 1584, vol. I, f. 527v. Thevet would also have other contacts with the English embassy in the 1580s, principally through Richard Hakluyt.

[31] André Thevet, *Cosmographie Universelle d'André Thevet cosmographe du roy illustrée de diverses figures des choses plus remarquables veues par l'auteur, & incogneuës de nos Anciens et Modernes*, Paris, P. L'Huillier, 1575.

[32] "a booke of Cosmografie in frenche of Andreas Thevet makinge" and "a newe world of Andreas Thevett englishe and frenche bookes ij smalle" in Exchequer King's Remembrancer, E164, vol. 35, N° 16, cited in James McDermott, *The Account Books of Michael Lok, Relating to the Northwest Voyages of Martin Frobisher, 1576-78*, Master of Philosophy, University of Hull, pp. 148-149.

[33] The chart found in the *Cosmographie Universelle* (of 1575) is not clear on this subject, for a symbol hides the spot where the Northwest Passage is located.

[34] A. Thevet, 1575, *op. cit.*, vol. II, f. 1001r. Thevet must have been referring to the voyages of John Hawkins in the 1560s.

[35] F. Lestringant, 1990, *op. cit.*, p. 218.

[36] A. Thevet, 1584, *op. cit.*, vol.I.

[37] Cf. F. Lestringant, *op. cit.*, p. 219.

[38] Dionyse Settle's account of the voyages of Frobisher was later published in other languages: first in French (1578), then German (1580) and Latin (1580).

[39] Cited in F. Lestringant, *op. cit.*, p. 220, note 72.

[40] A. Thevet, 1584, *op. cit.*, vol. I, f. 378.

[41] A. Thevet, 1584, *op. cit.*, tome II, fol. 378r.

[42] A. Thevet, 1575, *op. cit.*, f. 1010r.

[43] A. Thevet, 1575, *op. cit.*, f. 1015r.

[44] It is likely that he had died sometime between 1589 and 1595, for the last news we have about him dates from 1589. Additionally, in a letter of 1595 he is referred to in the past tense, which leads us to believe that he was no longer alive. Cf. *CSP, Foreign (1595)*, Letter from Thomas d'Arques to William Cecil (14 February 1595).

[45] Other information concerning Geoffroy Le Brumen can be found in *The New Found Land of Stephen Parmenius, the life and writings of a Hungarian poet drowned on a voyage from Newfoundland, 1583*, (ed. David B. Quinn and Neil M. Chesire), Toronto, University of Toronto Press, 1972.

[46] Francis Walsingham and Michael Lok talk about him as being a "Frenchman." Cf *CSP, Domestic*, N° 25, (22 March 1577) "Mr Lockes Discours touching the ewre."

[47] Le Brumen was engaged in 1567 under the orders of Jacques Kerfer, leader of the militia in the municipal district of Sainte-Geneviève in Paris. Cf. *Archives Nationales* [Hereafter *AN*], H 1784, fol. 400r-401r (5 and 8 August 1567), cited in François Bonnardot, *Registres des délibérations du bureau de la ville de Paris vol. 5*, Paris, Imprimerie nationale, 1892, p. 599 and 600.

[48] *AN*, H 1780B, fol. 156v (19 April 1569) cited in F. Bonnardot, *op. cit.*, vol. 6, p. 99.

[49] According to specialists, destitution amongst the Parisian militia was frequent at this time, and simply rumour of being Protestant was a sufficient cause for dismissal. Cf. N. Weiss & Ch. Read in *Bulletin de la Société de l'Histoire du Protestantisme Français*, [hereafter *BSHPF*] vol. 50, 1901, pp. 575-595; N. Weiss in *BSHPF*, vol. 72 (1923), pp. 86-97 and D. Richet, *De la Réforme à la Révolution, Études sur la France Moderne*, Paris, Aubier, 1991, pp. 15-51. We would like to thank M. Robert Descimon for helpful advice on this matter.

[50] There is no trace of Le Brumen in any of the publications of The Huguenot Society of London (Cf. W. Page, *letters of denization and acts of naturalization for Aliens in England 1509-1603*, Lymington, *The Huguenot Society*, 1893, vol. 8) as well as in the Aliens Return list (Cf. PRO, *SP12-82* November 1571).

[51] *CSP, Foreign*, Letter from Jacques de Somere to Davison, (3 July 1579).

[52] *Mémoires inédits de Michel de La Huguerye publiés d'après des documents autographes pour la société de l'histoire de France*, [Hereafter *MMH*] (ed. A. De Ruble), Paris, Renouard, 1878, p. 36.

[53] *CSP, Foreign (1583)*, Letter from Geoffroy Le Brumen to Walsingham (9 June 1583).

[54] He was particularly interested in the Earl of Sussex's state of health.

[55] This was the case, for example, in spring 1577. Cf. also *CSP, Domestic Addenda (1580-1625)*, pp. 78-79, Letter from Le Brumen to Walsingham (31 October 1582) in which he wrote to Walsingham of "cushions" of arsenic hung around the neck as prevention against the plague.

[56] *CSP, Foreign (1583)*, Letter from Le Brumen to Walsingham (29 January 1583).

[57] *CSP, Foreign (1582)*, Letter from Le Brumen to Walsingham (14 June 1582).

[58] Saltpetre was the main ingredient used to make gunpowder.

[59] *CSP, Foreign (1583)*, Letter from Le Brumen to Walsingham (29 January 1583). This is probably Joachim Gaunz (of Prague), translator of a work on metallurgy by Lazarus Erker. Gaunze actually did obtain the privilege to make saltpetre in London. Cf. (Cecil Papers 276.5 Hatfield House), in D. B. Quinn, *Roanoke Voyages I* (1955).

[60] *CSP, Foreign (1579-1580)*, Letter from Jacques de Somere to Davison, (3 July 1579).

[61] Jacques de Somere states that Le Brumen has "a delicate judgement in public affairs. He knows all that goes on here and can talk at length to you on the likehood of peace or war, and the result of one or the other; also about the position of Maestricht... ." Cf. *CSP, Foreign (1579-1580)*, Letter from Jacques de Somere to Davison, (3 July 1579).

[62] *CSP, Domestic, (1581-90)*, p. 383. Letter from Le Brumen to Walsingham (28 January 1587).

[63] It is not impossible that the French authorities were aware of his activities in France at this time. Cf. "lettre de l'agent anglais Geffrey (G. Le Brumen) à M. de Walsingham," in *LCM*, vol. 8, (18 avril 1583).

[64] The French embassy in London for instance, was constantly watched by the men of Walsingham and Burghley. Castelnau de La Mauvissière gives a good idea of this kind of situation in November 1577 in a letter to the King of France. Cf. BN *CCC* N° 337 (20 November 1577).

[65] *CSP, Foreign (1579-1580)*, pp. 1-2, note 3 (3 July 1579).

[66] *CSP, Foreign (1582)*, p. 333, N° 342 (17 September 1582).

[67] *Cecil Manuscripts Hatfield House*, part 3, p. 267 (30 June 1587).

[68] C. Read, *op. cit.*, vol. 2, pp. 34-35, note 5, and vol. I, pp. 281 and 286. Michel de La Huguerye was, however, right about the activities of Le Brumen, which he emphasizes in his memoirs: "[...] ledit Sr Wolsinghant nous feist advertir par maistre Geoffroy, chirurgien françoys [...] Maistre Geoffroy, qui le gouvernoit, en obtint ung [passport] par le moyen du Sr Pasquier, qui estoit secrétaire du roy en la charge dudit Sr de Mauvissière, soubz le nom de deux marchandz allans à Paris." Cf. *MMH* vol. II, p. 36.

[69] Alison Plowden, *The Elizabethan Secret Service*, Harvester Wheatsheat, St-Martin's Press, 1991.

[70] Alan Haynes, *The Invisible Power, the Elizabethan Secret Service*, London, Alan Sutton, 1992.

[71] De Lamar Jensen, *Diplomacy and Dogmatism*, Cambridge, Harvard University Press, 1964.

[72] They all seem to have come up against the problem of the documents sent to Walsingham, only written in French by Le Brumen.

[73] This widespread remedy in the 16th century was contested, however; among other things, its price rendered it available to the wealthy only.

[74] Cf. "The doing of capt Frobisher (may 1579)" in PRO, *SP12-131* N° 20.

[75] This man may be John, Godfrey, Thomas or Nicolas Wheler, who came from Germany to England in the 1550s and 1560s and whose names are mentioned in the acts of naturalization. Cf. W. Page, *Letters of Denization and acts of Naturalization for Aliens in England 1509-1603*, Lymington, The Huguenot Society Publication, 1893, vol. 8.

[76] Cf. J. McDermott, *Michael Lok, Mercer and Merchant Adventurer*, in this volume. In 1571, Giovanni-Baptista Agnello was living in Saint Christine parishe of London. Cf. Aliens Return, PRO, *SP12-82* (November 1571).

[77] Richard Collinson, *The Three Voyages of Martin Frobisher...*, New-York, Burt Franklin, 1867, p. 97.

[78] *PRO*, SP12-122-17, (24 January 1578[NS]). Its existence was mentionned in *CSP, Colonial (1513-1616)*, (24 January 1578) and in *CSP, Domestic*, (24 January 1578).

[79] R. Collinson, *op. cit.*, pp. 172-173.

[80] Markaschâtsâ means rock, Cf. R. Metz, *Visage des minéraux et des pierres précieuses*, Paris, Museum d'Histoire Naturelle, 1978 (1964), p. 92.

[81] Jewelers today still sell jewels called marcasite which are actually made of pyrite crystals. Most specialists tend to restrict the term marcasite to a whiter kind of iron sulfide whose crystals grow in a radial orientation but which contain the same chemical substance as pyrite (FeS_2). Cf. P. Bariand & J. P. Poirot, *Larousse des pierres précieuses fines ornementales organiques*, Paris, Larousse, 1985; Tardy & Dina Level, *Les pierres précieuses...* Paris, (5th ed.), 1980, p. 315.

[82] Marcasite is one of three species of mineral commonly called "fool's gold."

[83] Magnets were part of the basic tools of most goldsmiths and refiners and could be used to identify imitation jewels made out of iron and covered with gold or silver. See for example the inclusion of a magnet in the inventory of a 16th century gold and silver refiner: *AN*, notary Nyan, XXIII-204 (7 January 1561).

[84] D. D. Hogarth, P. W. Boreham and J. G. Mitchell, *Martin Frobisher's Northwest Venture 1576-1581: Mines, Minerals Metallurgy*, Hull, Canadian Museum of Civilization, 1994, chapters 3 to 5.

[85] See for example the XVIth century specialist Georg Agricola who did not make a clear distinction between pyrite, flintstone, and iron ore. Cf. "Georg Agricola: Bermanus" in Wolfgang Paul, *Mining lore; an illustrated composition and documentary compilation[...]*, Morris, Portland [Oregon], 1970, pp. 229-311.

[86] Such as the instrument maker, Humphrey Cole, whose short biography can be found in E. G. R. Taylor, *The Mathematical Practitioners of Tudor & Stuart England*, Cambridge, Cambridge University Press, 1954. I would like to thank Lt. Cdr. D. W. Waters for this information.

[87] For instance, George Woolfe, who took part in the assays performed after the second voyage, is mentioned in "A little bundle of the tryeing of ye Northwest ewre..." Cf. *CSP, Domestic* (vol. cxxii, N° 62), published in R. Collinson, *op. cit.*, p. 176.

The Medical Record of the Frobisher Voyages of 1576, 1577 and 1578

Sir James Watt

Clinical details of the Frobisher voyages are sparse. There are no extant medical journals and no observations attributed to their surgeons have been reported. The medical record has therefore to be constructed from allusions to medically-related incidents in the logs or journals of other participants. That is not to suggest that any medical assessment must be considered unreliable, for it is possible to arrive at a reasonably coherent account of accidents, sickness and mortality by co-ordinating the various reports of perceptive and dependable witnesses. It is only in the third voyage that we are confronted by imponderables, because of the atrocious weather conditions which scattered the large fleet and prevented any one journalist from obtaining an overall picture of a confused and constantly changing situation. Even George Best, captain of the *Anne Francis* during that voyage, who appears to have drawn heavily upon the memories of others for his accounts of all three voyages, was able only to offer a very rough approximation of the total number of deaths believed to have occurred.

Mortality and morbidity, however, are but one facet of the medical record and cannot be considered in isolation, nor can they be judged as adequate criteria for comparison with other voyages in similar conditions. Health statistics are obviously affected by the training, skills and experience of the surgeons and also by the quality of their instruments and medicines. But mortality and morbidity are influenced even more by the nutrition and natural immunity of the individual which, in part, are attributable to the nature and condition of his victuals and whether they provide enough calories and accessory food factors to meet the demands of his workload and environmental conditions in terms of energy expenditure. This, in turn, is affected by the nature of the task and the efficiency of his tools. Such factors as living conditions, cooking, clothing, hours of sleep and psychological stress are equally important components in the equation which determines surrender or survival. Before meaningful conclusions can be reached, the influence of each factor upon the health record of the voyages needs to be examined.

Medical Personnel

While the names of the surgeons in all three voyages are known and their seniority can be deduced from their wages, only two can be positively identified. They are John Paradice, senior surgeon of the third fleet, who sailed in the *Judith* and William Beton, also of that fleet, who sailed in the *Thomas of Ipswich*, a commissioned ship. References to John Paradice appear several times in the Court Minute Books of the Barber-Surgeons Company of London and he appears to have been an active member, prepared to accept the discipline of the Company. He was admitted to the freedom on completion of his apprenticeship, on 11 November 1571 and licensed to open his shop in April 1573. He had been apprenticed to a Thomas Pratt who died about this time, and Paradice appears to have taken over his practice under an arrangement with his widow by which she would benefit from a proportion of his fees. She appears to have believed that she was receiving inadequate information about the number of cases he was treating and appealed to the Master to arbitrate. This he declined to do, but made an arrangement which seems to have satisfied her. The matter may not be unconnected with a complaint made by Paradice himself against a colleague, Henry Lusche, "for that he said Henry Lushe called the said John Parradize knave, and he p[d] his fyne xijd and they toke hands and were ffrends."

Then, on 2 October 1576, there was a complaint against Paradice by the father of a girl who had died while under his care, the plaintiff asking for the return of a gown he had given to Paradice in lieu of a fee. The Court decided that Paradice would return the gown but the father of the girl would have to pay for the hire of the boat used by Paradice to take him to Putney. While on the face of things it might appear that Paradice was a troublesome fellow, it is nevertheless noteworthy that the Master and Court thought highly enough of him to find in his favour and never criticised his practice or judgement. He does not appear in the Minute books after 1577 when he contributed to a tax levied on the Company by the Lord Mayor for the equipment of soldiers.[1]

William Beton, or Bedon, was an altogether different figure. He was one of the small circle of experienced surgeons seeking to promote recent advances and was a close friend of William Clowes who used one of his remedies. They were both on the staff of St. Bartholomew's Hospital in London and its journals and ledger for the period frequently record bonuses paid to Beton for good work. He was an assistant-surgeon in 1567 when, on 28 June, he was awarded an extra 40 shillings "in consideration of his pains." In 1569, he became a full surgeon and in 1572 was granted, "10s for his pains in healing the leg of a poor man outside the hospital." He retired from full-time work in 1575, but remained actively associated with the hospital until his death in 1581. In consideration of his contribution to the hospital, it leased to him a house in Duck Lane for 43s.4d. a year. The only complaint recorded against him is that he failed to cure a bubo and his answer to the charge reveals his professional philosophy, for he was prepared to undertake the treatment only "yf he will be ruled by him."[2] Like his modern counterparts, the idea of a sea voyage in the early years of his retirement had obvious appeal.

The surgeon of the first voyage, Phillipe Bocket, was hired on 8 June 1576, apparently at Blackwall on the Thames and was accommodated in the *Gabriel*. His name has usually been given its English equivalent, Philip Becket, but that may be a mistake, for, at that time, ships were manned by cosmopolitan crews, many of whom were French Huguenots and Huguenot doctors were active in England. It is therefore quite likely that he was French.[3] Edward Cooley in the *Ayde* was paid 50 shillings a month as senior surgeon of the second voyage and he had to assist him, Anthony Thompson, described as "surgeon's boy" who was paid 10s. a month. John Netherclifte was in *Gabriel*, paid 30s. a month, and William Edwardes in the *Michael*, 25s. a month.[4]

The medical manning of the third voyage raises a number of questions. Paradice, the senior surgeon was borne in the *Judith* and served under Fenton for 50 shillings a month, while Frobisher in the *Ayde* carried the most junior, John Harwood, paid 36s. a month, who may well have been recruited at Bristol, where his chest was purchased for £5.8s.0d. Moreover, he is described as "sailor and surgeon" which suggests that he may not have completed a formal training and was unlicensed. Indeed, a search of the Bristol burgess and apprentice indexes has failed to identify anyone of that name, and the Bristol City general names index is equally unhelpful.

The second surgeon, Robert Hind, paid 45s. a month, was in the small *Michael*. William Beton, the only distinguished surgeon in any of the voyages, was in a commissioned ship, the *Thomas of Ipswich*,[5] one of the larger vessels [130 tons], and was perhaps engaged as surgeon for all the commissioned ships. Alternatively, he may have acted as a surgical consultant in medical matters for the whole fleet, and Frobisher's orders in matters of hygiene and sanitation suggest he was conversant with current medical thinking. Beton would therefore have been housed in more comfortable quarters than the Company's ships could offer, as befitted his status.

It does not explain, however, why the *Ayde* had the most inexperienced surgeon unless it implies that Frobisher had had differences of opinion with his surgeons on previous voyages and had his own ideas about medical matters. If so, he would not have been alone, for captains often took medical decisions themselves well into the nineteenth century. Surgeons would usually have had the assistance of a surgeon's boy, whether specifically designated as such or listed as a seaman and giving part of this time to surgical duties.

English sixteenth-century medical records are inadequate and incomplete, the chief sources being the minute books of the Barber-Surgeons Companies of London, Bristol, Norwich, York and Newcastle, Munk's Roll of the Royal College of Physicians and the archives of St. Bartholomew's and St. Thomas's Hospitals. Episcopal licensing of doctors and surgeons and Bishops' licences in the Diocese of London occasionally provide information, but by the end of the Tudor period, most practitioners were satisfied with the qualifications of their examining body and saw little value in an ecclesiastical sanction requiring a further examination. Testamentary records, however, are invaluable if they can be found, since they sometimes list the chests, instruments and libraries of surgeons to provide a far more accurate picture of the character and practice of a particular individual than entries in minute books, while marriage licences and church memorials provide additional information.

Little further knowledge has been gleaned from such sources, but a William Edwardes was buried at St. Botolphe, Billingsgate in January 1593;[6] a John Harwood at St. Martin's Ludgate in March 1611;[7] and a Robert Hynde at St. Botolph, Aldgate in September 1604.[8] All were London parishes. The names are spelt in various ways in different entries and simply reflect the clerk's interpretation of their phonetic character.

Other medical men were associated with the voyages. William Crowe, who was paid five pounds for the autopsy on the Inuit [Eskimo] man and for embalming him after the first voyage, was an eminent member of the Barber-Surgeons' Company and became Master in 1585.[9] He was a close friend of Clowes and Banester, prominent activists within the Protestant medical network. John Gymblet, who was paid five shillings for his care of the Inuit child who died in London after the second voyage,[10] was an active member of the Barber-Surgeons' Company and probably served on the Court of Assistants. "A chest full of surgery wares" was bought from a surgeon, Arnold Langly, for £2.13.4. Since we know that Hugh Morgan supplied the chest of drugs, this must have been a case of surgical instruments bought from a surgeon who had perhaps retired. An Arnold Lanygam, or Langham, probably the same man, was buried at St. Botolph, Aldgate in October 1593,[11] and there was an interesting eighteenth-century memorial to Dr. James Jurin in the church of St. James, Garlikhythe which mentions two generations of Arnold Langleys, possibly indicating a continuing medical tradition.[12]

Of the physicians, Dr. Edward Dodding provided a report in Latin of the illness and death at Bristol of the Inuk brought back from the second voyage, which he attributed to pneumonia.[13] He was a Fellow of Trinity College, Cambridge and only gained his M.D. in 1576 before practising in Bristol. He subsequently moved to London and was buried at St. Dunstan's in the West in April 1592.[14] Burchard Kranich, whose role in the Frobisher voyages was that of metallurgist and assayer, was nevertheless a conspicuous court physician and, as Dr. Burcot, may have exerted considerable medical influence.

Finally, there was Dr. William Gilbert, the most distinguished of the Elizabethan physicians, who was paid five shillings "for fyssyke for Jonas" [Schütz], the assayer.[15] His scientific interests, particularly in the field of magnetism, brought him into close touch with personalities like Francis Bacon: he was consulted by the Navy Board on both medical and scientific matters, became Physician to Queen Elizabeth and, in 1600, President of the College of Physicians.[16]

Apothecaries' Supplies and "Necessaries" for the Sick

Instruments carried by surgeons in their various boxes and chests have already been described and a detailed list of medicaments purchased from the apothecary, Hugh Morgan, can be found in the account books of Michael Lok for the first voyage; Edward Elmore supplied the surgeon's "necessaries" to supplement the diet of the sick. Morgan supplied — in his own words — "Ambra grisi oriental, cibetta, rhubarb, agarisi, turpenti, ddiagridii calam aromatici, arios, galanga, mirrha-fine, mastichis, araenti vita, laddiri, aumine gomme, opponopax, oppin, alloes-fine, bellzona, styrax calum, myrobboralia chebug bellerichi ana, Indiorum citrini, ledoria, spica nardi, cardomonii, ligni Rhodi, coloehutis, margarite, boli oriental, lapis lazuli, cantalii citem, corallina, coralli rubri, borax, camphera, castorium." For these, he was paid £4.13.8d.[17]

Ambra grisi [*Ambra grisea*] was a wax-like substance from the sperm whale's intestine found floating in the Indian ocean, as distinct from amber, a fossilised resin from which a volatile oil was extracted. Both were used in medicine as stimulants, and Monardes mentions it as a New World component of ointments and plasters. He also emphasises the importance of balsam [balm] consisting of various resins which "heals wounds without suppuration and joins their lips together."[18]

Several resins and gums appear on the list — *turpentine*, *myrrh*, *mastic*, "aumine gomme" [probably *Gum animé*, so named because of the number of insects entrapped within it], *Oponopax*, *Styrax calemita*, "*Ledoria*" from Cyprian resinous shrubs and the resinous juice of *Rhodes wood* or candlewood, a West Indian tree.

"Bellezona" was probably *Benzorium* or *Belzoe*, a refined gum from the East Indies of two varieties, mild and strong. It was taken internally for lung complaints and applied externally to wounds threatening gangrene, where fragrant *Spica Nardi* [Spikenard] was a welcome additive. External applications often included *camphor*, used in cooling lotions, for instance, in burns, and *borax* was used as a powder for skin complaints or in surgical plasters. "Diagridii" probably refers to *diaglaucium*, an eye lotion or collyrium which contained the juice of the herb *glaucium*.[19]

Arios or *Irios* was used for its anodyne properties in painful wounds and Banester added *Gallanga* to his wound lotions.[20] It was extracted from the root of that name which came from the East Indies and was dissolved in vinegar or wine. Dioscorides had commended the virtues of coral, and since his reputation was at its height among apothecaries in the mid-sixteenth century, it is no surprise to find both *red coral* and *coralline* on the list. There is no evidence, however, that contemporary surgeons made much use of it, and this seems to suggest that Morgan compiled the list himself, perhaps after discussion with apothecary colleagues or from his own experience of what surgeons normally requested.

Other preparations were for internal use to treat common medical problems, apart from "Araenti vita" which was probably some clerk's attempt at *Argentum vivum* — quicksilver or mercury. It was made into an ointment for external massage in patients with venereal disease. "Oppin" was probably *Opion* or opium, used prior to operations and in severe dysenteries or "fluxes." Then there was a group of laxatives of varying strengths. "Coloehuthis" was probably a copying error for *Colocynthus*, the most violent purgative, while "Myrobboralia chebug" was *Myrobalani chebuli*, a mild laxative, rather like *rhubarb* which was also included. *Aloes* was a stronger purgative and was sometimes used in wounds to assist healing while *Boli orientali* were given to arrest diarrhoea. *Calam aromaticus* was a bitter antidote for bites and poisons and was a constituent of *theriac* with its numerous ingredients. "Ladderi," probably *Ladanum*, was a resinous juice from a shrub, the *lada*, and was probably an expectorant for those with coughs and colds.

Several of the "surgical" resins, like *Belzoe* were also administered as internal remedies in such cases. For other minor complaints like flatulence and dyspepsia, there was *Cardomom* and "Indiorum citrini" or *Cyperus*, an aromatic tropical plant. *Castorum* came from the anal glands of the beaver which provide the animal with a powerful defensive odour and "Cibetta" was probably "Civetta" or musk from the civet. Both helped to disguise the odour from septic wounds or gangrenous members. It is difficult to understand how *Margarite* [pearl] and Lapis lazuli found their way into a sea surgeon's chest, since they usually appeared only in prescriptions for the wealthy unless they had been included in some previous prescription for Frobisher or Kinderslley. "Cantalii citem" has not been identified.[21]

In addition to drugs, apothecaries or grocers also supplied "necessaries" or comforts for the sick. The list supplied by Edward Elmore for the first voyage is similar to that for the second, but there is no information on this item for the third. The various ingredients were probably used by the cook to provide more readily digestible foods, and highly flavoured to stimulate the appetite. They would have included puddings and pies. Cloves, mace, nutmegs, ginger, cinnamon, raisins, currants, dates and almonds were therefore provided and also grains [of mustard]. Alum, an aluminium and potassium double sulphate, was used as an astringent and styptic in granulating wounds. Cotton wool also appears on this list, together with a number of dyes, coperas, "gaules" [galls], cochineal and "Annea Crasea Indico." They may have been used to colour medicines, but some were considered to have medicinal properties.

Copperas or green vitriol, was a sulphate of iron, which had been used on wounds from antiquity. Iron was believed to be antiseptic and some metal sulphates are. Galls, excrescences on the leaves and bark of certain trees, usually the oak, caused by the eggs of insects, were used to produce ink and were probably provided for that purpose. However, Galen used ink in wounds and it had been Greek practice to delineate fractures of the skull with ink,[22] although indigo might have been used by Elizabethan surgeons for that purpose. *Indigofera* is one of the Indian and East Indian leguminous plants which produce the dye, and Elmore's description suggests it was a particular variety, the *Indigofera anil*, which was grown in India itself. Soap, expensive in those days, was obviously considered an essential in the sick bay.

One particular item supplied by Elmore deserves special mention. That is licorice which, only in comparatively recent years, has been found useful in treating gastritis and gastric ulcers from which seamen might have been expected to suffer. The carbenoxolone it contains reduces inflammation of the stomach. It was also taken as a linctus for chest complaints.

Large quantities of two other provisions of medical relevance appear on the general victualling list of the second voyage. Honey was used, not only as a sweetener, but also in wound balms and has a marked antibacterial effect derived from an enzyme, inhibine, secreted by the bee's pharyngeal glands.[23]

The ships were also provided with no less than one hogshead [54 gallons, if an ale and beer measure, and even more if a wine hogshead] of "sallet oil." This seems to have been one of the earliest attempts to prevent scurvy at sea. Turner refers to it in his herbal of 1551, where it is described as "the oil crushed out of those green herbs that most usually constituted a salad" and possibly augmented with other oils and preservatives.[24]

Diet, Victualling and Food Values

It is therefore evident that considerable thought had been given to health requirements and this appears to be reflected in the victualling arrangements. Unfortunately, while the nature and cost of victuals is recorded for all three voyages, the precise allowance per man per day is only provided for 115 men on the second voyage. Any attempt to deduce allowances for the first and third voyages requires unjustifiable assumptions, but the daily rate per man for the second voyage can be assumed to have been the standard, particularly since it follows closely the prevailing rate in the navy which has been considered already. While the routine of four meat days and three fish days a week was the same, quantities of some foods varied. Only 1lb of meat or pork was allowed as compared with 2lbs in the navy, while the Frobisher mariner was allowed double the amounts of butter and cheese on fish days.[25] [Table 1]

	Sunday	Monday	Tuesday	Wednesday	Thursday	Friday	Saturday
Beer [gallons]	1	1	1	1	1	1	1
Biscuit [lbs]	1	1	1	1	1	1	1
Salt Beef or Pork	1	1	1	-	1	-	-
Stockfish [portions]	-	-	-	$1/4$	-	$1/4$	$1/4$
Butter [lbs]	-	-	-	$1/4$	-	$1/4$	$1/4$
Cheese [lbs]	-	-	-	$1/2$	-	$1/2$	$1/2$
Peas [oz]	8.8	8.8	8.8	-	8.8	-	-

Table 1 : The weekly allowance per man on the second voyage

Peas were supplied by the bushel, a dry measure amounting to 32 dry quarts, and 1 quart was to be divided among four men on each meat day, an allowance of 1/2 pint per man. In terms of dried peas, this would be equivalent to approximately 8.8oz. After boiling, peas would double in weight and lose much of their food value, but it seems clear that the allowance was for unboiled peas.

The most variable item of diet was fish which might be salted cod or ling or haberdine [sun-dried cod].[26] Wheeler, working on fish remains in late medieval Kings Lynn, found both inshore fish, which were smaller, and large deep sea cod. Since weight bears a logarithmic relationship to length, he was able to estimate the weights of gutted cod of varying lengths.[27]

The navy was supplied with the larger Newfoundland cod, which would have been gutted before salting or drying, so it seems reasonable to accept his weight of 6-20kg for large fish. Taking an average of 13kg and allowing for nearly 50% wastage during the salting or drying process, something like 7kg would be available for four men, *ie*, 1.75kg or

3.86lbs per man on fish days. A further problem arises in estimating the beer allowance, since Elizabethan ale gallon measures varied slightly, some being of greater capacity than others.[28] In view of the ever-present possibility of leakage, this is probably not significant.

It will therefore be evident that any attempt to arrive at the energy value of the diet can only be approximate but, provided assumptions are realistic, a reasonable estimation of the calorie and vitamin content of the mariner's food can be made. [Table 2] Calculations have been based upon the Special Report of the Medical Research Council on the Composition of Foods [McCance and Widdowson, 1960],[29] since later tables reflect the very different constituents of modern foods.

| Victual | Allowance | Composition in grams per ounce | | | K.cals per oz |
		Protein	Fat	Carbohydrate (available monosaccharides)	
Biscuit	16oz	1.70	2.40	23.2	116.0
Beer	1 gallon (128.4oz)	0.05	Trace	0.46	7.0
Beef	16oz	7.50	6.00	0.00	86.7
Pork (as alternative to beef)	16oz	6.40	7.50	0.00	96.0
Peas	1/2 pint [8.82oz]	2.00	Trace	5.40	28.0
Stockfish (gutted)	1/4 cod (61.76oz)	9.10	0.30	0.00	40.0
Butter	4oz	0.10	24.20	Trace	226.0
Cheese					
Cheddar	8oz	7.2	9.80	Trace	120.0
Dutch		6.9	6.50	Trace	88.0 (mean 104)
Additional to allowance for sick or in lieu of deficiencies or for occasional use					
Rice		0.60	0.10	8.40	35.0
Oatmeal (as porridge)		0.40	0.30	2.30	13.00
Bread (coarse brown flour)	In lieu of biscuit	2.50	0.60	14.20	68.00
Honey		0.10	Trace	21.70	82.00
Milk		0.90	1.10	1.40	19.00
Eggs		3.40	3.50	Trace	46.00
Duck & fowl caught locally		6.50	6.70	0.00	89.00
Sick Comforts					
Aquavite		—	—	Trace	63.0
Prunes (raw)		0.30	Trace	4.80	19.0
Raisins (dried)		0.30	Trace	18.30	70.0
Almonds		5.80	15.20	1.20	170.0
Licorice		1.10	0.60	21.00	90.0

Table 2: Composition in grams per ounce and energy value in k.calories per ounce of standard victuals, substitute foods, occasional extras and sick comforts during the second voyage

While an attempt could be made to establish the approximate vitamin content of the various foods, it would prove a pointless exercise because assumptions even have to be made by experienced researchers working with well controlled groups. The type and length of cooking seriously affects the vitamin content and we know that fresh bread, fresh beef and other foods were supplied while ships were fitting out,[30] while supplements were taken in at ports of call such as Plymouth, Harwich, the Shetlands and Orkneys. Best, in his account of the second voyage, states that some victuals were acquired at Harwich and that fresh poultry, eggs and fish were bought from the Orkney islanders. Since he also comments on their milk and oatcakes it is probable that they purchased these too.[31] It is clear that the basic ration was intended to be supplemented by fresh foods, for lines and nets were supplied.[32]

Fishing was actively pursued near the coast of Greenland where halibut were caught, and in his account of the first voyage, Best tells us that the Inuit brought Frobisher salmon, and other types of fish and fresh meat.[33] There are references to wild life available for food such as fowl, bears, hares and deer, and Best again enlightens us about dietary supplements when he mentions killing seals and animals on the third voyage.[34]

Both Settle[35] and Best[36] observed that the Inuit ate greens as well as raw meat and fish and this would have contributed to their freedom from scurvy. In fact, Frobisher, ever health-conscious, brought back a sample from the first voyage[37] and perhaps had already appreciated the importance of cresses and other greens in keeping men healthy. That this was so, is suggested by the large quantities of "sallet oil" he carried which would certainly have been antiscorbutic.[38]

Without, however, any idea of the amount and character of dietary supplements, we are in no position to consider whether dietary accessory food factors were adequate, for the basic allowance provided no vitamin C, and minimal, but probably sufficient amounts of the B complex of vitamins, and vitamins A and D from butter and cheese. We are on firmer ground with its caloric value, bearing in mind that it was, or at least could have been, augmented by local meat, fish and fowl [Table 3].

Table 3 seems to represent what was intended, but there are some ambiguities. An allowance of meal [flour] was included — 30 tons for 13 months of 28 days, or 364 victualling days, providing 1.6lbs per man per day. It has usually been considered that flour was carried for the purpose of baking more biscuit or baking loaves after the biscuit was expended, since biscuit was easily spoiled by weevils and maggots which, apart from their revolting appearance, destroyed any food value the biscuit might have had. However, flour may have been carried, as it often was, to make pies and puddings, so that a proportion of this must be added to the daily allowance; for instance, 16ozs per man per day would provide an extra 1520 calories.

Nor is there any instruction about the use of beef and pork, but it seems that pork, which kept better than beef, was meant to be used after the beef had been expended, since peas, which were only issued on meat days, were provided for 18 months, the total period of beef and pork days combined. It will be noted that pork yields rather more calories than beef. Nevertheless, Elizabethan naval victualling allowed two pounds of meat a day per man and it was issued in 2lb pieces.[39] Pork only became a regular issue in 1596.[40] After that, according to Fuller, there were two beef days and two pork days a week.[41]

Victual	Calorie value per man per week [weight in ozs x calorie value x days served]	Total K.calories
Biscuit	16.00 x 116.0 x 7	12992
Beer	128.4 x 7.0 x 7	6292
Beef	16.0 x 86.7 x 4	5549
Peas [after boiling]	8.82 x 28.0 x 4	988
Stockfish [gutted]	61.7 x 40.0 x 3	7404
Butter	4.0 x 226.0 x 3	2712
Cheese	8.0 x 104.0 x 3	2496
		38433
	Average daily intake per man per day 5490 K.calories	
[Pork as alternative to beef	16.00 x 96.0 x 4	6144]

Table 3 : Average weekly and daily calorie equivalent of basic victuals during the second voyage

Suffolk or Cheshire cheeses were usually provided, the latter being a little more expensive, but Essex and Dutch cheese was also bought.[42] A further ambiguity lies in the extent to which wine was used. It was certainly given to the sick in lieu of beer and, as McDermott suggests, may have been carried in case beer deteriorated; but even in the third voyage, it is the lack of beer which is bemoaned, and wine is not mentioned. Although 5 tons of wine were carried in the first voyage, 4 tons remained unused which does not suggest it was issued to ordinary seamen.[43] An average nutritional value has been used in Tables 2 and 3.

Damage, leakage or corruption of victuals was common on long voyages and an allowance was made for this, though provisions obviously kept better on Arctic voyages. Nevertheless, when all these variables have been taken into account, the basic allowance per man for the second voyage appears to offer an acceptable formula for calculating energy values. This works out to approximately 5490 calories per man per day — 6085 when pork was used, and an additional 1520 if 16ozs of flour were added; this provided a total calorie intake of 7010 per man per day, or 7605 calories if eating pork rather than beef, quite apart from calories supplied by occasional food supplements. These figures of course imply that the food was in prime condition, and there are reports, particularly in the third voyage, that food was damaged or rotten and often, on that voyage, inaccessible. As a working basis, it might therefore be better to ignore the contribution of supplementary supplies. In any case, a calorie intake of anything between 5490 and 7605 calories is far in excess of what is customarily considered necessary for men doing the hardest manual labour in an adverse environment.

Energy Expenditure : Workload and Environmental Conditions

The energy value of the sledging rations carried by Scott and Amundsen in their assault upon the South Pole in 1911 was 5100 and 5000 K.calories respectively.[44] It might appear, therefore, that Frobisher's men had ample reserves. However, Amundsen survived and Scott perished, because Amundsen expended considerably less energy than Scott, whose food and fuel resources proved inadequate for the techniques he employed. Moreover, members of the Trans-Antarctic Expedition of 1957-8, driving Sno-cats and wearing modern protective clothing, lost weight on a basic diet of over 5000 K.calories which rose to 7000 when peak performance was required.[45] The adequacy of the diet in Arctic and Antarctic regions is related to energy expenditure in terms, not simply of effort, but of the individual's physiological response to the conditions in which the effort is made, while the vitamin content is critical. Amundsen's party received enough vitamin C from the dogs they ate. Scott's calorie-deficient men perished from scurvy.

McDermott has painted a vivid picture of the physical, climatic and psychological stress experienced by men of Frobisher's third voyage who, under the relentless pressure of determined officers and the exhortations of a dedicated minister, were driven beyond the limits of human endurance in their efforts to avoid being crushed by ice during attempts to enter Frobisher Bay. The sheer physical exhaustion of towing ships with small boats, reinforcing the ships' sides with whatever heavy equipment happened to be available, fending off icebergs with poles and oars, and often jumping from floe to floe, in gale force winds with snowstorms which soaked them to the skin, made overwhelming demands on their metabolism.[46]

Only the foresight of the organisers of the voyage in providing abundant warm clothing and the insistence of captains that men should keep dry with the assistance, no doubt, of the cookhouse fire in the hold, averted a major human disaster. Best reported that sailors needed five or six shifts of clothing and even then "hadde scarce one drie threade to his backe," and he added, "which kinde of wette and coldnesse, together with the over labouring of the poore menne amiddst the ise, bread no small sicknesse amongst the fleete."[47]

Despite Herculean efforts, ships were holed by ice. Men in the *Ayde* and *Anne Francis* were obliged to spend desperate hours working the pumps[48] while emergency measures were taken to stop the leaks, and the bark *Dennis* sank after one such incident within half an hour.[49] Although all were rescued by the ship's boats of the *Beare Leicester*, some would undoubtedly have suffered the medical sequelæ of sudden immersion in icy waters.

There were also unexpected hazards. Ropes froze every night, cutting men's hands while handling them.[50] Such injuries are slow to heal, readily become infected and even lead to the loss of fingers owing to reduced peripheral circulation in sub-zero temperatures. A further factor is that excessive labour in the Arctic causes clothing impregnated with perspiration to freeze, thus adding to its weight and increasing the effort required to perform the same task.[51]

It was too much for some. The *Thomas of Ipswich* gave up the struggle and returned to England, taking with her much needed beer and other victuals. The ship's company of the *Anne Francis* became so desperate that they even contemplated constructing rafts to be towed ashore by the ship's boat, until they realised that they could never survive in the Arctic climate by living off the land,[52] while only the powerful exhortation of Master Woolfall "a good godly precher" rallied the men of the *Judith* when all seemed lost.[53]

Such then were the vicissitudes and psychological terrors of the voyage, yet no sooner were the ships anchored at last in safety, than men were immediately employed in mining ore from rocky, frozen and unyielding ground. They used the heaviest of implements — crowbars weighing 30lbs, for instance, with sledges laden with heavy ore,[54] to be dragged across the unforgiving ground of the "Countess of Warwick's [Kodlunarn] Island to ships" boats engaged in the constant traffic of loading, rowing and unloading into the ships. This ceaseless activity continued for over a month before the ships were ready to depart, having loaded almost 1200 tons of ore, though deprived of the miners borne in the *Thomas of Ipswich* and, for a time, those in other ships, which only arrived later.

Frobisher's determination, however, to use spare capacity in the *Emanuel of Bridgwater* to amass the maximum quantity, led to a fatal delay and caused the fleet to be tossed about and scattered by a sudden, violent tempest which, says Best, led to widespread devastation, with "some men stricken overboorde into the sea, and utterly lost. Many lost yards and masts and ropes parted because [they] had become rotten through freezing."[55] The storm prevented the large mining party on the island from rejoining their respective ships and left the two small overcrowded, undervictualled barks and the *Judith* to face a stormy Atlantic crossing with men deteriorating in health without adequate food.

The third voyage therefore matched the endurance of all subsequent Arctic explorers, far better equipped and provisioned. It must have been a harrowing experience, in contrast to the first voyage where relatively benign conditions instilled wonder rather than fear, though even in that voyage, the defection of the *Michael* and the loss of five men and the only boat, taken by the Inuit, curtailed exploration.

The second voyage, however, despite its low mortality, had also experienced problems from the rigours of the Arctic climate, for mining had had to be aborted when, despite the high spirits with which it was undertaken, "shoes and clothes were well worne, their baskets bottoms torne out, their tooles broken" and some men "with over-straining themselves received hurtes not a little dangerous, some having their bellies broken and others their legges made lame."[56]

Nevertheless, the fitness of the seamen during that voyage is illustrated by the way they repaired the rudder of the *Ayde*, which split during a storm. In the words of Best, he "flung halfe a dosen couple of our best men overboorde, who taking great paines vnder water, driving planks and binding with ropes, did wel strengthen and ment the matter, who returned the most parte more than halfe deade out of the water, and as God's pleasure was, the Sea was calme vntill the worke was finished."[57] It is amazing that none of the twelve died, for sudden immersion in ice-cold water may cause immediate death, or cause disordered rhythm and changes in the blood-clotting mechanism which may have long-term consequences.

Johnson has pointed out that overwork and exhaustion were common in nineteenth-century polar expeditions where man-hauling was a feature, because it caused conductive heat loss and, in exposure to snow and ice, the body can radiate energy at a dangerous rate, particularly at night, when there is no sun to provide energy.[58] When wind chill is a factor, body cooling is rapid and can quickly lead to death. To survive in the Arctic, food must be of sufficient quantity and quality for the task, physical work within the individual's capacity, transport efficient and housing adequate to protect against cold and wind chills.[59]

Several of these criteria were not met during the 1578 voyage, especially in regard to workload, but it is clear that Frobisher and Fenton were well aware of the need to protect their men against the elements by providing abundant warm clothing and adequate shelter. One reason for abandoning the idea of a colony was that a robust enough house could not be built in the time available, while the inadequacy of tents to house the miners was recognised; a cave was found to afford adequate protection, but had to be abandoned when it proved to be damp.[60] Nevertheless, reports of the concluding phase of each of the voyages, particularly the third, suggests an energy imbalance with output exceeding intake.

The Medical Record

In attempting to compile the medical record of the voyages, we are immediately confronted by a dilemma — the conflicting reports of the numbers carried in each expedition. It is not merely an academic exercise, because medical effectiveness can best be judged by the proportion of fit men available to accomplish the task on which the success of the mission depends and by the proportionate mortality. Hogarth has made a praiseworthy attempt to assess the numbers carried on each voyage by identifying personnel from pay lists.[61] While reasonably accurate for the first two voyages, this approach resulted in a significant shortfall for the third voyage which was large by contemporary standards — 15 ships in all.

From publications and manuscripts, Hogarth later compiled a list of minimum numbers in the Cathay Company's ships, in the ships commissioned by the Company and in the unauthorised ships which Frobisher had acquired to increase the ore-carrying capacity of the third voyage after exploration had been abandoned in favour of mining and, no doubt, with an eye to personal profit.[62]

McDermott, working from official statistics for authorised ships only, in the account book of Michael Lok (who was responsible for the organisation of the voyages and therefore likely to be the most accurate) listed both the number of men carried in these ships [451] and the number appointed by the Commissioners [278].[63] From this, it appears that considerable overcrowding occurred even in the authorised ships which would be increased by the greater bulk of victuals required and may have been the reason why, with her relatively small complement and large capacity, the *Thomas of Ipswich* was carrying most of the victuals; an irreparable loss when she deserted.

McDermott's numbers compare well with Hogarth's figures for officially sanctioned ships [460] but unauthorised ships carried a further 87 to give a grand total of 547 for the third voyage including the 154 miners who were carried. This is just a little above the miners identified by Hogarth from paylists [147]. It is clear that McDermott is correct in stating that only 278 men on the third voyage were appointed by the Commissioners, for Frobisher's Instructions for the third voyage expressly laid down a total of 270 men, of whom 100 were expected to winter in Meta Incognita with Fenton. They included 160 miners and refiners.[64]

If a reasonably accurate figure can be reached only with difficulty for the third voyage, there are also problems with numbers for the second voyage. State Papers for 26 March 1577 provide for the victuals of 115 men in the three ships — 85 mariners and 30 soldiers[65] — but Frobisher's Instructions sanction 120 men — 90 mariners and artificers and 30 miners, refiners and merchants.[66] However, accounts for wages on return show payment for 100 mariners, 26 soldiers and 14 gentlemen, 140 in all.[67] Hogarth, *et al*, provide a figure of 154 and McDermott, from Lok's accounts, 143. Frobisher had been warned, in a letter from the Commissioners which he received at Harwich before sailing, not to exceed 120 and, according to Best, "discharged many proper men, whiche wyth unwilling myndes departed." In addition, he also dismissed all convicts who had been pressed into service.[68] Both Hogarth and McDermott report men discharged before the commencement of the voyage [19 mariners and six miners, and 22 mariners respectively], but whether or not they were the same men is difficult to say. It seems clear, however, that at least 143 men sailed, which Best confirms, and it is therefore possible to provide a reasonably accurate assessment of the number who sailed on each of the three voyages [see Table 4]. It should be emphasised that these are the minimum numbers likely to have been carried.

Crude mortality rates are an unreliable means of assessing the medical record, for they need to be considered in the light of prevailing conditions, the nature of the deaths and the competence of the medical personnel. In the first voyage, problems were created by the defection of the *Michael* which left *Gabriel* alone to pursue exploration in hazardous, unknown Arctic waters. The loss of five men taken by the Inuit with the ship's boat, curtailed the intended period of exploration and added to the labours of the small and depleted ship's complement. They had also lost the pinnace, intended for inshore exploration, in a severe storm off Greenland. Best, who was not on the voyage, suggests that the four-man crew of the pinnace was lost.[69] Christopher Hall merely mentions the five carried off by the Inuit,[70] but Lok, who ought to have known, suggests three were also lost in the pinnace which reduced the ship's company of *Gabriel* to "but xiii men and boyes so tyred and sik with labour."[71] Since *Gabriel*'s complement was fifteen and she had lost five men to the Inuit, this suggests that, out of a total of nineteen, only one was lost in the pinnace, the mortality for the voyage being six in all.

First Voyage :	32 men in the two barks [28] and pinnace [4]
Second Voyage :	143 men in the *Ayde* and two barks, including 8 miners
Third Voyage :	451 men in 4 Company ships and 7 ships commissioned by the company
	87 men in 4 unauthorised ships, a total of 538 men carried on the third voyage, including some 154 miners.

Table 4 : Probable numbers of men borne on each of the three voyages

Both Best and Settle, who sailed on the second voyage, agree that there were only two deaths, one of a seaman who had been ill before leaving but who had insisted upon going, and the other the young, able and popular master of the *Gabriel* who was swept overboard with the boatswain in high seas. The boatswain grabbed a rope, but could not hold William Smyth, the Master, until he was rescued. As in the first voyage, none died from illness contracted on board.[72]

Reference has already been made to the problems of assessing mortality during the third voyage where Best's estimate of "not above fortie persons"[73] is considered reasonable. Selman gave details of 13 deaths. Four died on Newland Island near Winter's Furnace mine, where they were buried on 16 August. They were Philip Ellarde, in charge of clothing aboard the *Ayde*, Thomas Trelos or Trelease, a seaman, of the bark *Dennis*, which had foundered on 1 July, and who had no doubt succumbed to the after-effects of cold immersion, one from the *Armonell* and one from the *Frances of Foy*. He also reported the deaths of Anthony Sparrow, quartermaster of the *Ayde* on 31 August and Roger Littlestone, also of the *Ayde* and Frobisher's servant, from "the pox" on 28 of that month. On 2 September, *Armonell* lost a boat and one man and there were a further six deaths during the stormy homeward passage: George Young, a miner, died on 17 September, Walter Kelley, a carpenter, on 24 September, Thomas Cunningham, a seaman, on 25 September, Cornelius Riche, a Dutch seaman, on 27 September and John Wilmot, a seaman, on 28 September. All were from the *Ayde* in which Selman himself was borne, so reflect only the deaths in that particular ship.[74]

Since there were twelve others at sea at the time, the number of deaths in the rest of the fleet could have been proportionately greater. Fenton reports four deaths in his log, but

Figure 1: A burial at sea during the Portuguese expedition of 1580, portrayed in the Hales Memorial in Canterbury Cathedral. Copyright Ben May, Photographer.

they seem to be among those already reported by Selman. In addition, Best reported heavy losses when a sudden storm struck the *Emmanuel of Bridgwater, Gabriel, Michael* and the *Anne Francis* during a last attempt to obtain ore from the Countess of Warwick Island before departure. The storm caused the loss of some 20 boats and pinnaces throughout the fleet which had just left for home "and some men stroken over boorde into the sea, and utterly lost."[75]

Taking into consideration the number of implied deaths, Best's estimate of "not above fortie" appears justified and not excessive in the conditions experienced. However, more would have died after arrival in England, from injuries received through the hardships encountered during the voyage, the back-breaking toil of mining and the lack of adequate victuals in overcrowded ships during the voyage home for, at Weymouth, Fenton "sett divers sick men on shoore, and others willing to departe to their frindes, the Shippe being personned with, 67 men, the most parte whereof infected with the skirvie and other gingerfull diseases."[76] It should be noted that *Judith*'s normal complement was 38. The *Emanuel of Bridgwater* ended her voyage a wreck on the coast of Ireland, but the cost in terms of human life is unknown, though Hogarth found three miners unaccounted for.[77]

Injury and sickness receive little detailed attention from the journalists, but enough to indicate some of the problems the surgeons had to deal with. During the first voyage, lost hands who were critical to the success of the voyage, prevented exploration which might have had significant influence upon plans for subsequent voyages. Their absence imposed a heavy penalty on the remaining crew obliged to take over their duties and resulted in "faynt and weake men" undermined by "so great labours and diseases suffered at the sea."[78] They were finally "so tyred and sik with laboure of their hard voyage" that they were barely able to reach Harwich on 2 October "where they taryed to refresh their sick and weake men."[79] Michael Lok's poignant account of their condition suggests a legacy of injury and chronic illness from which they might be slow to recover.

Reference has already been made to Best's description of the various injuries sustained by miners during the second voyage from which it is evident that they developed hernias, back problems, sciatica and perhaps fractures. All this imposed a great burden on the surgeons and it is noteworthy that they were never once criticised for incompetence. In fact, the number of injuries and amount of sickness they treated without losing any patient on the second voyage is a tribute to their skills. In a skirmish with the Inuit, Giles Wallis was dangerously wounded in the abdomen by an arrow,[80] and he survived well under medical care, but was nevertheless disabled enough to receive compensation for it later.[81] In another such skirmish, Frobisher himself received an arrow in his buttock — a potentially dangerous injury — but seems to have been treated so effectively that he was scarcely inconvenienced,[82] though Settle, in his detailed description of Inuit arrows, mentions how destructive they could be.[83]

The journalists were too occupied with the terrors of navigation in the third voyage to give much time to sickness and injury. As we have seen, even deaths were rarely mentioned. Fenton describes how a man on the foreyard cut away a sail which fell on a boy and knocked him overboard. He saved himself by grasping the foresail sheet, but his face was beaten and chest bruised.[84] Selman tells how Francis Austen, the *Ayde*'s helmsman, was struck by a following sea during a stormy return passage,[85] but the most Best tells us is that they were plagued by stinging gnats which left red blotches.[86] However, we can assume that crushing and lacerating injuries, aggravated by frostbite and hypothermia, must have been one consequence of desperate attempts to prevent the ships being crushed by icebergs, while lacerations of the hands caused by frozen ropes have been noted. The feet would not escape under these conditions, for gangrene of the toes can occur. Similar, if not more dangerous, mining injuries than those of the second voyage would have occurred in the relentless pursuit of ore, and constant exposure to wind and snow would bring its quota of chest and circulatory problems.

Their extent is communicated by the continuing list of deaths reported after mining had got under way, while Fenton's description of the scurvy-ridden *Judith* on arrival at Weymouth probably reflects the state of the whole fleet. It is therefore to the credit of the surgeons that, under such circumstances, losses were so few; they must have been constantly employed. The later deaths might well have been avoided, but for Frobisher's last-minute redeployment of ships in his passion for ore, which caused unnecessary loss of life when they were surprised by a sudden tempest and which resulted in overcrowding in ships with inadequate, spoiled or unsuitable victuals.

There are two other factors. One is that the priority given to ore prevented fishing and a search for fresh foods which had been a feature of the two earlier voyages. Secondly, there remains some doubt about Frobisher's probity. As McDermott has pointed out, he was responsible for victualling the *Ayde* and was accused of putting men on short rations in order to maximise profit.[87] In his "Abuses of Captain Furbisher agaynst the Companye" dated 1578, Lok claimed Frobisher took an extra four unapproved ships and 100 extra men on the third voyage for his own purpose, charged to the Company, but without its knowledge, and could not leave Fenton's 100 man colony as ordered, because he had already expended their victuals on his own ships for which he had made no victualling provision. Furthermore, he had received money to victual the *Ayde* at Bristol, but made money from the deal, "whereas the Companye allowed him to vittel her wth fleshe 4 days in the weeke, he sarved the men thereof onlye 3 dayes, and 2 dayes in the weeke, and the rest of the weeke wth evill fishe, and that wth scarsetie wherebye manye of them died, as the men do reporte."[88]

Discussion

It seems evident that the stimulus to medical thinking and social reform — caused by the upheavals of the sixteenth century, and the impact of the Reformation, which generated an international network of physicians, surgeons, apothecaries and naturalists, together with the propagation, following the dissolution of the monasteries, of radical ideas on hygiene, sanitation, discipline and diet — had a profound influence upon the Frobisher voyages. The new spirit of self-confidence provided not only the stimulus to exploration, but also the initiative, stamina and determination which enabled men to overcome the most daunting hazards by super-human efforts.

The victuallers and apothecaries appear to have provided supplies of the highest quality and were probably selected by Lok because of their association with the network. Certainly the apothecaries were eminent in their field and were discriminating enough to recognise that priority should be given to basic ingredients for the treatment of wounds and burns and to simple remedies for chest infections, stomach and bowel disorders and skin conditions. Morgan resisted any inclination to include the latest exotic import unless he believed it necessary. The presence of two sophisticated and useless remedies — pearl and lapis lazula — must therefore have been at the insistence of one of the gentlemen, perhaps even Frobisher himself.

There was no criticism of the quality of victuals supplied, and victualling problems arose because of damage suffered by casks during storms, through unsatisfactory stowage or through failure by Frobisher to follow his instructions which clearly laid down that victuals should be equally distributed throughout the ships in case of loss or accident.[89] His failure to do this caused severe food shortages during the third voyage when the *Thomas of Ipswich* deserted, carrying the bulk of the fleet's victuals with her.

Lok's indictment of Frobisher, however, carries a much more serious charge as we have seen, for he not only deprived the *Ayde*'s men of victuals but, contrary to the company's policy and his instructions, engaged men of such poor calibre that they caused disorder and increased the mortality rate of the *Ayde* in the third voyage.[90]

The Company obviously believed that success depended upon a high degree of selection and this policy was usually enforced, for it appears that all men were medically examined. The names of seven who were hired for the third voyage and subsequently discharged medically unfit appear in the accounts.[91] Finally, Frobisher was roundly condemned by all for the losses he incurred through hazarding the fleet for such a trivial purpose before its departure.[92]

The depressing medical record of the third voyage was therefore no reflection on the surgeons, who appear to have coped admirably with a variety of injuries and medical problems, but can be largely attributed to Frobisher's self-interest. His cavalier approach to victuals, a key element in any voyage of discovery, is highlighted by an incident when the ships were beset by ice. After the *Ayde* was holed, it was found that the pumps were not ready to empty water which was filling the hold, so "beef and other provisons" were used to plug the gash in the hull.[93] It seems clear that the Company intended victuals to be supplemented by fresh foods which were known to be necessary to keep men healthy and avoid scurvy, despite the antiscorbutic carried in the form of "sallet oil." While it appears that this policy was followed during the first two voyages, the requirement seems to have been subordinated to the search for ore during the third.

Despite these weaknesses and a disturbing tendency to undermine the authority of his officers,[94] perhaps with the intention of enhancing his own, Frobisher had his strengths, both physical and moral. He was immensely powerful, was largely responsible for righting the *Gabriel* during the first voyage when she was flung on her side in heavy weather,[95] and captured the Inuit man by single-handedly lifting him and his kayak from the sea into the ship.[96] A born leader, he invariably took the initiative and was utterly fearless in the face of danger. He encouraged teamwork and allowed no difference between officers and men when a job had to be tackled, always setting the example himself.[97]

He seems to have taken seriously the instructions of Sebastian Cabot for the Willoughby and Chancellor voyage of 1553, particularly in regard to hygiene, the exercise of caution, and the equal sharing of labour, although he turned a blind eye to Cabot's insistence upon scrupulous control of victualling expenses.[98] In matters of hygiene and sanitation, however, he went much further than Cabot. A letter from Sir William Monson to Frobisher in 1592 suggests that they were on intimate terms,[99] and Frobisher may have obtained some of his ideas from Monson who held advanced views on hygiene and sanitation.[100] More likely, they both received them from the same source, the Protestant initiative which, through a series of authors, was an active subject of debate in court circles, led by Haryngton and others. In any event, Frobisher was nearly 300 years ahead of his time, for he forbad anyone to wash in a spring of running water which he specifically designated for the dressing of food. He gave strict orders for the hygienic dispersal of waste from the ships and allocated a tidal area under cliffs for "easement," where all excreta would be washed away. Disobedience carried heavy penalties "for the better preservation and health of everye manne."[101]

Friel has drawn attention to the significance of the cooking facilities which suggest the possibility of boiling or stewing meat and fish, and frying or roasting meat on spits, and has suggested that the variety of cooking available bolstered morale and helped to combat debility caused by environmental conditions and hard labour.[102] This is true, although there were dangers inherent in the use by sailors of the large amounts of dripping they obtained from cauldrons and spit trays, which could prevent the absorption of vitamins and lead to scurvy.[103] Attention has already been drawn to the generous provision of clothing which allowed five or six changes of apparel during the height of exposure to the raging elements which undoubtedly saved lives. It included Kersey cloth and a variety of garments, caps, boots and shoes. Kersey was a coarse cloth, usually ribbed, made from long wool and therefore warm.[104]

Finally, a word needs to be said about the injuries sustained by miners, which were crippling and carried long-term implications, while some comment is also required on the consequences of pushing men beyond the limits of tolerance. The provision of "8 dossen cruell gerdles" [crural', *ie*, leg girdles or trusses],[105] is a measure of the frequency of herniæ among seamen. Muscular injuries were common enough on board ship, but did not compare with the severe and frequent musculo-skeletal injuries sustained by miners using rough tools on rocky ground and driven by their officers to achieve maximum output. They have already been described, and accidents would involve wounds and fractures.

Investigation of the high injury rate during training among recruits for today's Armed Forces has revealed a high incidence of stress fractures, particularly in smaller, heavier men. This is because remodelling of bone occurs in the process of the body's attempt to remove damaged areas and replace them with stronger buttresses to sustain the continuing load. During the process, the bone is weaker for a period and vulnerable to potential damage.[106] Commonly, this occurs about three weeks after the commencement of a heavy workload without preliminary training, and seems to have happened to the miners who were flung into an arduous task without preparation for it. Little wonder that lameness occurred. The long-term effects of these and more serious injuries would have led to deformities and arthritis, which would have reduced wage-earning capacity.

Everyone needs to be under a certain amount of stress to maximise effort. However, when a combination of factors act in concert to cause unsustainable effort, increasing effort becomes self-defeating, performance falls short of expectation and extra effort leads to exhaustion without reserves to meet the unexpected emergency, and physical and mental breakdown occur [Figure 2]. The immune system becomes increasingly deficient causing vulnerability to illness.[107] For athletes, additional psychological stress can cause sudden collapse.[108]

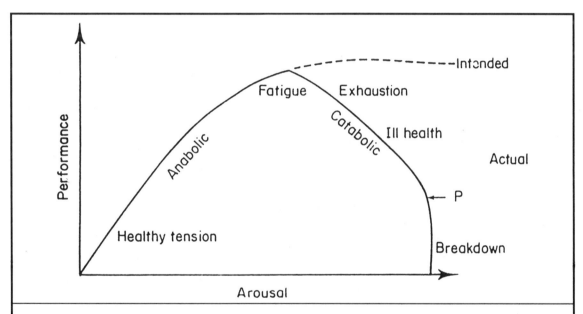

Figure 2: *The Human Function Curve: a performance-arousal curve used as a model for a systems or biophsychosocial approach to clinical problems. P = point of instability where little extra arousal is required to produce breakdown*   *[Nixon, 1989]*

To these adverse consequences of stress must be added adverse metabolic influences, for the high energy output demanded by the conditions of the third voyage would have resulted in massive loss of sweat, since heat production is directly related to the intensity of physical activity. Sweat loss also caused loss of electrolytes, vitamins and iron, further undermining resistance to illness,[109] while the increased weight of clothing caused by frozen sweat would add to the effort required to achieve the same output. Such factors, together with the nutritional deficiencies already noted, would help to explain the tragic cavalcade of death which characterised the third fleet's homeward passage. To that must be added the unknown number which succumbed to illness and injury sustained during the voyage. William Beton, for instance, died shortly afterwards and John Paradice is not heard of again.

Conclusions

The medical aspects of the Frobisher voyages can only be assessed in their contemporary setting. The wind of change sweeping through Europe in the wake of the Renaissance and the Protestant Reformation brought together like-minded individuals impelled by the curiosity and dynamism which these two movements created. The leading figures in medical, mercantile and naval circles shared similar convictions and readily adapted to changing concepts of social structure, hygiene, sanitation, diet, surgery and medical care. They aroused fierce loyalties and bitter antagonisms which identified leaders who commanded obedience and respect. In the medical world, improved standards of training and practice separated the competent from the bogus. Integrity, the hallmark of true Protestantism, found an effective exponent in Michael Lok, whose experience and relationships ensured that victuals and medical stores would be of the highest quality, while the health record of the voyages must be considered a tribute to the surgeons' skills.[110] No man was lost through clinical incompetence, the medical record of the first two voyages was excellent and the less favourable outcome of the 1578 voyage was entirely due to Frobisher's mismanagement.

Yet Frobisher was a man of his time, and if he displayed a stubborn and venal streak, he could also show kindness towards those in distress and a fatherly concern for his own men. Above all, he had the vision and leadership to see the task through whatever the privation it entailed, and he set the example himself. To appreciate the quality of his leadership, even the third voyage can be compared favourably with those of contemporaries in similar circumstances. Eleanor Gordon, describing Munk's voyage to Hudson Bay in 1619, deplored the total failure of Munk's leadership which so lacked inspiration and initiative, that his men simply crept into bed and died. Though decent, pious and conscientious, he lacked the resourcefulness which Frobisher so magnificently displayed in crisis. Of Munk's 65 men, 62 succumbed to the climate.[111] It takes more than drugs and medical care to weather the rigours of the Arctic.

Acknowledgements
I am most grateful to Dr. Bernard Allaire for his helpful information and I am especially indebted to Mr. James McDermott for so generously sharing his intimate knowledge of accounting and organisation of the voyages. Mr. J.S.Murray, Archivist of the Worshipful Company of Barbers of London, Mr. J.S.Williams, Bristol City Archivist and Mr. Malcolm Beasley, Botany Librarian at the British Museum [Natural History], have given much assistance. Mr. Eric Freeman, Librarian of the Wellcome Institute for the History of Medicine and his staff have been particularly helpful and my special thanks are due to Mr. William Schupbach who kindly translated into English Dr. Dodding's report in Latin on the illness and death of the Inuk [Eskimo man] from the second voyage. Finally, Emeritus Professor David B.Quinn has drawn my attention to important sources of information.

Notes

[1] *Court Minute Book*, 26 May 1573; 2 March 1573; 2 October 1576; 15 March 1577, Worshipful Company of Barbers, London: Barber-Surgeons' Hall.

[2] N.Moore, *The History of St Bartholomew's Hospital*, London: C.Arthur Pearson, 1981, 595-6. *Court Minute Book*, Barber-Surgeons' Hall, *op.cit.*, 11 April 1570.

[3] G.V.Scammell, "Manning the English Merchant Service in the Sixteenth Century," *Mariner's Mirror*, 1970, 56, 131-154.

[4] *Exchequer King's Remembrancer*, 35, London: Public Record Office, 18, 144, 145.

[5] *HM715*, Huntington Library, San Marino, ff 15, 16, 20 and D.D.Hogarth, "The Ships' Companies in the Frobisher Voyages," in N.W.Fitzhugh and J.S.Olin, eds., *Archeology of the Frobisher Voyages*, Washington D.C: Smithsonian Institution Press , 1993, Appendix 1, 244, 246.

[6] *MS 9054 Archdeaconry Court of London, Probate and Admin Acts*, 2, 1588-1594, 16 January 1593; London: Guildhall Library.

[7] Ibid., 5, 1611-1626, 19 March 1611.

[8] Ibid., 4, 1603-1611, 1 September 1604.

[9] S.Young, *The Annals of the Barber-Surgeons of London, compiled from their records and other sources*, London: Blades, East-Blades, 1890, 6, 184.

[10] *EKR*, E164, 35, 14.

[11] MS9054, Archdeaconry Court of London, *op.cit.*, 2, 1585-1594, 18 October 1593.

[12] A.J.Jewers, *Index to Monumental Inscriptions in City Churches*, 1910-1919, MS2480/2 Guildhall Library, London.

[13] *Calendar of State Papers, Colonial 59, Domestic Eliz, cxviii, No.40, i*, "Doctor Doddyngs report of the sicknesse and death of the man at Bristoll wc Capt. Furbisher brought from the north-west: and of the nature of the woman of that contrie yet livinge." An English translation by William Schupbach appears in the paper by James Watt and Ann Savours found in this volume.

[14] W.Munk, *The Roll of the Royal College of Physicians of London, 1*, London: R.C.P, 1878, 86-7.

[15] *EKR, E164, 36*, 150.

[16] W.Munk, *op.cit.*, 77. *Acts of the Privy Council*, 16, 1588, 5, P.R.O.

[17] *EKR, E164, 35*, 45.

[18] J.Frampton, *Joyfull Newes out of the New Founde Worlde written in Spanish by Nicholas Monardes, Physician of Seville and Englished by John Frampton, Merchant*, 2, London: Constable, 1577, 44.

[19] W.Smith, *Latin-English Dictionary based on the works of Forcellini and Freund*, London: John Murray, 1877, 318.

[20] J.Banester, *An antidotarie chyrurgical containing great variety and choice of all sorts of medicines that commonly fal into the Chyrurgion's vse, partlie out of Authors, olde and new*, London: Thomas Man, 1589, 2.

[21] The minutes of the various drugs are as described by either Turner or Lemery: W.Turner, *A New Herball*, in 3 parts, Facsimile of 1st edition 1551, ed. G.T.C.Chapman and M.N.Tweedle, Cambridge: Cambridge University Press, 1989; N.Lemery, *Dictionaire Universel des Drogues Simples, contenant leur Noms, Origine, Choix, Principes, Vertues, Etimologie*, 3rd edn., Paris: D'Houry, 1733.

[22] G.Majno, *The Healing Hand, Man and Wound in the Ancient World*, Cambridge, Massachusetts: Harvard University Press, 1975, 169.

[23] Ibid., 117.

[24] W.Turner, *op.cit.*, 772 n.50.

[25] CSP, *Colonial 33, Domestic Elizabeth, cxi, No.48, i*.

[26] M.Oppenheim, ed., *The Naval Tracts of Sir William Monson*, 4, London: Navy Records Society, 1913, 56.

[27] A.Wheeler, "Fish Bone," in H.Clarke and A.Carter, eds., *Excavations in King's Lynn, 1963-1970*, London: Society of Medieval Archeology, 1977, 403-8.

[28] R.D.Connor, *The Weights and Measures of England*, London: HMSO, 1987, 159.

[29] R.A.McCance and E.M.Widdowson, *The Composition of Foods*, Medical Research Council Special Report Series No.297, London: HMSO, 1960.

[30] *EKR, E164, 35, 15* states "Fresh victuals daily to ships while fitting out" and this was the customary practice.

[31] G.Best, A True Reporte of such things as hapned in the second voyage of Captayne Frobysher, 1577. In R.Collinson, *The Three Voyages of Martin Frobisher in search of a Passage to Cathaia and India by the North-West*, London: Hakluyt Society, 38 (1867), 123-4.

[32] CSP, *Colonial 33, Domestic Elizabeth, cxi, No.48, i, 16 March 1587.*

[33] G.Best, A True Discourse of the Late Voyages of Discoverie for finding of a Passage to Cathaia by the North-West, under the conduct of Martin Frobisher, General, 1578, in Collinson, *op.cit.*, 73.

[34] G.Best, The Thirde voyage of Captaine Frobisher, Pretended for the Discoverie of Cataya, by Meta Incognita, 1578. In Collinson, *op.cit.*, 254.

[35] D.Settle, A true reporte of the last voyage into the West and North-West regions, 1577, worthily achieved by Capteine Frobisher of the sayde voyage the first fynder and Generall. In V.Stefansson and E.McCaskill, *The Three Voyages of Martin Frobisher in search of a passage to Cathay and India by the North-West, A.D. 1576-8, 2*, London: Argonaut Press, 1938, 20.

[36] G.Best in Collinson, *op.cit.*, 286.

[37] Ibid., 75.

[38] CSP, *Colonial 33, Domestic Elizabeth, cxi, No.48,i.*

[39] M.Oppenheim, *A History of the Administration of the Royal Navy and of Merchant Shipping in relation to the Navy: from MDIX to MDCLX*, London and New York: Bodley Head, 1896, 140.

[40] W.Beveridge, *Prices in England from the Twelfth to the Nineteenth Century, 1*, London: Longmans, Green, 1939, 510.

[41] T.Fuller, *The Worthies of England*, 1662, ed. J.Freeman, London: George Allen and Unwin, 1932, 716.

[42] Ibid., and *EKR, E164, 36*, 64.

[43] J.McDermott, *The Account Books of Michael Lok relating to the northwest voyages of Martin Frobisher, 1576-1578: Text and Analysis*, unpublished Thesis, University of Hull, 86-7.

[44] L.G.C.Pugh, "The Logistics of the Polar Journeys of Scott, Shackleton and Amundsen 1901-12," in Medical Aspects of Polar Exploration, *Proceedings of the Royal Society of Medicine*, 65 (1972), 43-7.

[45] A.F.Rogers, "The influence of Diet in Scott's Last Expedition," in J.Watt, E.J.Freeman and W.F.Bynum, eds., *Starving Sailors: The influence of nutrition upon naval and maritime history*, London: National Maritime Museum, 1981, 166.

[46] J.McDermott, "Frobisher's 1578 voyage: early eyewitness accounts of English ships in Arctic seas," *Polar Record*, 32, [183], 1996, 325-334.

[47] G.Best in Collinson, *op.cit.*, 250.

[48] Ibid., 251, 266.

[49] C.Jackman, Fragment of Journal in *Harleian MSS, 167, No.40*, f 181 transcribed by J.McDermott for ARTAF.

[50] G.Best in Collinson, *op.cit.*, 261.

[51] A.F.Rogers, *op.cit.*, 164.

[52] G.Best in Collinson, *op.cit.*, 242.

[53] C.Jackman, *op.cit.*, 182.

[54] *HM715, H.L.,* ff 9-11.

[55] G.Best in Collinson, *op.cit.*, 279.

[56] Ibid., 152.

[57] Ibid., 154.

[58] R.E.Johnson, "Doctors Abroad. Medicine and Nineteenth Century Exploration," in *Starving Sailors*, 105.

[59] Ibid., 106.

[60] E.Fenton, *Log. MS1125,* f 8, (Saturday 9 August; Tuesday 29 July 1578), Pepys Library, Magdalene College, Cambridge.

[61] D.D.Hogarth, *op.cit.*, Appendix 1, 241-250.

[62] D.D.Hogarth, P.W.Boreham and J.G.Mitchell, *Mines, Minerals, Metallurgy: Martin Frobisher's Northwest Venture, 1576-81*, Hull, Quebec: Canadian Museum of Civilization, 1994, 27-9.

[63] J. .McDermott, *Account Books of Michael Lok*, 381. EKR, E164, 36, 98.

[64] CSP, *Colonial 93, Conway Papers.*

[65] CSP, *Colonial 33, Domestic Elizabeth, cxi, No.48i.*

[66] CSP, *Colonial 39, Domestic Elizabeth, cxiii, No.12.*

[67] CSP, *Colonial 55, Domestic Elizabeth cxvi, No.14.*

[68] G.Best in Collinson, *op.cit.*, 122.

[69] Ibid., 71.

[70] C.Hall, The First Voyage of Martin Frobisher to the Northwest, for the search of the straight or passage to China, 1576, in Collinson, *op.cit.*, 153.

[71] M.Lok's Account of the first voyage, in Cotton MSS: Otho, E.viii, f 46, British Library.

[72] G.Best in Collinson, *op.cit.*, 153, 157 and D.Settle in Steffansson and McCaskill, *op.cit.*, 2, 25.

[73] G.Best in Collinson, *op.cit.*, 280.

[74] E.Selman, Journal, Harleian MS No.167, 42, ff 166-180.

[75] G.Best in Collinson, *op.cit.*, 279.

[76] E.Fenton, *Log*, f 69, Monday 29 September 1578.

[77] D.D.Hogarth, P.W.Boreham and J.G.Mitchell, *op.cit.*, 63 and 71n.10.

[78] M.Lok, *op.cit.*

[79] Ibid.

[80] G.Best in Collinson, *op.cit.*, 142.

[81] CSP, *Colonial 89, Domestic Elizabeth, cxxiii, No.50*: "James [Giles] Wallis, hurte and maymed by the countrey people."

[82] G.Best in Collinson, *op.cit.*, 128.

[83] D.Settle in Steffansson and McCaskill, *op.cit.*, 18-21.

[84] E. Fenton, *op.cit.*, Monday, 8 July 1578.

[85] E.Selman, *op.cit.*, 14 September 1578.

[86] G.Best in Collinson, *op.cit.*, 286.

[87] J.McDermott, "A right Heroicall heart: Sir Martin Frobisher", in this volume. McDermott's review of Frobisher's life exposes the flaws in his character which, despite his undoubted professional abilities and charismatic leadership, could never quite resist the temptation for personal gain. Though finally obtaining the respectability he craved, he nevertheless remained a pirate at heart.

[88] CSP, *Colonial 122, Domestic, Elizabeth, cxxx, No.17* The Abuses of Captain Furbisher agaynst the Companye, Ano 1578 [8].

[89] CSP, *Domestic-Addenda, Elizabeth, XXV No.81.*, March 1578. Instructions to be observed by Martin Frobisher.

[90] CSP, *Colonial 122, Domestic, Elizabeth, cxxx, No.17*, [21].

[91] V.Stefannson and E.McCaskill, *op.cit.*, 2, 221-2.

[92] E.Selman, *op.cit.*, 310.

[93] Ibid., 303.

[94] Ibid., 306-7. Frobisher refused to support Fenton when he reported men of the *Ayde* to Frobisher for disobedience of orders. Later the men apologised to Fenton stating that they did not know Fenton was Frobisher's deputy. Fenton felt "let down and dishonoured," presumably because of Frobisher's attempt to undermine his positon. Jackman, master of the *Judith*, also found that Frobisher made it difficult for him to maintain discipline and determined never to serve with him again. [See "Abuses," item 14].

[95] C.Hall in Collinson, *op.cit.*, 159.

[96] Ibid., 164-5.

[97] G.Best in Collinson, *op.cit.*, 248-255. During the third voyage when the *Emanuel of Bridgwater* struck fear into all hearts by accounts of her privations. Frobisher provided firm leadership and resolution, winning respect and compelling obedience. Immediately mining commenced, Frobisher ordered allocations of work for gentlemen and miners alike, as he had done in the second voyage when "shewing fyrst a good president of painfull labourer & a good Capitaine in himselfe, gave good examples for others

to follow him, wherevpon eueryman, both better and worse, with their best endeuors, willingly laide to their helping handes" [Best, 137].

[98] Ibid., 256. Frobisher's Orders in Meta Incognita, 2 August 1578 — Compare Sebastian Cabot's Ordinances of 9 May 1553 in C.R.Beazley, *John and Sebastian Cabot. The Discovery of North America*, London: Fisher, Unwin, 1898, 186-195.

[99] *Lansdown MSS 70, f48, July 12, 1592.*

[100] M.Oppenheim, ed., *The Naval Tracts of Sir William Monson*, 4, 60-3.

[101] G.Best in Collinson, *op.cit.*, 256-258.

[102] I.Friel, "Frobisher's Ships. The Ships of the North-Western Atlantic Voyages,1576-1578," in this volume.

[103] J.Watt, "Medical Aspects and Consequences of Cook's Voyages," in R. Fisher and H.Johnston, eds., *Captain James Cook and His Times*, London: Croom Helm, 1979, 129-157, 250-5.

[104] CSP, *Colonial 33, Domestic, Elizabeth, cxi, No.48, i. EKR, E164, 36, ff 46, 50.*

[105] *EKR*, E164, 35 48.

[106] J.Etherington, *Prediction of stress fractures by ultrasound*, Paper presented at joint meeting of the Section of United Services and Section of Sports Medicine, 10 October 1996, London: Royal Society of Medicine.

[107] P.G.Nixon, "Human Functions and the Heart," in D.Seehouse and A. Cribb, eds.,*Changing Ideas in Health Care*, Chichester: John Wiley & Sons, 1989, 31-65. Fig.1 is the illustration used by Nixon to illustrate how actual performance falls increasingly short of that intended if individuals are stressed beyond tolerable limits.

[108] J.Fazey and L.Hardy, *The Inverted-U Hypothesis: catastrophe for sport psychology?*, Leeds: British Association of Sports Sciences and National Coaching Foundation, 1988, 4-24.

[109] R.J.Maughan, "Fluid and electrolyte balance during exercise," and J.Kent, E.Jacob, A.Berg, H-H.Dickhuth, M.Lehmann and G.Huber, "Performance in relation to vitamins, iron and sports anæmia," in D.H.Shrimpton and P.B.Ottaway, eds., *Nutrition in Sport*, London: Echo Press, 1986, 17-45.

[110] J.Watt, "The Medical Climate of Frobisher's England: Maritime Influences," in this volume.

[111] E.C.Gordon, "The Voyage of Captain Munk to Hudson Bay in 1619: An Analysis of a Medical Catastrophe," in *Transactions and Studies of the College of Physicians of Philadelphia*, ser.5, 11[1], 1987, 13-27

Notes on Contributors

Bernard Allaire

After a college training in the Sciences, Bernard Allaire's interests turned to the study of history, leading to a Masters from Université Laval (Quebec city), a DEA at l'École des Hautes Études en Sciences Sociales de Paris, and a Ph.D (Laval) on the history of the European fur trade. Having worked for some years for the Paris office of the National Archives of Canada, he is presently working on a book entitled *Pelleteries, manchons et chapeaux de castor, le commerce des fourrures nord-américaines à Paris*. He is involved in various research projects involving notarial, administrative and diplomatic sources in Europe, in collaboration with Canadian, American and European historians and archaeologists. His interest in the historical context of European exploration of North America led to his involvement with both ARTAF and the Laval CELAT team (the latter investigating the Frobisher expeditions through archaeology).

Robert Baldwin

Educated at the City of London School and St. Chad's College, Durham University to 1980, Robert Baldwin later worked for the Museum of London, the National Maritime Museum, and from 1992, as a Research Associate for ARTAF. He is the author of *Globes* (Greenwich, 1992) and *Cartography in Thomas Harriot's Circle*, (Durham, 1996). Published articles include: "The interchange of European and Asian navigational knowledge in the Far East before 1620", *Five Hundred years of Nautical Science*, (Greenwich, 1981), pp.80-92; "The charts and surveys of James Cook", in *James Cook, Navigator*, (Sydney, 1988), pp. 88-101; "British Assistance to the Preparations for Malaspina's expedition, 1789-94", *Spain and the North Pacific Coast*, (Vancouver, 1991), pp. 69-77; "The Maritime Heritage", *Manual of Heritage Management*, (Oxford, 1994), pp.171-186. A Fellow of the Royal Society of Arts and of the Linnean Society, and a Member of the Royal Institute of Navigation, he is active in conserving archaeological and industrial contexts through the Nautical Museums Trust and the Railway Heritage Trust.

Ian Friel

Born 1954 in Hitchin (Hertfordshire), and educated at Hitchin Boys' Grammar School and the Universities of Lancaster, Leicester and Keele (Ph.D in medieval maritime history, 1990), Dr. Ian Friel was employed at the National Maritime Museum from 1977 to 1988, and at the Mary Rose Trust from 1988 to 1992. Since 1992 he has been Curator (and latterly Museum and Community Arts Officer) at Littlehampton Museum, West Sussex. He has published over twenty papers and books, including *The Good Ship: Ships, Shipbuilding and Technology in England 1200-1520* (British Museum Press, 1995) and is currently working on a maritime history of the British Isles.

Sir Ian Gourlay

Sir Ian Gourlay assumed the role of Chairman of the Archival Research Task Force UK (ARTAF) in the summer of 1992 at the invitation of the Chairman of the Meta Incognita Project. A leader with a career maritime experience as a former Commandant General of the Royal Marines, he served for fifteen years (1975-1990) as Director General of the United World Colleges, the international educational movement devoted to the world-wide development of international understanding. His role as Chairman of ARTAF has been to coordinate the research work and writings of ARTAF's group of scholars, and to serve as a link between that group and the Meta Incognita Project Steering Committee.

Donald Hogarth

Dr. Donald Hogarth was a professor in the University of Ottawa's Department of Geology from 1959 up to his recent retirement. It was as a geologist that he participated on several archaeological expeditions to the Frobisher sites in the early 1990s, but his interests in broader aspects of the voyages led him to conduct extensive archival research. His writings on the subject include the book *Martin Frobisher's Northwest Venture, 1576-1581: Mines, minerals and metallurgy* published by the Canadian Museum of Civilization in 1994.

James McDermott

James McDermott, B.A., M.Phil., is a Special Adviser to ARTAF. His master's thesis, *The Account books of Michael Lok, relating to the Northwest voyages of Martin Frobisher, 1576-1578: text and analysis* provided the first complete transcription of the financial records of the Frobisher voyages. Leaving university, he pursued a career in industry, but has since returned to full-time academic employment. He is currently preparing a forthcoming Hakluyt Society volume on the third (1578) voyage to Baffin Island, and has recently completed a "popular" biography of Martin Frobisher.

David B. Quinn

Dr. David Quinn is Emeritus Professor of History in the University of Liverpool; he has also taught at a number of American universities including The College of William and Mary and the University of Michigan at Ann Arbor. Most of his research and publications (apart from Irish history) have concerned North America, including Canada and Bermuda. His Roanoke Voyages (1955 and 1991), North America from Earliest Times to First Settlements (1977) and (with A.M. Quinn and S. Hillier) New American World (5 volumes, 1979) are his best-known works. His most recent is European Approaches to North America 1450-1640 (1998). He has been involved with ARTAF since its initiation.

Richard I. Ruggles

Dr. Ruggles is Emeritus Professor of Geography at Queen's University (Kingston, Ontario). An undergraduate at the University of Toronto, he took graduate studies at Syracuse University (New York), and at the University of London (England). He specialized in cartography, and regionally in Soviet studies and geography, the fields in which he lectured at McMaster University (Hamilton, Ontario) and the University of British Columbia before he founded the department of geography at Queen's University in 1960. He was cartographic editor of the first provincial atlas, British Columbia Atlas of Resources, and joint author of the first provincial historical atlas, the award-winning Historical Atlas of Manitoba, prepared for the centennial of Manitoba. One of the leading experts on historical cartography, among other publications in this field he wrote the award-winning *A Country So Interesting: The Hudson's Bay Company and Two Centuries of Mapping, 1670-1870*. He is a Fellow of the Royal Geographical Society and of the Royal Canadian Geographical Society.

Ann Savours

Ann Savours (Mrs. Ann Shirley) was educated at London University and the Sorbonne. She held posts in the University of Aberdeen Library, the Scott Polar Research Institute (Cambridge), and the National Maritime Museum, where she was Curator of the Arctic Gallery, sometime Archivist and member of the *"Discovery"* Project team. She retired in 1987 and continues working as an independent scholar, at present writing a history of the search from the Northwest Passage from Frobisher's time. A long-time member of the National Trust, she has served on the Councils of the Royal Geographical Society and the Hakluyt Society, and as Secretary of the Society for Nautical Research. Her publications include an edition of *The "Discovery" Diary of Edward Wilson* (1966) and the books *Scott's Last Voyage* (1974) and *The Voyages of the "Discovery"* (1992, reprinted 1994), which merited a "Best Book of the Sea" award.

Kirsten A. Seaver

Kirsten Seaver is an historian of early North Atlantic exploration as well as a novelist and translator. Her work focuses primarily on Norse Greenland and on early Norse and other European voyages to North America, and she takes a particular interest in the early cartography of that region. She does most of her research in London and is a Fellow of the Royal Geographical Society. Educated in her native Norway and in the U.S., she is the author of six books and a number of articles in English and Norwegian, including *The Frozen Echo: Greenland and the Exploration of North America ca. A.D. 1000-1500* and three articles on the "Vinland Map".

William H. Sherman

Dr. William Sherman's doctoral work was on the polymath John Dee, and he is the author of *John Dee: The Politics of Reading and Writing in the English Renaissance* and of numerous articles on Renaissance literature and culture. He is currently co-editing an anthology of texts related to Shakespeare's *The Tempest* and is co-writing a study of Elizabethan reading practices. He has been a Junior Caird Fellow at the National Maritime Museum (U.K.) and is currently Associate Professor and Director of the English Honors Program at the University of Maryland, College Park.

Thomas H.B. Symons

Founding President and Vanier Professor Emeritus of Trent University, Professor Symons is a teacher and writer in the field of Canadian heritage studies. He is the author of *To Know Ourselves*, the Report of the Commission on Canadian Studies, and of numerous studies and articles dealing with education, human rights, cultural pluralism, Aboriginal and northern studies, international relations, and other aspects of public policy in Canada. His service on many national and international bodies has included the Chairmanship of: the Historic Sites and Monuments Board of Canada; the Canadian Polar Research Commission Study; the National Library Advisory Board; and the National Statistics Council. Professor Symons has acted as Chairman of the Meta Incognita Project Steering Committee since the Project's inception in 1990. He is a Fellow of the Royal Society of Canada and a Companion of the Order of Canada. In 1998 he received the Governor General's International Award for Canadian Studies.

David W. Waters

Lieutenant Commander D.W. Waters, R.N., joined the Royal Navy in 1925 and during the 1930s served as a torpedo/bomber pilot in the Fleet Air Arm. He saw active service in the Siege of Malta (1940), and was a prisoner-of-war in Italy and Germany from 1940-45. Thereafter he served as Admiralty Historian from 1946-60, undertaking a study on the Defeat of the Enemy Attack on Shipping. He was Head of Navigation and Astronomy at the National Maritime Museum from 1960-76, its Deputy Directory 1971-78, and Caird Research Fellow there from 1979-83. Lt.Cmdr. Waters is a Fellow of the Royal Historical Society. His publications include *The Art of Navigation in England in Elizabethan and Early Stuart Times* (1958, 1978) and *The Rutters of the Sea, the first French and English printed Sailing Directions* (1968).

Sir James Watt

Sir James Watt KBE, MS, MD, FRCS, FRCP, FSA trained in medicine and surgery at the Universities of Durham and Newcastle, followed by Fellowships of the Royal College of Surgeons of England and Royal College of Physicians of London. In the Second World War he joined the Royal Navy and continued to pursue a navy career after the end of the war, rising to the position of Medical Director General (1972-77) with the rank of Surgeon Vice Admiral. After retirement he became President of the Medical Society of London and of The Royal Society of Medicine, and was a visiting Fellow of University House, Australian National University, and of the University of Calgary. He has written extensively on surgery, medical history and Christian ethics, and is currently involved in various academic, professional and charitable organisations.